While the Kettle Boils

Edited by Thomas Bartram

GRACE PUBLISHERS

While the Kettle Boils

*A selection of letters & quotations
from readers of
Grace magazine over 40 years
ending December 2000*

Edited by

Thomas Bartram

While the Kettle Boils

Life goes by so very quickly,
Little time to stand and stare,
Days of gladness, times of sorrow,
Daily problems, daily care.

Sometimes just a welcome tea cup
Helps us to relax, unwind,
See things from a new perspective
And discover peace of mind.

Let us take a quiet moment,
Put aside the daily toils,
Join together, sharing friendship,
While the kettle boils.

Iris Hesselden

GRACE PUBLISHERS
Mulberry Court, Stour Road, Christchurch, Dorset BH23 1PS. (UK)
Tel: 01202 476868. Fax: 01202 480559

Halcyon days . . . when we sit quietly by the window watching wildlife in the garden come and go, pausing to read a letter from a friend, accompanied by a refreshing cup of tea.
Photo: Clifford Robinson

Preface

OVER THE YEARS I have received thousands of letters arising from Grace Magazine. Often, I have been asked: "Why don't you reprint in a book?" At last, I endeavour to rescue from oblivion personal experiences of readers.

I have formed the opinion that members of Grace Family are inveterate readers. What can be more interesting than the subject of good health – physical and mental?

A majority of letters I receive are from those who have found a solution to their health problems through alternative medicine, which some suggest works as well as many prescription drugs. True, herbal medicine will not do everything. Yet the proof of the pudding is in the eating.

We all have a good cause to be grateful for some of the marvels of modern medicine, yet we are impressed by the volume of research into medicinal herbs that are opening-up a whole new world of healing.

More members of the medical profession are turning to these natural remedies instead of some of the questionable products of modern pharmacy. Almost every month, research reveals the efficacy of herbs over a wide range of disorders. These include benefits to sufferers of arthritis; bowel, liver and intestinal conditions; memory loss, depression and nervous complaints.

We are amazed at the rate new discoveries are coming out of the laboratories . . . from Saw Palmetto (prostate gland), St John's Wort (depression), Garlic (heart disorders), Fenugreek Seeds (diabetes), and others.

This book, as you will see, is my excuse for repeating some of the fascinating letters received in our office at Grace Magazine. Of course, not all the contents of the Magazine are concerned with health. We live in a world of disquieting news, mental stress, and a speeding-up of the general tempo of life. From time to time we all need something to give the heart a lift.

"Grace" is for busy people to enjoy during the quiet hour when we can draw aside from the world and all its cares, to allow 'the soul to catch up with the body'.

Have you put the kettle on? You may wish to browse through the following pages before sinking into the depths of your favourite armchair, aided by a soothing cup of tea.

Thomas Bartram, January 2002.

WHILE THE KETTLE BOILS

For my son, Roger, and
Ursula, my daughter-in-law.

© 2002. Thomas Bartram
First published January 2002.

ACKNOWLEDGEMENTS

THE EDITOR expresses his gratitude to all whose letters appear in this book. He trusts they will rest assured that their testimony will be of practical help to many readers. He is grateful for permission given by owners of copyright. Our sincere thanks to authors or agents we were unable to locate. The Editor acknowledges with sincere thanks the expertise of Mr Tony Purvis, his team at GreenShires Group Ltd., Leicester, and all others engaged in the production of this book.

The Editor is sorry he cannot prescribe for health conditions. This book is not intended to replace or conflict with advice given by your doctor or health professional who has records of your medical history and general health. He, or she, is in a situation of forming professional judgement of the reader's case. We cannot accept responsibility for any liability arising from use of this book.

Cover photograph.
Tea in the garden.
Roy Westlake

Contents

Spring

Spring comes gently to the country, slipping into our lives while the last scraps of snow lie neglected, the remainder of winter's last fling. Blustery winds give way to fresh breezes that sweep away winter's gloom and usher in the gentle rains to warm the earth. Next summer's flowers stir and stretch in their winter beds, poking an inquiring green finger toward the sun to see if spring is really here . . . and finding it is so, growing and blooming, a riot of bobbing, colourful faces smiling at the world. The fruit trees don their party dresses, their full skirts fluttering in the breeze as they bow and curtsy, flirting with the staid old cedars and making brash promises about this year's harvest.

All about us the bleak, colourless landscape is merging into soft pastels, the stark black trees wearing the soft fuzz of buds, roadsides becoming carpets of violets, and here and there a brazen dandelion peeping through, a sure harbinger of summer. From the new kittens in the barn and the blossoms on the apple tree comes the reminder that spring brings us a new beginning each year, that the dismal winter is over, and that the season of sweetness and light is upon us again, with the chance to sow the seeds of new friendships, new adventures, and the things that will make a summer of tomorrows warm and bright and wonderful.

Jean Marion

I know a bank whereon the wild thyme blows,
Where oxlips and the nodding violet grows
Quite over-canopied with luscious woodbine,
With sweet musk-roses, and with eglantine: . . .
A Midsummer Night's Dream

Woodland Primroses in Wiltshire   *Jane Miller*

Mrs. Frank Deacon, Philadelphia. U.S.A.
I can't remember ever receiving a Magazine I enjoy more. It is so inspiring, helpful healthwise, and heartwarming. I have always dearly loved the English people and your beautiful Island, and have been fortunate in being able to have travelled there often. I admire the innate courtesy of the people.

Liverpool store magazine.
A real salesman can see by his customer's eyes what degree of interest he has aroused. No interest is signified by the pupil being small, the iris large and the upper lid coming down to the upper edge of the pupil. As interest grows the pupil enlarges and the upper lid lifts.
   When it lifts to the top edge of the iris, the desire to purchase is aroused.

Miss L. A. Parnell, Fulham, London.
Two things I found very helpful may help other readers. Five years ago I had an operation and now have to wear a stoma urine bag. A few months ago I had a vague feeling that something was not quite right; nothing you could pin-point. I am not a religious person, but I did pray for guidance and help. After a few days I was led to a health magazine and flicked it open and the page which it opened at was an article on Fenugreek. I went along to the herbalists and bought some. I have been taking a teaspoonful every night since, for a few weeks, two months roughly. One night a huge clot came away. A bit frightening, but the relief was marvellous. Since that time I have had no trouble.
   All my life I had brittle nails, and since I retired I decided to do something about them. After taking one vitamin A tablet, daily, for three months there has been vast improvement.

Anonymous.
Who's afraid of the big bad wolf? Certainly not your husband – if he snores at night. Scientists claim: "Men snore to keep wild animals away from the 'cave'. And the woman whose husband snores should be proud that her husband is protecting her so well.
   "However, a *woman* who snores is aggressive – for she is taking over a masculine job." Quiet, girls!

Mrs. M. J. Harries, Devon.
In the autumn *Grace* I was particularly interested in the extracts from a book by Dr. Smalpage dealing with the excessive use of common salt as the chief cause of cancer. This confirms the findings of Dr. Maude Tresillian Fere as stated in her book that she has proved to her own satisfaction (since she cured herself of cancer of the bowel) that excessive sodium chloride (common table salt) is the chief cause of cancer.
   She has also cured more than 100 other sufferers. Incidentally, a strict vegetarian diet is part of her treatment. Her book also contains one of

the strongest condemnations of fluoridation of our water supplies I have yet encountered. She says, "I am whole-heartedly with those doctors who condemn fluoridation of public water supplies. There is no doubt that this practice would very much increase cancer, because of the impossibility of avoiding excess of *sodium* in such a water supply . . ." A very sober thought. Under fluoridation it would become impossible to cure cancer because the patient's system could not be rid of excessive sodium through diet. With all good wishes to the Grace Family.

Mrs. S. J. Rondesbosch, Cape, S. Africa.
Living in a boarding school, it isn't easy for me to follow the health hints, but I try my best and am happy to say that I enjoy good health.

For the past nine months I have been making up a mixture of 20 oz. Soya Oil and 4 oz. Wheat Germ Oil. I take one dessertspoonful after meals. Since taking the oil my skin has become soft and clear and my hair glossy. My weight is right for my height and age. I have not put on any weight since taking the oil. My nerves are good and, believe me, looking after 82 girls can be a pretty full-time job, needing good nerves. The oil is most palatable and does not leave the mouth feeling oily.

Mrs. D. Hoult, St. Leonards-on-Sea, Sussex.
Some time ago I was operated on my spine; a few weeks ago a small blister came up and I was in terrible pain, so kept putting on a cabbage leaf. For five weeks fluid kept coming out. Then something over two inches long came out – a splinter of bone. It had been pressing on the spinal nerve. What a relief!

E. James, Lincolnshire.
People take all sorts of sophisticated medicines for their bowels. Some are downright dangerous, but no one seems to enlighten the public. Liquid Paraffin for instance, has now been silently dropped since it is believed to be injurious to the lining of the bowel. One old-fashioned thing which can be overlooked is one we all know – the cheapest, the smoothest, the least toxic, and the easiest. I give you one guess. Here's an epitaph for you.

> Here lie I and my three daughters,
> Died from drinking health spa waters.
> Had we but stuck to Senna pods,
> We wouldn't be under these 'ere sods.

Doris Morgan, Handsworth, Birmingham.
I was surprised to read in *Grace* that folk were still suffering from migraine.

I started attacks at 45! I spent 20 years in hell. A wonderful experience delivered me. People had been praying. I reached out a hand and turned the knob of the radio to hear a voice saying: It is thought that some

people are born without a filter in their blood to an element in certain foods: this element has so far been isolated in cheese and chocolate."
That was IT. I had lived on cheese. When I was depressed I turned to chocolate. Very often I meet similar sufferers and pass on the good news.

"Member of Grace Family", London N1.
They say life begins at 40. It began much later for me. I didn't marry until over 50, commenced going out to work (part-time) at 55, learned to play golf at 60, became President of the club at 65, learnt to paint at 70, took a course in home decoration at 75 and now, at 80, have so much to occupy my mind that there is never a single dull moment. My husband is 83 and takes a lively interest in all my 'hobbies'.

Mrs L. Bacon, King's Lynn, Norfolk.
We moved house. As I looked round disconsolately late at night I said, "Wouldn't it be nice to go away and when we came back to find all this furniture in our new house, and all the work done?"
The next day I was called away urgently to help a friend with an accident. There was nothing for it, I had to go. Imagine my surprise when a group of young people, in one fell swoop arranged the whole job for us. They had our new house spick-and-span, all ready for us to move into, before I arrived back a week later. So you see, my wish was granted.

Anonymous, Newark, Nottinghamshire.
I see you have given a remedy for hiccups. There's no guaranteed cure for hiccups – only counter-irritants. Nearly everyone has his or her own cure for hiccups. Some try drinking water from the wrong side of the glass. Others hold their breath until they go puce, and many more think that dropping a cold key down the front of the chest is a cure.
Each of these methods may work – the first time. They owe their success to the power of concentration, or shock.
ED: *Thank you for writing. How very true. However, we know old codgers who still swear by onion juice or chamomile flowers.*

Mrs. D. Dailey, San Tropez, France.
I felt I must include you, this season, in with my dear friends. I thank you very much for all the joy *Grace Magazine* gives me. I have sailed the Atlantic, West Indies and Bahamas; crossed Africa twice from the Congo to Lake Tanganyika by car; seen pigmies and held their babies in my arms. I have travelled the country down to South Africa and seen the beauty there. Among the Greek islands I have just spent three years, having experienced wonderful peace and beauty, and unbelievable sunsets and sailing on starlit nights above phosphorescent waters. Your beautiful *Grace Magazine* recaptures all those wonderful moments. Thank you.

Mrs. W. G. McNeel, Memphis, Tennessee, USA.
Grace still means lots to me. It is the hand that reaches across oceans to people of kindred minds and says "Greetings, Neighbour". It has such a warmth within its pages it takes you away from the things that are wrong in the world, and makes your soul feel at peace.

There is one thing I might share with the readers. For quite a few years I had trouble with having to get up nights. I read an article some place where if you used honey only as a sweetener it would correct this condition. I began to use natural honey from a good farm nearby and now I am not afraid of these all-day meetings, spending the nights away from home, etc., as I am no longer bothered with this condition. Thank you so much.

Mrs. M. Mathieson, West Chiltington, Sussex.
I have recently returned from visiting an old friend at Kilve in Somerset. While there, she told me that she had had an inflamed finger which did not heal despite remedies from the chemist. Then a woman in the village told her to try wrapping round her finger the leaves from one of the lily plants in her garden, Lilium Candidum (the white Madonna Lily). This she did and the finger cleared up extremely quickly. You probably are already aware of the healing properties of these leaves.

Miss G. Bowden, Saltdean, Sussex.
Some of the things recommended in *Grace* are wonderfully good. One is Elderflower as a cure for colds. I have found it good myself and when a young neighbour of mine was in despair because she was going to a very special dance and had started a shattering cold, I gave her some (rather wondering whether she would take it) – but she did and told me afterwards that it worked like magic.

ED: *Dose: Place one heaped teaspoonful Elderflowers in a teacup and pour on boiling water. Allow to infuse for ten minutes. Strain. Drink hot at bedtime.*

Mr. R. W. Collins, Sheffield.
Having given up smoking, I have been eating chocolates and sweets fairly frequently to overcome the habit. I have now put on too much weight, and now it is a full-time job trying to break up the "sweet" habit. What do you say to this?

ED: *Health-giving alternatives to sweets are nuts and raisins, which are cheaper bought separately and mixed at home. Nuts are an excellent form of protein and raisins contain iron. Nuts should be avoided by sufferers from chest complaints. That is, with the exception of Sunflower Seeds which are beginning to give sweets a run for their money. Rich in magnesium, they tend to strengthen weak hearts and, of course, the Russians found them powerfully good for eyesight – even to the point of allaying cataract. Sunflower seed chewing was endemic in Russia, as confectionery shops were few and the deleterious effects of white sugar not yet caught up with its people.*

Look at pictures of Russian and American soldiers on parade. Whole rows of Americans are shown with glasses. If a single pair is seen among the Russian ranks it is quite unusual. We believe this to be due to heavy white-sugar intake in the New World.

Miss M. L. Felgate, Basingstoke.
Some years ago I developed a large double wart on my wrist which irritated continually. One day an elderly friend said I could get rid of it with chalk. I did as she instructed and kept the wart dry by always having a stick of blackboard chalk on my dressing table, in my pocket, and in the bathroom, so that I could constantly be rubbing the chalk on the wart to keep it quite dry. I kept this up until the wart completely disappeared, a matter of several months, but well worth the effort. And the wart never re-appeared. Regards to the readers.

Dr. H. E. Spencer, Detroit, Michigan 48208.
I thought that you might like to pass the following herbal combination to others:

Years ago we lived in the country and the only doctor around there made up his own herbal remedies. I remember – for severe nerve convulsions – the good doctor used Poplar Bark (white). The thin outer coating of the bark was to be scraped off. Then the bark was to be shaved downward from the limb. About an ounce of the bark was put in a pan and one pint of water added, then brought to a good rolling boil. A few sips of the tea were to be taken every day. It was very bitter. No doubt many sufferers suffer from constipation, and this tea acts as a cleanser – It is laxative.

Mr. F. Green, Basingstoke, Hants.
I hear that America will soon be able to land space-craft on Mars. Already they are able to bounce off its surface bleeps and blurps. Somebody refers to it as a kind of space music. I wonder if it would consist of Mars bars?

Barbara Edwards, Guildford, Surrey.
A freckle-like spot below my right eye began to get larger and was found to be eczema, which did not respond to any suggested treatment.

Suddenly I was seized by an overwhelming desire for at least six oranges a day. The spot grew rapidly, spreading down my face and becoming very red. Then it grew pale from the centre outwards, and inside a week, had gone.

Miss M. Mansley, Chorley, Lancs.
There are so many letters of advice in your magazine and in the Spring
issue I see someone asks for a herbal aid for bronchitis. I do know that
for a cough it is a good thing to cut up finely one large onion, sprinkle
over this a dessertspoonful of honey and leave it to allow the juice to
form. Drink the liquid by the teaspoonful when required (eat the onion
too if you feel so inclined!).

Miss Joan Roberts, San Diego, California, U.S.A.
Can you give me a line on Migraine? My life has been spoilt by these
blinding headaches for years. Is there something I can get in the States?
ED: *Lacto-bacillus Acidophilus, the bacteria which turns milk sour, is a
new treatment for this distressing complaint. Its use was recently discovered by a Swedish physician who described his unexpected success in "The
Lancet." He cured a fifty-three-year-old woman of migraine and colitis of
twenty years' standing. Since then, Dr. Erik AskUpmark, Royal University
Hospital, Uppsala, Sweden, has used the same treatment on other migraine
patients. "Substantial improvement" occurred in eight of the ten, all of
whom had also previously suffered from intestinal disturbances.*

Mrs. Margaret Hanson, Burlington, Washington, U.S.A.
Grace is the sunshine and breath of fresh air that lifts the spirit and keeps
it light and fortified to withstand adversity.

Mr. T. Simpson, Glasgow, Scotland.
What would you recommend for prostatitis where the gland is swollen
and for when I simply 'cannot get started' when getting out of bed in the
cold in the wintertime?
ED: *Try rectal insertion of two garlic perles into the anus on retiring.
Persevere for some weeks. Consult one of the many excellent homoeopathic or herbal practitioners in Glasgow.*

Albert George Williams, Aldershot, Hampshire.
When we were young we lived in the country where my grandfather
always made a fomentation for my grandmother's arthritic wrists and
hands, from herbs he gathered on his way home from work.
  My wife now has similar stiffness and swelling, and what wouldn't I
give to know what he used? He's been gone these past thirty years so
there's no way of finding out, unless you have any ideas.
ED: *Try these, Mr. Williams. One of any of the following: Ragwort,
Goutwort or Tansy, which should relieve pain. These are also helpful for
gout and joint troubles generally, but of course they could never free an
ankylotic fusion.*
  *Place a handful of the fresh herb or an ounce of the dried herb and
infuse in a quart of boiling water. Strain, and immerse a piece of gauze,*

dressing or material in the liquor. Wring out. Bind around the joint. When the dressing becomes dry, repeat the routine. Do this two or three times. Do not take internally.

Monica Grant, St James, Jamaica, West Indies.
I have been a member of Grace Family for the past six years and commend you on a really beautiful magazine. Every article is worth reading, and cover such a wide range of interests that there is always something to learn. The pictures are magnificent. I look forward to each issue and read the old copies over and over again. It is a magazine that gives one a sense of peace and sanity in a world turned upside down. Yours sincerely.

Miss J. Mercer, Burnham on Sea, Somerset.
I would like to praise Aloe Vera Gel as a wonder-help in healing my small yet persistent leg ulcer which defied all medical treatment. It has healed after constant use for weeks.

Louise Vacher, Bridgewater. Somerset.
I read, with concern, the letter about Mrs Sharp's grandson in the Winter issue of the magazine. It was about a 4-year-old boy who had a bed-wetting problem.

When Head of an Infants' School (now retired 9 years), I used to advise mothers to put the younger child (if there was one) to bed first of all, then give the older child time on her lap, a cuddle, a story and tell him that she loved him, before she put him to bed.

Often, there was a change over-night. I remember on one occasion, a mother coming to my office to tell me that her son had wet the bed. She had punished him, stopped his T.V. and she was going to take him to the doctor. I did not say anything. The mother observed, "You don't agree with me?"

I replied that I did not agree, and gave her my advice. To my surprise, the mother returned within a fortnight and said: "Mrs Vacher, we have done what you said and we have not had a wet bed since." Yours sincerely.

The Balti Garden, Bristol, offers:
"Lentils with garlic friend in butter".

Mr A. Williams, Southampton.
Regarding a letter from Mrs H. Johnson, Market Harborough, on the subject of urticaria. Long ago I, too, suffered from this and was told I was "allergic to something". As I am a gardener by trade, the "things" I could have touched were so numerous. So the doctor gave me lotions, pills and potions, all to no avail. I heard of a Homoeopathic doctor who treated me with Rhus Tox and the complaint cleared up within two weeks, never to again return. Best of luck.

Members of 'Grace' Family – June, Amanda (holding Penny) and Olive Morris, Evington, Leicester.

Staying young
CORNELIA ROGERS

TO BE YOUNG is not a matter of years. Youth lives forever in a love for the beauty that is in the world, in the mountains, the sea and sky, and in lovely faces through which shines the kindliness of the inner mind.

It is the tuning into the orchestra of living sound, the soughing of the wind in the trees, the whisper and flow of the tide on wide beaches, the pounding of surf on the rocks, the chattering of brooks over the stones, the pattering of rain on leaves, the song of the birds and of peepers in the spring marches, and the joyous lilt of sweet laughter.

Youth lives without counting the years in a fluid mind which is open to new theories, fresh opinions, changing impressions, and in the willingness to make new beginnings.

What is it to stay young? It is the ability to hold fast to old friends, and to make new ones, to keep forever our beloved in dear remembrance, and to open our hearts quickly to a light knock on the door.

Youth is to remain faithful to our beliefs, to preserve our enthusiasms, to trust in ourselves, to believe in our own courage, and to follow where courage bids us go.

And, at last, youth means that, like an unquestioning child, we place our hand without fear in the hand of the Gentle Guide, who will lead us through the little gate at the end of the winding road.

Mr. H. C. Miller, Vancouver, British Columbia, Canada.
Obesity is surplus gone to waist. Usually the end product is gout. There is no better illustration than the following overheard conversation.
"Yes, sir, I was never more surprised in my life. You could have knocked me over with a brick church. What? Oh, I thought I'd told you. I've got the gout. How did I find out? I was playing squash in London. I put over a fast one and whoosh . . . I crumpled right up there on the court. Foot just refused to carry me. I said to my wife that night, 'I'll bet I've got the gout.' She said, 'Nonsense, you're always having something!' "

Mrs. J. Ewart, Edinburgh, Scotland.
My doctor seems a reasonable sort of man and tells me he thinks a lot of tea is not too good for my rheumatic and neuralgic pains. What can we take in its place?
ED: *We assume your doctor has no objection to tea, provided excessive quantities are not taken over the day. An excellent alternative is Vichy Water (Celestins) which is a natural spa water from France. It is rich in valuable minerals, promotes digestion, is good for acidity (which can be a cause of rheumatism) and is good for rheumatic troubles generally. Some time ago, we discovered how to make an excellent Vichy cocktail. Take a large wineglass. Half fill with Vichy Water, fill up the rest of the glass with Apple Juice. Do not overlook the wide range of interesting herb teas on sale at your Health Food Store.*

Mrs. L. Thomas, London, N.W.1.
I never was very big. When on holiday at the seaside I saw outside a fish shop "Fresh shrimps walk in". I simply couldn't resist a peep inside and a quick glance round.

Mrs. E. Leatherbarrow, Ormskirk, Lancs.
I found the juice of a raw onion the most effective remedy for a wasp sting. I have also heard of applying cigarette ash. Also another herbal remedy – tobacco leaf.

Mrs. J. V. Clarke, Oakroyd, Horam, E. Sussex.
I thought you may like to know of a treatment I used successfully recently on a Bantam hen. She seemed to have ceased laying till we found that she was laying shell-less eggs at night, and the others were eating them.
I gave her one Calcium tablet (from Health Stores) a day, and three Biochemic tablets of Calc. Phos. After three days she laid a normal egg, and continued to do so. I kept up the treatment for several more days.

Mrs. L. E. Sinclair, Flintshire.
I would like to share this experience. Last August and September I had a severe attack of Shingles. The pain and irritation was very trying. Any

clothes, whether soft and cool, did not help. In desperation I said to myself, "What can I do to ease this?" and I distinctly heard, "Put some pear juice on the shingles." I did and the result was wonderful. Cool, peace, and all of the lesions cleared within a day or two. I may add it was the juice of fresh pears I used.

Mrs. Allaway, Birmingham.
Early this year a neighbour lent me some of her old *Grace* magazines to read, and in the Summer 1976 one I read about the book Harry Benjamin had written "Better Sight Without Glasses". At the time I was having trouble with the fit of my glasses and was tired of going back to the Optician. I sent for the book and started in February to do the exercises, and very soon noticed my improved vision. As I have a Cataract growing in each eye, I go for annual examination by a Surgeon at our local Hospital, last Thursday, 21st he told me my vision was very good and he would see me again in eighteen months' time instead of the usual twelve.

Mrs. Ivy M. Eyre, Corfe Mullen, Wimborne, Dorset.
About thirty years ago I had a nasty varicose ulcer. Some months later, as it was still as bad, a different doctor told me to keep off my legs as much as possible for two months. I was to lie on a sofa all day and bandage the ulcer with Castor Oil ointment, morning and evening. It worked wonders. It left a large brown scar which gradually disappeared. I am 94 years old, and feeling fit and well.

Moira Grassby, Western Australia.
Thank you for your letter of friendship and welcome to Grace Family. I certainly hope to enjoy a long and happy membership.

Your magazine is as refreshing as a shower in summer (something we never experience here!). In this age of hustle, bustle and materialism, it's wonderful to find a magazine filled with the realities of life: peace, laughter and poetry. I wish most sincerely, that you will prosper for the next hundred years, at least, and find yourselves able to teach as many people as possible. Please accept the enclosed donation and use in whatever way you find best. Thank you for making rainbows. Have a lovely day. God bless. Sincerely . . .

Miss P. Stephens, Highgate, London, N.9.
My doctor says I have an under-active thyroid gland which is making me dull and stupid. Can you tell me something good for weakness and continual tiredness? No appetite.

Kelp tablets. Made from seaweed. They contain iodine, which is always in short supply in the body in thyroid insufficiency. They should gradually restore some of your lost vitality and put a gloss on your hair, which I guess is dull to the point of falling. Good for debilitated constitutions.

Mrs. Mollie MacKillop, M.A., London SE24
In the Summer issue of *Grace* I read with interest your Editor's comments on a Bill for compulsory Fluoridation of our drinking water, which is at present being rushed through Parliament. The dentists want to add sodium fluoride to all public water supplies.

I continue to be astonished at the absence of serious 'homework' by dentists in this field. They keep on endorsing the Department of Health propaganda described in 1963 by Sir Cyril Black, M.P. for Wimbledon, as "most biased, most partial and most misleading by reason of its many omissions", and I feel at this juncture that a few FACTS conveyed as briefly as possible would not be out of place:

1) Sodium fluoride is a poison, 15 times stronger than arsenic.
2) Part of even the smallest amount taken tends to accumulate in the system – (Dr. Jonathan Forman (M.D.), world-renowned specialist in allergy).
3) A cumulative poison, its effects on humans never yet adequately, i.e. over a lifetime, tested; HIGHLY REACTIVE.
4) Damage to heart muscle (Goodman & Gilman published research) – Washington told cardiovascular maladies have reached epidemic proportions – official publications show significant death-rate increases in Grand Rapids, Mich. and Newburgh, N.Y. (both fluoridated 1945) – Antigo, Wis. research shows death-rate 7-8 times the national average after 20 years' fluoridation.
5) Interferes with natural processes of cells – no slightest quantity of sodium fluoride for expectant mothers, warns D. G. Steyn, Prof. of Pharmacology, University of Pretoria.
6) For children no fluoride in any dose whatever in any circumstances whatever – (Danish Dr. Kaj Roholm, world's greatest authority on fluoride).
7) Illness from fluoride in drinking water develops over a number of years. Is easily mistaken as due to other causes (Dr. A. W. Burgstahler, Prof. of Chemistry, University of Kansas).
8) At 1 part per million in water system equals 10 times the amount in British water supplies – no safety factor (Nesin, Edwards, Sargent, Stockinger, Patrick – authorities in water toxicology).
9) On July 21, 1975 U.S.A Congressman James J. Delaney recommended to Congress that artificial fluoridation of water be suspended 'pending further investigation'.

Two out of four experimental areas in the UK have thrown out fluoridation. A third has voted massively to throw it out after 20 years' trial. In the fourth, resistance continues to grow.

Not only can a doctor not force a patient to follow his orders, but there is nothing in any Water Act that specifically permits a water system to be used for the dispensing of a substance added to it for the purpose of affecting bodily or mental function.

Archibald Cook of Glasgow.
Christmas and the New Year loom nearer on the calendar. Soon, we shall all be celebrating, and how we are looking forward to it! I would like to pass on to members of the Family a useful tip for merry-makers who may over-indulge in the "spirit" surrounding festivities. Honey helps you to overcome the misery of the morning after. Sometimes even the best of home-made wines can have a disturbing effect.

Honey, which contains sugar fructose, increases metabolism, i.e. promotes the "combustion" of the body. Like vitamin B6 it helps to eliminate toxins, and has a sobering and sedative effect. Honey combined with this vitamin has proved helpful in treating alcoholism.

Quoted in "The Communicator"
The executive of a large hire-purchase company sent this letter to one of his defaulting customers. "Dear Sir, after checking our files, we find we have done more for you than your own mother did. We have carried you for sixteen months."

Kennedy Runion, Foxfire, California.
I can cure the average kitchen burn in just a few minutes. Cut an Irish potato in two at the middle and lay it on a cloth. A handkerchief is a good thing. Bind the handkerchief with the potato in it around the site of the burn. In ten minutes you can't even tell you've been burned. I've doctored myself. I know. You can scarcely believe it. Let the potato stay there until it turns black. When removed, the site of the burn will be as white as cotton. You've got the fire out of it. If you get it on fast enough, it won't even blister!

Anonymous, Birmingham.
I have had tonsillitis, off and on, for the past four years and being in my thirties am not keen to have my tonsils out. I am taking Poke root and Echinacea, just starting them. What do you think? I think my children are affected too.

ED: *Tonsillitis is a distressing condition where the lymphoid tissue in the nasopharynx and tonsils is enlarged and engorged by waste secretion. The lymph vessels are the drains of the body, and while they can become blocked-up, they can also thicken into hypertrophy and obstruct function. This is where an eliminative diet can prove helpful. Children are very susceptible because of our permissive dietary.*

As you have not taken the Poke root or Echinacea for any great length of time, I would continue with them. Go carefully on starches and fats. Eat plenty of salads and vegetables, going easy on the potatoes. Artichokes are nourishing and not high in calories. They are a good form of diabetic starch, and do not put on weight. Their flavour is not unpleasant, and quite a change from the everlasting potato. Take sunflower oil with salads, and do not be sparing with cooked and raw beetroot.

(continued on page 30)

27

JUICE COCKTAILS FOR HEALTH

SOME of the principal vegetables and fruits whose juices may be used for making palatable and healthy drinks are:

Carrot—Contains most of the vitamins and acts as solvent in ulcerous conditions.

Beetroot—Contains iron, sodium and a little calcium. Is beneficial in cases of high blood pressure, varicose veins and hardening of the arteries.

Celery—Has a high mineral content, is a distributor of calcium and is especially helpful in nervous and arthritic conditions.

Tomato—Is rich in most of the vital elements, and tends to neutralize acids.

Cabbage—Contains vitamin C, sulphur, chlorine, and iodine and is beneficial in cases of peptic ulcers.

Swede and Turnip (also Turnip Tops)—Contain vitamin C and are rich in potassium and calcium. Help to combat hyper-acidity and to harden teeth and bones.

Lettuce—Has a high mineral content, especially iron, manganese and silicon.

Spinach—is excellent for cleansing and regeneration of the digestive tract and in combating pyorrhoea.

Parsley—Very potent; an excellent adjunct in the treatment of disorders of the genito-urinary tract and of kidney and bladder complaints.

Watercress—Has a high sulphur content, and is also rich in most of the other minerals. A good intestinal cleanser.

Cucumber—Contains potassium, sodium, chlorine, calcium, phosphorous, silicon and sulphur. Promotes the secretion and flow of urine and stimulates hair growth.

Grapefruit and Lemon—Have a strong alkaline reaction and are useful in treating rheumatism and arthritis.

Orange—Contains vitamin A, B and C. Its uses are similar to those of grapefruit and lemon.

Apple—Is an excellent blood purifier and is good for the nervous system.

Pineapple—Is good for the digestion and is good for relieving sore throats and bronchitis. (Pineapple, honey and carrageen moss combined make an excellent drink for those suffering from sore throats and chest troubles.).

Grapes—Contain the B vitamins, potassium, iodine, calcium, etc., and are valuable in treating heart troubles.

It may be as well to reiterate that the juice of lettuce, spinach, parsley and watercress should be used sparingly, and should always be mixed with carrot or apple juice.

—Health for All

Maté Tea

Synonyms: Paraguay tea. Jesuit's tea. Yerba Maté.

DID you know that fifty million people in South America use Maté Tea in place of ordinary tea? Why? Because it is good for those with rheumatic tendencies. Oh, no! It won't cure arthritis. But for rheumatism and fibrositis it can often bring relief and cut down acidity which is the cause of so much rheumatism. Containing some caffeine it is therefore a stimulant. Many people find it as enlivening as ordinary tea. It is also a diuretic. That's just a medical term for encouraging the kidneys to do their job and excrete wastes from the body via the urine. If taken strong, it will also tackle stubborn bowels. But for that department there are other helpful remedies like psyllium seeds and good old senna pods.

Taste is pleasant. Good for gout. Some members of the Family like to mix it with equal parts of ordinary tea for those twinges in the hinges.

28

Threshold of Life   *Jan Lukas*

Do not overlook the advantages of two or three tablespoons of bran, daily, together with a little wheatgerm. If, to this, you can add a dessertspoonful of molasses, so much the better. An alternative way of taking molasses is to dissolve one or two teaspoonfuls in a beaker of hot water. It is the ideal sweetening for dandelion coffee which makes a good alternative to tea and coffee for those who wish to keep the caffeine habit under control.

There is something to be said for six to eight kelp or seaweed tablets, daily; prunes and brewer's yeast. All fruits and vegetables may be taken with freedom, but avoid milk, especially cream, cheese and eggs. You may fear there is little else left that is real yummy to a lively appetite, but if you think around the subject you'll be surprised at the number of palatable items of diet to take their place. By the way – be as light as you can on the salt cellar. Should you be clever enough to be able to lure your children away from sweets and shop pastry, you're almost halfway home.

Mrs. D. F., Bournemouth, Dorset.
I was delighted to read what Mr. John Tobe had to tell us about "roses for noses" in a very old issue of the magazine, I well remember days of my childhood when mother would make sandwiches with deep red rose petals between bread and butter. We thought them delicious. I do not think tastes will have changed. They are not only good for perfume, but for food and medicine. Older readers may remember how Queen Victoria loved these sandwiches and served them to her guests at Osborne House, Isle of Wight. Regards to the Family.

Mrs. C. N. R., Co. Durham.
We have found another use for a packet of denture-cleaning tablets. They are good for keeping the inside of my teapot clean.

Mrs. L. J. Picton, Pinelands C.P., South Africa.
A friend of mine had shingles in her eyes. She was in a dreadful state. I had heard of an unusual cure for this condition of the eyes but had not tried it. As she was so desperate, I did it for her. People will wonder how such a simple thing could possibly work, but within a week she was very much better, and soon afterwards, the pain and terrible trouble cleared up altogether.

You get a glass bottle. It must be blue. Fill it with water. Let it stand in the sun for twenty-four hours. Bathe the affected parts with the water.

The bottle must be glass, and not plastic. I prepared mine in an old milk of magnesia bottle. I saw her this morning and there is still no sign of shingles.

At the present moment we are having summer weather in mid-winter! It's very beautiful. But we need rain badly.I am so excited when receiving *Grace Magazine* that I cannot put it down until I have read every word. Last time, it was well past midnight before my light went out. Very sincerely.

Mrs. Freda Norman, Wareham, Dorset.
Greetings! A few weeks ago an old school friend came to see me and I was very surprised to see her reading small print without glasses. When I remarked on this, she said: "Oh, yes, my sight has improved considerably since I began eating raw carrots.

Humbling sight. Letter in the "Sunday Post"
I was having tea in a cafe where three little girls aged about five to nine were facing me. They bought glasses of lemonade. The oldest girl went and bought three slices of toast on a plate. Each took a slice then folded their hands together, closed eyes and said *Grace.* I felt very humble indeed.

Mr. A. S. Earp, Newcastle-upon-Tyne.
I am 43, and developed redness of the nose a year ago, a non-smoker, and total-abstainer. Extremes of cold and heat make it more shiny. What do you recommend?

ED: *Without having seen the case, we would say it is likely to be a case of rosacea. There are four known causes. First, the patient may be seborrhoeic; secondly, the blood vessels of the nose may be dilated due to a constitutional disposition. The third cause is psychological stress, and the fourth may be a deficiency in the production of hydrochloric acid in the stomach. Diet is important, so exclude anything containing oxalic acid; this goes for chocolate and spinach. Are you heavy with the salt-cellar? Also, how strong do you have your tea and coffee? Try bathing the tip with a little witch-hazel. If of stomach-causation, the homoeopathic tablets Carbo Vegetabilis 6x, taken after meals, should prove helpful. Homoeopathic Sulphur, 6x, four pilules night and morning, have been known to overcome this distressing trouble. Fresh raw vegetables and fruit.*

Mrs. Mitchell, Wooton Grove, Sherborne.
Bathing, or cleaning skin ulcers or old rashes with milk can sometimes be successful. I knew a girl who had a severe rash on her hands which defied all manner of treatments. One day she met a farmer and married him. Every day it was her job to wash out the milk churns. Soon the rash improved, and finally disappeared.

John Tobe, Canada.
In a book written by Dr. Abraham E. Nizel, called *Nutrition and Clinical Dentistry*, he claims that sodium chloride (common salt) enters into a struggle with calcium in the body and invariably calcium is the victim. The results – inadequate calcium for the body's needs. You know, they say calcium is vitally important for bone and teeth structure.

So if we believe Dr. Nizel, and there is no reason why we shouldn't, we now have a logical, clear-cut case against the use of salt . . . because

(continued on page 34)

Wild Violets

Wild Violets

(Viola Odorata, L.). The perfume of this modest spring visitor can now be enjoyed on the Sussex Downs. Indeed there are few English counties where they cannot be found. A powerful grace abides in this specie. Symbolizing constancy, it has been prescribed for every sort of complaint from cough to cachexia. For catarrh, take a handful of green or dried leaves; place in a saucepan and cover with two teacupfuls of cold water. Bring to boil. Remove the vessel on boiling. Strain when cold. Drink half teacupful morning and evening, after meals. This infusion would also be invaluable for chronic coughs, especially in children; it is best taken hot. In whooping cough it is especially useful.

A teacupful of Violet Tea serves to dispel violent headaches or migraines. Many cases of migraine are brought about by eating too many eggs, or by partaking of bacon, ham, pork or liver. If you are a victim of headaches, try cutting these out of the diet. You will be surprised how much better you will feel after a few days. I will tell you another thing. It is surprising how you will be able to think more clearly and to concentrate more deeply with these foods out of the way. After all is said and done, the pig is an unclean animal and one of the God-appointed scavengers of the animal world.

Violet Tea has a beneficial effect upon the lymphatic glandular system. Congestion of these glands is responsible for many troubles. You will not be slow to perceive the benefits of a daily drink of this powerfully prophylactic herb to keep the blood sweet and clean, and to discourage the onset of chronic degenerative diseases which today plague civilized peoples of the world.

Some use the infusion for stomach troubles, and others find it an excellent gargle for sore throats—especially if that throat has defied the best efforts of other medicines. An old folk practice was to bring violet leaves to the boil and to immerse in the liquor a piece of linen. This was rung out, and wound round the neck as an external application. I have heard of many people who have taken a daily health drink of this homely remedy, and who have had a jovial old age well into the nineties. Try it and see.

La Lettre. By Abraham Solomon 1824-1862.
Fine Art Photographic Library Ltd & Walker Galleries.

Life is an Art

As long as I live I want to seek beauty and the goodness which springs from the soft brown soil of our fertile valleys and the hard unyielding rock of the high hills. From the midst of a troubled and perverse generation I can still reach out my hand to touch the face of the One who swings the stars in their spheres, who implants His seed in the rich womb. To a heart's inner dimension is brought a conscious awareness of the essential goodness investing the world in which we live . . . majesty of oak and lofty cedar, the high courage of a songbird in the act of defence of its young, calm and storm. All these speak to me of an infinite patience, harmony in the midst of discord, hope in despair, and a vibrant expectation of joy where all was once contention and strife. As my outstretched hands welcome the dawn of another day my mind dwells on those positive healing words which have somehow found their way into the English language and which penetrate my subconscious mind to become part of my life: Balance, Gratitude, Tranquillity, Law, Love, Freedom, Peace, Pity, Self-control, Kindness, Growth, Mystery, Tenderness, Abundance.

Life is an art. There is no more beautiful experience than for you and me to meet a man or woman who lives life to the full. Such a one can always call today his own, bearing lightly what must needs be, who sees beyond the mud in the ditch to the sun casting its first glorious rays upon the tree-tops. He is the full man – the man of all seasons.

A Cup That Cheers

A WOMAN with a history of over 15 years chronic acidity and indigestion found surprising relief when she discontinued Indian tea and took an occasional cup of English Chamomile tea. Within a few months her life was completely changed. Nervous irritability gave way to perfect gastric harmony.

"I've never felt so well for years," she confessed. "I can now eat anything and my nerves are much calmer. What's more, I no longer lie awake at night thinking I've got an incurable disease. I sleep like a top. I put six to eight flower-heads in a teacup and fill with boiling water. I let it infuse for five or six minutes and drink it warm. I have one or two cups a day. It has made a big difference to my life."

A sequestered spot beside the stream in the garden of Mr & Mrs Styles, Oxon.   *Clive Nichols Garden Pictures.*

lack of calcium is one, if not the main, cause of dental cavities. Therefore, if you would have good teeth without holes in them, lay off the salt. Buster . . . lay off the salt!

Mrs. N. Butler, Torquay, S. Devon.
I felt I had to write to you to tell you about Agnus castus. In just a few days it really changed my life after being told for about a year that there wasn't any help for me, by having hormone replacement therapy (HRT) because I had a blood clot in my leg following an operation to deliver my boy 22 years ago.

Since taking Agnus castus it is as though a thick cloud has been lifted. Where my leg has always been swollen, it is really much reduced. I just had to say "Thank you".

Mrs. B. H. J., London W1.
Lobelia has done the trick. The hacking cough I had developed was quick to respond and I got relief.

Mr. J. Blake, Luton.
I have always had a high cholesterol level which has not helped my coronary or bad circulation. I now feel much better and am able to do more about the house and garden. The reason? Garlic.

ED: *If there is a medicine of the 2000s, it is likely to be garlic. Researchers have discovered its efficiency for heart disorders It could reduce the sequence of heart attacks. Dr J. Grunwald medical scientist, Berlin, had this to say at a conference:*

"The efficiency of garlic on cardiac infarction patients has been well demonstrated together with reduction of raised blood pressure and improvement of blood-flow. This results in a much better general circulation."

It just goes to show!

Natural Immunity

WE have lost reverence for the body, and have thereby become its slave. The living body is a matchless work of art of the Creator, a symbol and means of expression of the mind. We poison it deliberately and defiantly with wrong food and intoxicating drinks. We cut it off from the sun. We intervene brutally in its mechanism by chemical preparations and drugs . . . Every possible effort is made to establish immunity to illness by artificial means, but the strengthening and protection of natural immunity are not thought of.

—M. BIRCHER-BENNER, M.D.

34

Miss E. Darlington, Poulton le Fylde, Lancs.
Just to say "Thank you" for the booklets *Sincere Sympathy* and *Grace at Table* which I find very helpful; just as I have found *Grace Magazine* for the past 28 years.
Calamus root I find proves invaluable for my serious bowel complaint. I have diverticulitis and a prolapsed bowel. I place one level teaspoonful in a cup of cold water in the evening and allow it to stand overnight. In the morning it is strained, and I take sips before and after meals three times a day. Best wishes . . . and God bless . . .

Nell Dollimore, Exmouth, Devon.
A friend of mine called on a neighbour whose father had died and said how sorry she was. The neighbour smiled sweetly and said: "My dear, we have been fortunate. His Father didn't call him home till he was over ninety.
What a comforting remark!

Miss C. R., Kent.
The most efficient method of dealing with unwanted mail to date is the following:
I place it within a large envelope addressed, without a stamp, to one of the companies, with this message: "Congratulations, you are the lucky winner of all the junk mail that arrived at my door this morning."

(Dr.) Noel Olsen, London, W.1.
It is amazing how some people can still be ignorant of the facts of smoking.
The association between smoking and coronary artery disease is well established, and many carefully designed long-term studies – not least a twenty year follow-up study of 35,000 British doctors – have confirmed that smokers are at an increased risk of dying from a coronary attack.
Smoking is only one of several important factors in the development of coronary heart disease, but any smoker who refuses to recognise the risk is living in a fool's paradise.

Anonymous, Heathfield, Sussex.
Last summer a friend told me her son was going on holiday on the Continent the next day, and was very distressed because he had a large patch of warts on his face. They had been damaged by shaving and were wet and oozing. His doctor suggested an electric razor.
I looked up some references in my natural-health books and told him to rub Castor Oil well into the warts, night and morning (about twenty rubs each time) and to take a course of vitamin A (Halibut liver oil capsules). This he did. Within fifteen days the trouble had completely cleared. They were surprised, as his mother said he had been troubled with warts since childhood.

I was glancing through Eric Powell's little book: *"Health from the Kitchen"* (Health Science Press), When I noticed that fresh carrot tops are splendid for strengthening kidneys and bladder. They are also good for the eyes. Some friends let me have a good handful of carrot-tops from their garden every few days. I poured on them hot (not boiling) water, and let stand until cold. I took a medicine-glassful before meals, three times daily. I kept this up for as long as I could get carrot-tops. It completely cured my bladder weakness. Using it in an eye-bath several times a day, it gave me peace for months from chronic conjunctivitis and keratitis, which had been very troublesome in spite of occulist's prescriptions and other treatments. Now, I can't wait for carrots to sprout again!

Miss Nora Gayton, Wimborne, Dorset.
Regarding letters in the newspapers about Paraquat in weed-killers. About five years ago I suffered from the spray when the field next to my house was sprayed with Paraquat. I must be allergic to the poison because I only inhaled it as I walked up the road. I suffered much pain and took over a month to recover.

Readers may not be aware that a homoeopathic antidote has been prepared for this poison in the form of Paraquat 6 which I started with. I concluded the treatment with Paraquat 30. Yours sincerely.

From the Jewish Vegetarian.
He hadn't time to pen a note . . . He hadn't time to cast a vote . . .
He hadn't time to sing a song . . . He hadn't time to right a wrong . . .
He hadn't time to love or give . . . he hadn't time to really live.

From now on, he'll have time on end . . . He died today, my busy friend.

Winfred Spray, Kennington, Oxford.
I refer to page 18 of the Spring issue where the first voyage to the New World in the Mayflower was mentioned. In that first terrible winter when the Pilgrims were so sorely in need of food, they saw animals stripping bark off a tree to assuage their hunger. This not only saved lives but was when the virtues of Slippery Elm were discovered. The thick demulcent gruel cured their ulcers and colic. Even today, it proves itself an effective healer.

As a child I suffered from what was most likely a "grumbling appendix". My mother always had Slippery Elm food at hand with which I was fed during those uncomfortable spells of "tummy" ache.

Shortly after starting my nursing training (with no Slippery Elm food for treating the pain of a subsequent attack) I was soon whisked into the theatre – in the nick of time – for appendicitis. The appendix was on the point of perforation. I shall never know if Slippery Elm would have rescued me yet once again!

Member of Grace Family.
On page 18 of the Summer issue of *Grace* there was a page on prunes.
My wife and I believe that prunes keep you right and regular.
I reckon no healthy fella can get along without prunes. Prunes have personalities. Did you know that? I don't know who wrote the following:
"However young a prune may be,
He's always full of wrinkles;
You may get them on your face
Prunes get them every place.
Nothing seems to worry them,
Their life's an open book,
No matter how young a prune may be
He has a worldly look!"

ED: *Well . . . what d'you know about that?*

Mrs. Dora Whyte, Ealing, London W13.
I was reading of a letter in your magazine from Mrs Pollard of Cornwall
who asked if anything could be done whilst she is still on the waiting list
for an operation for gall stones.
This reminds me of how my husband was in terrible pain from kidney
stones. My parent told me to obtain some parsley (quite a lot), to boil it,
strain it, and give it to him to drink.
I did this. I kept on giving him this tea which he hated. But when he
went to the hospital for a further X-ray the stones had disappeared.
Whether they had dissolved or whether he had passed them, we shall never
know. Sincerely.

C. Henderson (Member of Grace Family)
I have suffered for the past two years from diverticulosis but the usual
run of treatment does not seem to touch it. It is wearing me out. I have
lost faith in drugs. I've had all kinds. What is the cause of it?
ED: *Diverticulosis is, unfortunately, now very common in Britain,
affecting people in the second half of their lives. We believe it has been
due to the introduction of roller milling reducing the bran content. Today,
neither white nor brown flour contains more than a trace of fibre. It is
a disease of the 'affluent societies': a legacy of science which has brought
us frozen imported meats, refined sugars and jams, and various additives
designed to improve shelf life but which kill vitamins and vital enzymes.
White flour is made by sifting the bran from the complete grain.*
*We must alter our eating habits if we are to effectively by-pass this irritating disturbance in the colon. The orthodox physician now recognises
how a deficiency of fibre (bran) causes diverticulosis.*
Unfortunately, it does not follow that if a sufferer starts taking wholewheat products he will immediately find a solution of his problem. During

his years on refined flours certain subtle changes have been going on in his colon, which may prove irreversible. It is at that point where he may well try the Gluten-free diet.

A gluten-free diet means cutting-out all breads and products made from wheat, barley, rye and oats.

But the curse of much modern diet is not confined to the human colon. A few people have been amazed to find improvement in such widely separated conditions as multiple sclerosis, diabetes, schizophrenia and coeliac disease when laying-off refined flour, sugar, and by a liberal addition of bran and vitamin supplements to their diets.

Mr. M. B., Kidderminster, Worcestershire.
One difficulty in gardening, I find, is the inconvenience of trousers. One afternoon before an hour's session with a spade, I turned out my pair of old Boy Scout's corduroy shorts. They were a splendid fit, though a little short in the leg. My mother reminded me that I wore them when I was fourteen. How's that for value?

Anonymous
You can imagine how I felt after my visit to my doctor's surgery. He went to the trouble of writing down some medical history. I was feeling more than usually depressed.

"How old are you?" he asked. "Forty?" "No, fifty-four," I replied. "I wouldn't have thought it," he said.

I walked out of that surgery a new woman: I didn't need any prescription!

Anonymous
I have read that is it not always possible to obtain adequate supplies of calcium for the body's needs, especially when bones lose their weight, British diets are said to be much below the minimum levels. How can we augment this diet?

ED: *Rickets is today very rare. Perhaps the worst form of calcium depletion in the world today is seen in the starved babies in disaster areas of the globe. But we can often see its counterpart in ageing of the population over forty. Calcium may drain from the tissues during the menopause and at any time during the adult life, especially old age.*

Lack of calcium may follow high-cereal diet which produces a surfeit of phytic acid, and which can interfere with absorption of calcium from other foods. For this reason people with a rapid loss of weight are advised to switch from one hundred per cent wholewheat bread to the eightyone per cent loaf. Apart from such cases one hundred per cent should be the golden rule.

Those having any doubt about their calcium intake may always resort to supplements. This is sometimes worth bearing in mind in sleeplessness and low calcium conditions which result in excess nervous energy. You see this in the child who cannot sit still, and in adults with the 'jitters' whose legs may 'jump' in bed at night. Probably no other mineral plays such an important part in our lives.

Mr. W. Allen, Ponder's End, Middlesex.
My wife thought I needed some powdered kelp to keep me fit. It tasted horrible. Not one for wasting things, I dissolved it in water and fed it to plants in my greenhouse. One, especially, which looked as if it had had it, took on a new lease of life and is now beautiful enough to move into the house. All the others appear to be doing well. If only I could take the wretched stuff!

Notice in a shop window
"Would the person who took away a jacket from this shop last week please return its contents. If it's the contents you want, please return the jacket. If you require both please call around for the trousers."

Mrs. C. H., Liverpool 8.
After lunch, feeling like nothing on earth, and with the usual mountain of ironing waiting to be done, I could hardly drag myself around. Suddenly, I remember my neighbour had given me a pep tablet. It was upstairs in my dressing gown pocket.

I hauled myself laboriously up the stairs, fumbled about in the wardrobe, found what I wanted, and popped it into my mouth. I've never got through that ironing so quickly. I looked for other jobs. I chopped some sticks, cleaned the windows – even washed a blanket . . . which just goes to show how marvellous those things are!

When I went to bed that night I put my hand in my dressing-gown pocket and found the tablet. I'd swallowed one of my son's Smarties. Who said there was no such thing as mind over matter?

Miss A. Bradley, Freshwater Bay, Isle of Wight.
When we were young, mother had this poem on the wall.

I had a friendly smile . . . I gave that smile away . . . The milkman and the postman . . . Seemed glad of it each day. I took it out when shopping . . . I had it in the street . . . I gave it (without thinking) . . . to all I chanced to meet.

I gave the little ones my smile . . . and, though I'd much to do . . . I gave it to my neighbours . . . the old folk had it, too . . . I always gave my smile away . . . as thoughtless as could be . . . yet every time (how wonderfully), . . . my smile returned to me.

Mrs. B. S. Thompson, Hemel Hempstead, Herts.
I haven't had a holiday for years. but I'm having one now. *Grace* is my constant companion and cheers me. My husband and two sons are

having to fend for themselves. I'm now free to wallow in a comfortable arm-chair, enjoy headphones radio, have meals brought on a tray, and receive visitors. I've never been doted on like this, ever. My hospital bedside locker is full of good things kind people have brought. I'm making the most of it while it lasts. Though only a small 'repair' job, it's like having it done in a five-star hotel. Having the time of my life!

Anonymous.
I am told my trouble is Buergher's disease, and my medical dictionary tells me it is thromboangitis obliterans which, I believe, is another name for a reduced blood flow through the veins and arteries. I am taking herbs but what do you advise in diet?

ED: *This is usually a heavy smoker's hazard. There is a diminished flow of blood because of clotting or coronary obstruction, often with pain in the leg on walking (intermittent claudication). Hawthorn and vitamin "E" are helpful. Avoid salt, sugar and alcohol. Take no caffeine drinks such as tea and coffee. Caffeine increases free fatty acids in the blood stream and destroys the vitamin B complex. A good mineral supplement is indicated, with special emphasis on time-released vitamin C. It is most vital to restrict fats to not over ten per cent of calories in your diet.*

Sunflower oil and wheatgerm may be taken with salads and cooked vegetables. A lack of vitamin E can worsen circulatory troubles. It can be a means of encouraging more blood to flow through constricted arteries and veins, bringing more nourishment to heart muscles and other organs. Known to nutritionists as fagopyrum, buckwheat contains rutin which helps strengthen small blood vessels. Do not overlook honey, for strength and energy. It is a fine heart sustainer.

And, of course, bread. What sort of bread? White or brown? A lady's son and daughter collected some tadpoles to see how they changed into frogs. Her son put crumbs of white bread in the bowl for them to feed on. Into her bowl of tadpole's the girl dropped some pieces of brown bread. The following day all the son's tadpoles were dead – floating on their backs upside down – but the daughter's were still living and continued to thrive.

Parsley has four times as much vitamin C as any other fruit or vegetable. It has an abundance of calcium, iron and phosphorous, and is a must for heart and circulatory troubles. Add a little chopped parsley to your salad every day.

Mrs. Yvonne Thomas, Winchester, Hampshire.
What is a good substitute for tea? Is there any truth in the saying that tea is bad for you?

ED: *Tea, not coffee, is the most popular beverage in the world. The tea plant belongs to the Camellia family and the important parts are the two top leaves and a bud from which our tea is made. Taken in moderation it is harmless, and its benefits are too well-known for repetition.*

Tea, like coffee, contains caffeine which is a powerful stimulant and the syndrome of caffeinism reads very much like a classic description of anxiety attack. Taken to excess it can be responsible for nervousness, irritability, headache, rapid breathing, agitation, insomnia and even ringing in the ears. Prolonged excesses burn up our precious supply of thiamine, or vitamin B1, the nutrient so necessary for tranquillity.

In your nearest health store you will find several excellent Dandelion coffees on sale. A newcomer on the scene is Rooibosch, or "Red Bush" tea from South Africa, which has a most tea-like flavour. This is not "Bush Tea" from Jamaica. Rooibosch contains no caffeine at all and is remarkably free from tannin. It deals gently with liver and kidneys, is of value for insomnia, and has some small reputation for rheumatism.

Roy Albert Lain, Coltishall, Norfolk.

Since it is now time for readers' tea-break a few class-room howlers may help restore the crinkle to a tired face and bolster a depleted optimism. By the way, did you know that a pessimist is a man who is never happy unless he is miserable? Even then, he is not pleased!

General knowledge: Milk is chiefly bought in tins, but it also grows in coconuts and cows.

Medicine: A skeleton is a man with his inside out and his outside off.

Stocks and shares. Debutantes are Debentures belonging to ladies.

History. Julius Caesar was a very strong man. He once threw a bridge across the Rhine . . . Henry 8th was very cruel to Ann Boleyn and ironed her. He pressed his suit on her.

Mr. A. W. Smith, 3 Victoria Street, Rochester, Kent.

The swallows make use of celandine, the linnet of euphrasie (eyebright), for the repairing of their eyesight.

Mr. W. Hubbard, Capetown, South Africa.

Is there a herb that can stop the tobacco habit? Or a special diet that will cure cigarette smoking?

ED: *There is no herb or diet that will supplant good old will power. Sorry, reader, but there is just no easy way of doing what in this case can best be done the hard way.*

Mr. William Tompkins, Liverpool.
Had you heard of the new cure? A woman, all doubled-up with arthritis, went to a Bingo session. Her first. She got so excited and carried-away that when she got up to go home, all her pains had vanished. They haven't come back yet, and she's got rid of her bath-chair. She said,"I completely forgot the pain in my knees and fingers and made up my mind to walk again." And she did.

H. C. M., Limerick, S. Ireland.
I gave up my exercises after my last baby was born and now I have quite a stomach. Is it too late to start now?
ED: *No. It's not too late. It will help abdomen and thighs by bending, twisting at the hips. Lying on your back, raise first one leg and then the other, keeping the leg straight. Push-ups. Try riding a bicycle in the air. Good posture and a good girdle are helpful. Keep an eye on the weight. On rising, be like a cat and s-t-r-e-t-c-h to your heart's content.*

Miss M. Freeman, Queens Park, Bournemouth.
I should like to tell you how very much I enjoy reading *Grace*. It is such a happy magazine and full of refreshing inspiration and interest. Shortly after reading the article on Euphrasie for eyes I came across the words of Milton: "Then purged with euphrasie and rue the visual nerve, for he had much to see".
ED: *Euphrasie (eyebright) and Rue (one of the old sacred herbs) have been used for impaired vision (not disturbances of accommodation) for centuries. They have also been used for infections of the eyes and diseases of the lids.*

H. Collins, London.
On my wife's birthday I took her to a show, and then to dinner in an expensive restaurant, where there were soft lights and sweet music.
As we were having our main course, a violinist came to our table and played gipsy music to us. It was so romantic, there were tears in my wife's eyes.
Still playing, the violinist bent down, and whispered in my wife's ear. When he went away, I asked, "What did he say?"
I shall never forget the expression on her face . "He asked me," she said, "what the chips were like."

Mrs. E. Hall, Cheltenham.
For my fidgety legs in bed, which entailed walking around two or three times every night, and sleeplessness, you recommend zinc tablets. I would like you to know that the zinc has almost conquered the problems. Very many thanks.

Lipika Tandon (14), Lancashire.
Customer: I would like to try out the suit in the window, please.
Assistant: I'm sorry sir, you have to try it on in the changing room like everyone else .

Lydia Darnton, Lancs.
I have experimented with all kinds of vitamins, minerals, evening primrose, etc., but have found that Agnus castus is the perfect thing for female complaints.

T. A. G., Herts.
I would like to alert all those who suffer from chilblains of a simple remedy that cured years of irritation for me overnight – Friar's Balsam. Soaked in cotton wool and dabbed on to offending toes, one or at most two applications should provide a permanent cure.

Mrs. L. Wells, Glasgow, Scotland.
Last night I was in the bath and the telephone rang. The call was from a friend the other end of the country and – of course I was glad to hear her voice – but fancy ringing-up at that time of night! I sat and shivered, anxious to get back into the bath to finish the job. But I thought it might not be wise to endanger a good friendship by cutting short the gossip. Today, I have a sniffly cold.

Just think of how much more convenient it would be to write a letter! Letters are precious, cheaper than the telephone, and can be cherished at any odd minutes during the day. A telephone chat is gone for ever. As I see it, there's nothing as nice as receiving a letter. Yours sincerely.

Mr. C. W. Piggott, Westgate on sea, Kent.
As many people have tried to do, I too cannot find words to adequately express my feelings of – what is it? – wonder, gratitude, comfort and help when receiving another issue of *Grace*.

The wise and helpful editorial, interesting articles, lovely pictures of countryside and animals, and the reports from readers of their successful treatments make it the best magazine I have read.

I would like to convey my congratulations to the Editor for his wonderful book 'Nature's Plan for Your Health.' It's most interesting reading apart from the invaluable advice on herbal treatment and the individual information on a selection of herbs. I keep it by my side and always follow recommendations when needing herbal treatment. God bless him and may he long continue to inspire us with his writings. Yours sincerely.

Charles Cameron, Denham, Bucks.
We were having tea one day last summer when a wasp flew in through an open window and buzzed around the head of our guest, who showed signs of alarm, jerking his head and waving his arms about.

43

"Don't mind him," said my youngest son. "It's only George."
We then had to explain that in our house the wasps were our friends and we gave them names – usually George!
Actually wasps are quite friendly creatures and will only sting when frightened. But the habit of blessing, or loving, that which threatens you does pay dividends. One of Buddha's disciples was once bitten by a snake and died. The other disciples were astonished and asked the Buddha how this could be. The Buddha replied: "His mind was unfriendly to the snake".
The writer was discussing this subject with a group of British and American actors in Hollywood recently and it was the consensus of opinion that by adopting a loving attitude of mind to all God's creatures – even poisonous snakes – one did find a measure of protection. This attitude applies even more so in our daily dealings with our fellow men.
A difficult customer in a shop; a tricky situation in business; a tiresome neighbour and so on: all these can be "healed", as it were by a loving frame of mind. After all, are we not commanded to love our neighbour? Not necessarily to like him, mark you, but to love him. There is a subtle difference.

Mrs. D. M. Grace, Headlands, Ossett.
Someone told us to scald red sage for my husband's boils and he hasn't had a boil for a while now.
When I was young, if I was a bit sluggish, my mother would scald the following in a quart of water: ¼oz. hops, ¼oz. wormwood, 2oz. honey, 1oz. mountain flax, and I had to take a wineglassful three times a day.

Mrs. Eaton, Bournemouth.
I have cured many severe cases of carbuncles and boils by using a cabbage leaf. In this way I have helped tradesmen from time to time. I take a cabbage leaf, tear out the stalk and midrib, and tear-up the leafy part into small pieces. I put these pieces of cabbage in a little heap over the boil and bind over a handkerchief or similar piece of linen. The leaf is, of course, washed before use.
I couldn't tell you the number of those who, doing this, have been amazed at the amount of pus extracted. The cabbage encourages it to burst and release all the poisons, which is much better than keeping them in the blood.
ED: *Thank you, Mrs. Eaton, for a useful contribution. This reminds us of the prediction of Maurice Woodruff in his book, "Know Tomorrow Today" (a Four Square Book). He says:*
"Nature is going to co-operate, once again, in the advance of medical knowledge. Just as penicillin was developed out of a natural mould, so a new antiseptic cure will be discovered in something as simple as, perhaps, a cabbage leaf . . . the outer leaf of a cabbage being placed over a particularly nasty, infectious-looking boil or surface growth – coming

away from the skin on the leaf. It will be discovered that there is some natural antidote in the outer leaves of the cabbage that has a particularly powerful "drawing" capacity which may well be developed by scientific research, into a powerful antibiotic."

Mr. C. Staddon, Ilfracombe, N. Devon.
Very many thanks for the year's *Grace* – a most healing publication deserving wider number of readers. As a retired pharmacist I appreciate greatly the simple things of life after 50 years of the world's rush and often useless antics. Some people try to alter Nature – but Nature always catches up on them. How nice it would be if, in sending you their subscriptions, our friends could order one copy to be posted to a friend, or to hand it on to others, thereby having a snowball effect. Yours sincerely.

From Miss L. Wright, Leicester.
I am finding great relief from the pains of arthritis by having a magnet in the bed. A few friends of mine have had a great success this way.
    ED: *This might appear to be a rather primitive practice, but surely any measure, no matter how simple, which can effectively eliminate pain, is a justifiable alternative to drugs. The trained physician has no right to smile down his nose in a superior manner just because a remedy is too simple to merit closer attention.*

Mr. M. J. Fox, Westmorland.
Some doctors say that Cod Liver Oil is of no value in arthritis or muscular rheumatism. They say it cannot reach the muscles to do them any good. This is all poppycock, because in my young days I was in the meat trade and I remember how the carcasses used to come in reeking with the smell of cod liver oil which used to be fed to animals to fatten them. And the flesh looked very healthy, on really fit animals.
    I followed Dr. Alexander's cod liver oil treatment for arthritis and am now free. Two tablespoons of the oil is shaken-up in orange juice and drunk last thing at night on an empty stomach. I had to do this for many months, but it was worth it. I know this oil does reach the joints and muscles. The capsules are no good for this purpose.

Mrs. Elizabeth Martyn, British Columbia, Canada.
However much of a wrench it is to part with our copies let us make up our minds that we will pass on at least four issues and that we will select the recipients carefully. Here are a few suggestions:
1. To send a copy to anyone known to be a keen gardener. Lovers of the soil will love *Grace*.
2. Send a copy to any branch of the R.S.P.C.A.
3. Send a copy to anyone interested in health. We can also remember

to use subscriptions to *Grace* as an easy and delightful Christmas or Birthday gift, sending to new recipients each time. It is all so simple. No letter need be written – just "With good wishes". Let us remember that freely we have received, and freely we can give.

K. H. Wilson, Moseley, Birmingham.
I know there are so many so-called 'cures' for arthritis, but what do you have to say?

ED: *One could fill a book with recommendations for treatment but I confine myself to one remedy only.*

In his book: "Hanssen's Complete Cider Vinegar", (Thorsons), Maurice describes the experience of a friend, Charles Walker, when he owned a Health Store in Birkenhead.

"An elderly man came in one day and danced around the shop. When questioned, he said he was not going crazy, he was demonstrating that he could dance. Two years before he had visited the store in a wheel-chair, crippled with arthritis. He had taken Cider Vinegar and Molasses for two years and now felt ten years younger!

Not everyone can expect such results, but they are at least a matter of common experience. Here is Dr D.C. Jarvis' advice for arthritis:

1. *Two teaspoonsful Cider Vinegar and two of honey in a glass of water, taken at each meal, or if not acceptable, between meals.*
2. *On Monday, Wednesday and Friday add one drop of iodine at one meal to the mixture.*
3. *One Kelp tablet at breakfast or at all three meals.*
4. *Avoidance of all wheat foods and cereals, white sugar, citrus fruits, muscle meats such as beef, lamb and pork, as these products have an adverse reaction.*

He says this regime helps rheumatoid arthritis, osteo-arthritis, bursitis and gout.

Howlers over the air.
John Snagge, on the Boat Race: I don't know who's ahead, but it's either Oxford or Cambridge.

Stuart Hibberd, reporting a volcano: Floods of molten lager flowing down the mountainside.

After a programme of Polish folk dances, an announcer commented: "You have been listening to Foolish Poke Dances.

Mary Kendle-Jackson, Deganwy, North Wales.
While cleaning my teeth in front of my granddaughter, she spotted the small plate I held in one hand which I was trying to conceal from her. "O, Granny," says she, "What is that?" I replied, "Well, Evie, these are not my own teeth." I had to laugh when she said, "Whose are they then, Granny?"

Harrogate in spring, the first warm day.   *British Tourist Authority*

WHAT Beauty glows in every cup
When tulips lift each challenge up!

1. *Harold Gwynne.*

47

Miss Mabel Morton, Wigan.
I was interested in Thurlow Craig's article on the sheepdog which ate grapes and became fit again.

I had a similar experience with my poodle only a week or two ago. He lost his appetite completely, and I could find nothing which would tempt him to eat. He began to lose weight.

One day I happened to be sitting by the fire eating white grapes. Suddenly the dog's eyes lit up-imploring me to give him some.

He ate them ravenously. Next day I gave him a few more and soon he was his old self again.

I read in an extremely old medical book that grapes were the "finest thing one could eat", being very beneficial for the liver and kidneys.

Do dogs know instinctively what would put them right?

Mr. P. Smithson, Reading, Berks.
What can I do for falling hair?

ED: *Diet is important. Make sure you are not taking too much salt. If you can cut it out so much the better. Wash the hair once weekly with green soft soap. Massage the scalp with a little coconut oil.*

Mr. H. Thorne, Oxford Road, Reading, Berks.
Is there any simple first aid measure for the relief of cramp?

ED: *In sudden attack of cramp relief may often be obtained by stretching the affected limb by elevating the heel as much as possible till the toes bend backward towards the shin.*

Osteopaths recognise the above simple treatment as a means of stretching the sciatic nerve. An even better result may be induced when a second person performs the manoeuvre. Assume the right leg has cramp. Let the patient lie on his back, relaxed. The operator should stand on the patient's right side, raising the limb to cradle it in his right elbow. His right hand will come to rest about half way up the shin. The operator's left hand should grasp the patient's knee joint, pressing downwards. to prevent bending of the knee.

Let the operator raise the whole of the patient's right leg in the crook of his right elbow until the limb is in the perpendicular position – at right-angles with the couch or bed. With firm pressure from the left hand the knee joint will not be allowed to bend and the sciatic nerve can be stretched and freed from any possible impingement at any point along its course or points of origin.

This is a reinforced version of what George, the gardener, does for the relief of his cramp. He says: "Strongly stretch out your heel, pulling the toes downwards."

This manoeuvre also stretches the Achilles tendon and leg muscles – not a bad thing for some cases of rheumatism or fibrositis. The secret is not to mind the initial neuralgic discomfort when the "stretch" is at its maximum intensity.

Anonymous.
My parents are on holiday for a week and for the first time in my twenty years I have been left to fend for myself. My eyes have been truly opened to the problems of loneliness.

Before, I had grand ideas of leaving home for a flat of my own. I realise now that nothing can replace a home and family.

The silence of an empty house was almost unbearable, and I eagerly awaited the sound of letters dropping on to the mat. Television became a companion; shopping was something to look forward to as a chance of conversation with other folk.

I understand now how lonely life can be for the housebound. My first call tomorrow? The local welfare office to see if one or two lonely folk nearby need a visitor for a few hours each week.

Dr. Benjamin Rush.
Science has much to deplore from the multiplication of diseases. It is as repugnant to truth in medicine, as polytheism is to truth in religion. The physician who considers every different affection of the different systems in the body, or every affection of different parts of the same system, as distinct diseases, when they arise from one cause, resembles the primitive peoples of the world who consider water, dew, ice, frost and snow, as different essences . . .

The sword will probably be sheathed for ever, as an instrument of death, before physicians will cease to add to the mortality of mankind by prescribing for the names of disease.

BALM TEA

Sweet Balm, or Lemon Balm, grows in most gardens. To make tea, place a few leaves (stripped from the stalk) into a teapot and infuse for 15 minutes. Drink freely. If honey and a little lemon juice be added it makes a most refreshing drink.

John Evelyn says, "Balm is sovereign for the brain. It strengthens the memory, and powerfully chases away melancholy (depression)". Combined with nutmeg and angelica root it has a great reputation as a remedy for nervous headache and neuralgia.

RASPBERRY LEAF TEA

I am a great believer in using Herbs to help to retain good health – you speak of RASPBERRY LEAF TEA, and I want you to know that I have been using it for a number of years to prevent cramps in my legs, caused by poor circulation. If I take the tea night and morning, I do not have cramps, but if I forget it for two or three days, then I suffer from the cramps . . .

Extract from a letter from Mrs. Dorothy Sheldon-Flynn, of Aliston, Mass., U.S.A.

Mr. E. Raynor, Inverness, Scotland.
When we had our first child my wife and I read all the Dr. Spock books and tried to carry out his advice. We did our share of patient persuasion with our son, explaining that little boys do not walk on your best plants to recover toy motors, lock puss in the garage, or lift an orange behind your back at the greengrocer's that you didn't discover until you got outside. For general naughtiness we were sweet reasonableness itself. Did it work? Not on your Nelly!

From the day I lost my temper and gave his bottom a resounding smack, we haven't had a single cause for complaint. What d'ye make of that?

Letter in a South African magazine.
I recently read an article which advised a cure for an inferiority complex. It suggested writing down on paper all the things that one could do, then reading back to raise one's ego. I thought I'd try that . . .

As I did so I became aware of many wonderful things I could do – though certainly not to my own credit. I could see, hear, walk, talk, laugh, cry, sleep, smell beautiful perfumes, and enjoy so many God-given things. I thought how very wrong it is to feel inferior when we have been made to such a splendid pattern. Surely inferiority borders on discontent.

I also realised even more clearly the tremendous courage of the people who have lost one of these faculties and have overcome it. They hadn't time to indulge in self pity as I had done. It was certainly a great cure!

Miss E. A. Hobden, Eastbourne, Sussex.
I should like to tell you of my success with nettles. Pick the tops out of nettles – about the first 4-6 leaves, wash well and cook for about 7 minutes. I find they are nicer if cooked with equal amount of greens of some sort. Of course I drink the liquor too, and I haven't had a common cold for four years! That is well worth the little bit of effort involved.

ED: *Thank you. Miss Hobden. We think cooked nettles taste like spinach – without the oxalic acid!*

Letter of appeal from a young woman to her Income Tax Inspector.
Please, may my case be investigated by one adult male, moderately attractive, single and approximately 35 years of age? Anything you can do to help will be appreciated. With your help and my wit, we might be able to decrease the number from two single tax returns to one joint return.

Mrs. Shirley Newman, Rednal, Birmingham.
Some time ago I discovered a method of successfully relieving headaches. Close your eyes. In your mind search for the central point of the pain, and fix it in the mind. Relax while you do so. It can be truly amazing how the pain just melts away.

Each time the mind wanders, the pain will return. By repeating this mental concentration the periods of freedom from pain increase; one becomes drowsy, and able to sleep. I understand this is an old Tibetan technique and can assure you it has really worked on headaches, and sprained ankles. It has even relieved pain after dental extraction. Thank you for all the wonderful articles. Keep up the good work. Yours sincerely.

Mrs. C. Nelson, Essex.
A letter from Mrs. Gladys Cooper in a past issue reminds me of my father. He was a sea captain who always slept with his head to the north, being convinced that it had real advantages. Incidentally, he was the first man to take a small steam ship across the Atlantic.

Mrs. E. Simpson, Andover, Hants.
May I mention something regarding dogs, as natural medicine and, spiritual healing applies to them as well as humans. I have a number of dachschunds and, some two months ago, my litter of five babies, then six weeks old, developed acute skin trouble, crustations forming, and in consequence sore places and loss of hair. The vet, said "mange" (they always do!) and he gave me some very expensive lotion which did no good at all. Friends said, "Put them to sleep, you'll never get rid of it." I then made up a lotion of one part flowers of sulphur and eight parts olive oil, applied it twice, then continued with olive oil only. Meanwhile I had written to an animal healer through whom I have had many miracles over the years – even curing a dog of paralysis (she is now back in the show ring).

These puppies are now three months old and all have lovely coats and are in excellent health. I pass this on in case other dog-lovers may find it useful.

Mrs. Alex Ingrey, London, Ontario, Canada.
My husband has been bothered with a stuffy nose for years, and reading where brewers' yeast is so good for everyone, also honey, I now put in a mug, about ½ cup of powdered milk, ½ teasp. brewers' yeast, fill up with hot water, add 1 tablesp. natural honey. This he takes once a day. Now his nerves are so much better and no more nose trouble. I ran out of honey for a while and then came back the nose trouble.

Mrs. D. H. Baxter, Bowd, Sidmouth, Devon.
Would this help Miss S. N. Carfree . . . ?
During a bronchial cough recently I found the more usual remedies not too helpful so I tried a teaspoonful of honey and five or six drops of Olbas Oil well mixed, and just a small amount on the tip of a teaspoon taken from time to time a very great help, allowing the mixture to be sipped slowly.

Here also is an amazing episode which happened in a very quiet lane as we were travelling slowly along in the car and talking about the poor hens kept in the dark and how we hoped to get eggs from "free range hens". In the lane we noticed a "white paper" which as we drew near and shifted, rose with a loud squawk and hurried away, leaving a really beautiful white egg in the middle of the road. Truly free range and newly laid.

Mrs. Turton, Sheffield.
For years I've tried various remedies for Piles without results. Lately I decided Comfrey was good for external use; why not internal? So I have been eating raw two or three small leaves of Comfrey in the morning, with wonderful results. I would like to pass this on to fellow readers of *Grace*.

Mrs. Eileen Marsh, "Lands End", Hamilton P.O., Bermuda.
I am going to tell you a true story that happened to me a few weeks ago. A young friend from Australia was staying with us. We went for a swim off the end of our garden (we live on the sea edge), and whilst swimming I was stung badly by a Portuguese-man-of-war jellyfish. I warned Campbell, but he was doing the Australian crawl and went slap into the same jellyfish. The tendrils were wrapped round his body and legs and he was badly stung. We got out of the water and I felt here was a chance to try an experiment. We had both been stung by the same jellyfish, so I ran up to the house and got a lemon and made him squeeze the juice on all the stings and let it dry. I did not use anything.

That night it was painful and I must have scratched the irritation for hours on end. The next morning my stings were red and angry and uncomfortable. Campbell had little tiny pinpricks where the stings had been, but no irritation whatsoever and no pain. By noon there was nothing to see on his skin, whereas mine lasted six solid days. That was one experiment that proved itself.

Two days after all this I fell into a bed of stinging nettles and my knees were covered with the stings. Again my thoughts turned to lemon and I rushed inside poured the juice on and within two seconds all the sting had gone and never returned. I feel this is a tip worth knowing, especially for children.

So now I am waiting for someone to get stung by a bee or a hornet and let me see if the lemon juice works. I'm sure it will. Any offers? The more I eat a completely uncooked raw food diet, the more convinced I become that this is the cure for almost every known ill.

God bless all the readers. You ask if any have had results by switching the direction of one's bed to face the magnetic north. Yes, indeed. Ever since we turned our bed to face the north we have slept much better and generally felt we had more energy. This definitely coincided with turning the bed round. Both my husband and I noticed it. So we quite agree with Mrs. Gladys Cooper whose letter appeared in a past magazine.

ED: *I never cease to wonder at the versatility of the lemon – one of God's healing gifts to men. I doubt if there is any one single discovery in the whole realm of medical science which is capable of curing so many different conditions.*

And don't you clever ones try to tell me that it is purely due to the citric acid and vitamin C it contains. It contains a whole context of inorganic minerals and trace elements, not to mention other invisible constituents science has not yet caught up with. I once read a very boastful pharmaceutical article claiming we already knew all there was to know about this common citrus fruit. Believe me. We have not yet turned over the first few pages in the book of the lemon.

The following conditions have disappeared by the use of lemon juice: biliousness, felon, erysipelas, innumerable colds and coughs, sore throats, hiccoughs, freckles from the face, corns, loss of voice, headache. One lady lost two stones in weight within six weeks from a lemon fast.

Mrs. Beaton had a use for it, too, the removal of rust stains. Some folk get a kick out of cleaning their teeth with it. Personally, I just haven't the courage to face up to lemon first thing in the morning!

Mrs. E. I. P. writes:
"Recovering from an illness, I was left so weak and low. Neither did I feel elated when my husband helped me downstairs, out into the car. We drove out into the country and stopped beside a church. The outlook was depressing indeed. I wished I were at home. Then, with a sudden burst the sun came out. What a transformation! Masses of daffodils lit up the grass with gold. How could I ever forget that moment?"

Leslie Russell, Birmingham 37.
May I join your many readers who express their appreciation of great pleasure on the delivery of *Grace*; so aptly named, and which makes such delightful reading.

The beautiful picture in the Summer number: "On the banks of the Cherwell" with Magdalen College tower in the background and part of the Botanical Gardens on the left brings back happy memories, tempting me to say, "Those were the days". I worked in the university Botanical Laboratory a little left of the picture.

(continued on page 56)

The value of pollen

By Professor Remy Chauvin, Paris

WHEN bees collect the nectar from which they produce honey, they also collect pollen from the flowers. Bees themselves eat honey, but they feed their larvae with nothing but pollen. Because of this diet the larvae grow 1,500 times their original weight in six days!

These small grains of pollen contain all the nutrition that can lead to the formation of a fruit and a new plant. Long before man, the bees discovered this remarkable source of energy and life and for the past fifty years scientists have been studying these little grains which in nature cause such unique, speedy growth.

Our modern food gives us, without our knowing it, sickness due to malnutrition, a fact which is becoming more and more known. Many important vitamins and minerals are absent because of the "purification" of our foods.

This causes disturbances which are all too well known to us and which give us great discomfort.

Tiredness, lowered resistance to illness, loss of appetite, weakness and depression, premature ageing and, especially, frequently occurring intestinal and digestive disturbances (constipation) and difficulties that arise because of food that is nutritionally insufficient.

Scientists can now, after many years of research, testify that "bee bread", as flower pollen is also called, is a very valuable product.

French and German scientists studying the bee have stated that it is a source of nutrition with an unusually large supply of vital elements and should therefore be used in cases of difficulties connected with diet, constipation, diarrhoea and sickness due to malnutrition.

All the amino acids, glutamatic acids, calcium, Vitamin B complex, Vitamins C and A as well as many traces of minerals are found in elements that can fill the deficiencies in our diet.

Pollen, which is not a medicine, is an ideal complementary food, absolutely pure and always harmless and easy to take.

While pollen is not a laxative, it has shown itself to be effective against constipation and intestinal disturbances. It restores the natural rhythm. Everybody's well-being depends to a large extent upon the normal functioning of the intestines.

For children's disturbances in their growing years, for convalescence, for over-exertion, which is so common in our days, for threatening premature loss of strength—in short, in all cases of physical and psychological exertion or because of malnutrition—without the dangers of chemical and synthetic stimulants.

In general, pollen brings about: a feeling of general well-being; restored physical and psychological vitality; greater resistance to illness; a better balance in the nervous system and improved appetite.

Pollen complements the daily diet, restores balance and harmony.

FRIENDS

The trees and the flowers
 Shall now be my friend;
The trees and the flowers
 That never pretend.
They keep to their nature
 As, quiet and true,
They grow to their stature
 And bloom in their hue.
 —*Mary F. Robinson*

54

Baby mine.   *J. Allan Cash.*

WHERE did you come from baby dear? *Out of the everywhere into here.*
Where did you get those eyes so blue? *Out of the sky as I came through.*
What makes the light in them sparkle and spin? *Some of the starry spikes left in.*
Where did you get that little tear? *I found it waiting when I got here.*
What makes your forehead so smooth and high? *A soft hand stroked it as I passed by.*
What makes your cheek like a warm, white rose? *I saw something better than anyone knows.*
Whence that three-cornered smile of bliss? *Three angels at once gave me a kiss.*
Where did you get this pearly ear? *God spoke and it came out to hear.*
Where did you get those arms and hands? *Love made itself into hooks and bands.*
Feet, whence did you come from, you darling things? *From the same box as a cherub's wings.*
How did they all come to be just you? *God thought about me and so I grew.*
But how did you come to us, you dear? *God thought about you and so I am here.*

Author Unknown.

55

I was "up" at Oxford when Sydney H. Vines was Professor of Botany and shall never forget the day when he caught me smoking a cigarette. He admonished me severely, giving me a lecture on the futility of the habit; then offering to pay for my further education – provided I gave up smoking! His own excellent health as a non-smoker was sufficient evidence for me. I gave it up.

And so the years have rolled by. I am now retired and thoroughly enjoy a full day's gardening, freshened up with an occasional drink of raw carrot juice. Many times during the past 50 years I have passed on that sound advice, so kindly given, in that laboratory beneath the "dreaming spires" of Oxford.

Mrs. F. H. Chubb, Southbourne, Dorset.
Quite by chance I discovered a marvellous way of getting off to sleep without drugs. One night, I thought I would have a drink of milk but was surprised to find there was none in the pantry. I felt I really must have something "to go to bed on", so I poured out a drink of boiling water and put in a teaspoonful of honey. It was insipid and not very palatable. I increased the honey to one tablespoonful and it made a most satisfying drink.

When I went to bed I slept like a log. I have taken it ever since. Milk and honey at night is an old remedy for insomnia, but the milk can give a little heartburn, so boiling water can do the job better for some people. Don't tell me that bees are the only ones who go drowsy in the wintertime.

Mrs. E. L. Weightman, Leigh-on-Sea, Essex.
My "daily help" came to me very distressed as her husband for years had been in misery with his feet, directly the hot weather started. He had been to many hospitals. But no relief. The same tale from each – "Bath, dry, powder". How many folk know or realise our skin breathes by the pores and through these are exuded the impurities from the body, the feet being the chief place? So where is the sense in washing and cleaning the pores, to fill them up again with powder? Impurities are kept in, which for some means blistered feet, and for others, ailments they might never have had. Exactly what do our Teaching Hospitals teach? Sure, the simple things confound the mighty. *Grace* is smashing. Long may it reign. Happy holiday.

Gerald North, Salisbury, Zimbabwe.
We have read a lot of literature in magazines and newspapers telling us of the dangers of smoking cigarettes. If they are as bad as all that, why don't we get warnings from the doctors?

ED: *Pleased to hear from you, Mr. North. Greetings from members of the "Grace" to you and your family down there in sunny Zimbabwe.*

No number of words from myself could possibly persuade habitual smokers of cigarettes to give up the habit. It is one of those difficult decisions we sometimes have to make. I can only repeat what a vast body of distinguished physicians, surgeons, and experimental scientists have stated:
"Studies of the past two decades have demonstrated conclusively that tobacco smoke contains carcinogenic chemicals and that heavy cigarette smoking is closely correlated with an increased incidence of lung cancer, and other major respiratory diseases. There is no longer reasonable doubt that cigarette smoking is a major cause of lung cancer."
Sorry, Gerald. There it is. We just can't find a single card in the pack to trump this ace.

Anonymous.
I find Peroxide of Hydrogen such a quick and effective cure for corns. Applied freely, daily, the corns seem to die. Their appearance does not change much, but in a very short time there is neither pain nor swelling. So simple. Yours sincerely.

Mr. Bannerman, Leeds.
I have tried Vitamin "E" for varicose veins and am amazed that we have heard so little about it. They are much better, and however many hours I spend on my feet, they now don't seem to bother me at all. I used to feel half awake, but am now full of vitality and want to do things in the evenings where, only a few months ago, all I wanted to do was to sleep. I have to write this by order of my wife.

Fruiterer's shop round the corner.
Little boy: "Half a pound of mixed nuts, please." After a pause: "And not too many coconuts."

From: The Reverend Arthur J. Wilson, Dartford, Kent.
I consider your *Grace Magazine* the best I have read. I am a retired priest of the Church of England, aged 82 years. I am correct when I say and write, that on my list of many books and magazines I read and have on my bookshelves, *Grace Magazine* is written third. The first is the Bible, the second the Book of Common Prayer. I have never read a magazine so well edited as *Grace*, and so very helpful in these days of rush and delinquency, drug addicts, robberies, assaults on young children and elderly men and women.

I worked in North Western Canada for eight years as a priest, where the weather in winter was often 65 degrees below zero. I lived alone in a nine-room rectory which I never locked up, even when I was away visiting the homesteads and farmers for a week from Sunday to Saturday. I travelled by horse-drawn buggy in summer and horse-drawn sleigh in winter.

I would like my relations and friends to know the joy and helpfulness your magazine can give. Therefore I enclose herewith from an old age pensioner a cheque to further your work. Many thanks for your help to me. I am almost housebound now after five operations but I look forward to many more years of joy.

Anonymous, Lincoln.
I read that rhubarb contains oxalic acid which can cause "stone" or interfere with the body's calcium. We grow and like the stuff. Do we have to go without it?
ED: *No . . . if you take with it calcium-rich foods such as eggs, bread and cheese. Oxalic acid is found in chocolate, cocoa, rhubarb, spinach, and you may not believe it . . . in tea. Even tea-drinkers can leach calcium from the body tissues, when drinking to excess.*

Roy Briggs, Bognor Regis, Sussex.
Can you tell me how did we ever manage to get the terrific population we now have without the help of special school programmes and today's so-called sex experts?

C. Martinet, Lausanne, Switzerland.
We duly received *Grace* – Autumn – issue, which we were looking forward to read and inwardly digest. You never fail to strengthen our faith and hope with every copy you send us. We are very grateful to you and your collaborators for sustaining our joy of living, sense of beauty in Nature and rewarding human contacts in the face of a grim and cheerless world.

Mrs. M. Morgan, Llanhennock, Gwent.
I must tell you that through reading *Grace* and the article on castor oil in it, I have got rid of my housemaid's knee after many years. I have so much to thank you for.

Mr. C. Carmichael, Liverpool 8.
Every time I clean my teeth my mouth fills with blood. My gums are so sensitive. When I wake in the morning my pillow is stained with blood.
ED: *It sounds very much like gingivitis or Vincent's disease. Inflammation of the gums is usually treated by your dentist. If he has been unsuccessful then it could be your opportunity to administer a little harmless "safe-help".*

THE REAL CAUSE

There is but one cause of disease – poison, toxaemia, most of which is created in the body by faulty habits and faulty elimination.

MAJOR-GENERAL SIR ARBUTHNOT LANE, M.D.

From your nearest herbalist or chemist obtain a small bottle (say, 30 mls.) Tincture of Myrrh, B.P.C. Take a tumber half-full of water and add five drops of the tincture. This will turn the water milky. Use as a gargle three times daily. Do not accept the tincture from any vendor where it is already milky. This implies that water has already been added. The natural tincture is a deep orange colour and turns milky as soon as it comes into contact with water. Results are poor where the change of colour has not been effected immediately on using. If the milky liquid has been already made up in a bottle some days or weeks ahead, results are impaired. Persevere for two or three months, if necessary.

A letter in a magazine.
Not long ago, I had a short spell in hospital. One evening during visiting time, I had no visitors. So I decided to put on the ear-phones and listen to some music. One of my operatic favourites was being played, which cheered me a lot. When the music stopped, I got a surprise. The whole ward was staring at me. Then they gave me a round of applause. I had been singing at the top of my voice.

Mrs. H. S. (Anonymous), Lowestoft, Suffolk.
A few days after my wedding six years ago I started with cystitis and I have had all kinds of treatment, but none have been good for long. I can't stand any more urine tests and antibiotics. Urination is painful.

ED: *Obviously your gynaecologist has done everything in his power. Why not tackle it from the aspect of a deranged hormone balance? Are you sure it is not due to taking the "Pill"? Herbal tablets of Agnus Castus may prove helpful, together with frequent drinks of Buchu infusion. Place one heaped teaspoonful of buchu leaves (barosma betulina) into a teacup and fill with boiling water. Drink half teacupful one hour before meals, three times daily. If well tolerated, dosage may be increased in severe cases.*

Anonymous.
The lady who chatted to me as I waited for the last bus home one night certainly enjoyed a natter. After minutes of it, I looked at my watch and remarked how late the bus was. "Oh, it's gone, my dear", she said, in a friendly way. But I'm not waiting for it. I live alone across the road, and generally come here for a chat before I turn in.

R. S. Bennett, Edinburgh, Scotland.
I get thirsty and wonder what to drink. Tea and coffee are supposed to be bad for my arthritis.

ED: *Vichy water. Spa waters are not very popular, these days. At the turn of the century they were taken for the rheumatic disorders. Maybe there is a place for it to tone up the digestive system and cut down acidity. It is a natural spa water, bottled as it flows from the famous springs*

*at Vichy. Is rich in valuable minerals, increasing enzyme secretion. Worth
a trial. Take tea in moderation.*

Mrs. C. Philip, Fareham, Hants.
I feel you should know what Comfrey Ointment has done for me (one
jar). I was bedridden and had a bad bedsore covering my right ankle bone,
all smothered each day in pus.

I dressed it thickly with Comfrey Ointment every day for three days
and then every other day. At the end of the tenth day the sore had sealed
over, very clean and tender, but healed. Thanking you with all my heart
for such a miracle.

I would also like you to know that giving my Scottish Terriers three
Comfrey Tablets (crushed-up) in their last evening meal has cleared-up
their skin eczema. There has been no recurrence for six years. Another
miracle.

Mrs. E. D. Leatherbarrow, Ormskirk, Lancs.
I remember reading in an article in *Grace* that someone else taking Vitamin
E capsules had experienced a similar effect followed by a complete heal-
ing of ulceration and asked if you had any experience of similar cases.
You replied that I could not do better than continue with Vitamin E.

After reading in *Grace* of someone using Peroxide on leg ulcers, I tried
it – just a drop on each of two and it did start to shrink them. I was also
taking the Vitamin E when this irritation set up. It was burning and itching so much one night that I wondered what to do to relieve it, when I
recalled reading of someone using Pear Juice on shingles with benefit.
Suddenly, I don't know why, I thought of Grape Juice, so I squeezed some
juice from a grape on to the irritation with immediate relief. I did this
twice a day for about two weeks and all the irritation cleared up. I spread
it on like a lotion, gently rubbing it around – now I can wriggle my ankle
which I haven't done for some time, with ease, and the ulcers, too, have
dried up and almost gone. The relief was fantastic. No doubt the combination of Vitamin E has helped, but others may like to know of the Grape
Juice.

Overheard on a London bus:
"I certainly hope I'm ill," said a passenger to her companion. 'I'd hate
to feel like this if I'm well."

John Tobe, Ontario, Canada. Publisher
I've just read about the passing of a Toronto financier at the ripe old age
of 53. That's a ripe old age now, you know! Or don't you know?

Well, this Toronto big-shot was the president of one of Canada's largest
processing meat companies. He was also president of one of Canada's
largest dairies. Besides this, he was at one time president of a large sugar

refinery. Most health-food-conscious people regard white sugar as the cloak-and-dagger villain capable of stabbing you in the heart when you least expect it. I almost forgot to tell you, the deceased was also president of the National Heart Foundation, as well as chairman of the Canadian Heart Fund.

Of course, what else? Naturally, he died of a heart attack. And all this just goes to prove that he who lives by the sword shall perish by the sword.

Paul Rendall, Woking, Surrey.
I met Brita at the last D.D.A. "Rally" at R.A.F., Locking, near Weston-super- Mare, on 21st July, 1968. We have much in common but for age (I'll be 42 in a week from yesterday, and Brita won't be 28 until 22nd May). We both drive hand- controlled cars, Brita's privately bought and "my" Mini issued to me as a War Pensioner.

When Brita Somerset was five, she had polio, and her parents were advised to "put her in a home", as it was said that she would never even sit up again, let alone walk. Her parents refused. Brita learnt to swim when she was seven, and that progressed so well (doubtless through her perseverance, will-power and determination) that, in 1964, she was chosen to represent South Africa in the Paraplegic Olympic Games held in Tokyo. There she won one Gold and two Silver medals for swimming, and a further Gold for archery. Two years later she was again chosen to represent her country in the Paralympics held here, at Stoke Mandeville, where she won two Gold and 1 Silver medal for swimming, and yet another Gold for archery.

She had to wear a caliper on each leg, and had a back brace. Some time ago she discarded these "aids" and walked with shoulder crutches, using her wheelchair only when at work as it enables her to "get around" faster. We both love music, ballet, poetry and literature.

Mr. J. Barlow, Birkenhead.
When a young man, I did not know what it was like to go through a summer without hay fever. I had asthma when a boy and could not be taken for a holiday at the seaside. My grandfather said he thought it was the cheese which was upsetting me. My father insisted I have no cheese, milk or dairy products whatsoever and I have never had asthma or hay fever since. I enjoy an annual holiday at the seaside with my family.

Mrs. H. Collins, Hull.
To enable the family to win some table-ware by collecting trading stamps for a certain breakfast food, we spent a lot of "housekeeping" cash before we collected the necessary number. My husband could not eat up all that breakfast food, and you can imagine my surprise when, coming down to breakfast one morning, I found the stack of packets nearly halved.

It was not until later in the day that I found out what had happened to them. Ugly cracks in the wainscotting in the bedroom had been neatly repaired. It just goes to show how, if cooked long enough, a good porridge has more uses than one.

G. Bryan Jones, London, S.W.10.
We are a big and growing family of *Grace*. We love it and do admire you for all the knowledge put into it. The drinking of Sage Tea was one of the health "tips" you gave us in the past; we have taken it ever since, and have felt the benefit of it.

Mrs. J. I. Hazelton, Cromer, Norfolk.
Grace Magazine arrived yesterday. Have you heard of Dr. Bach's Flower Remedies? I had great success with his Rescue Remedy for toothache. A drop or two was dropped, neat, into the hollow tooth. My dentist was amazed to see how the gums had healed up by the next morning. Trusting many readers will find comfort in your lovely magazine.

ED: *The Rescue Remedy is a combination of five remedies used by Dr. Bach in all cases of emergency. They are: Rock Rose, Star of Bethlehem, Cherry Plum, Clematis and Impatiens. A farm-worker broke his wrist. He was in a state of collapse and great pain, two still brandies helped him not at all. Then Bach's Rescue Remedy was given. It brought relief in half a minute. A sceptical nurse who was present, left marvelling. Nora Weeks, together with Victor Bullen carried on the work of the late Dr. Edward Bach, at Mount Vernon, Sotwell, Wallingford, Berks. A copy of their "News-Sheet" can be read with interest.*

Mr. Giles, Poole. Dorset.
My grandfather used House Leeks (fractured and rubbed on) for bee-stings. We used to bruise two plantain leaves between two stones, using the pulp for wasp-stings, with good effect.

Fred Willings, London, S.E.9.
For some months I followed the articles in *Grace Magazine* by Capt. Geoffrey Whitehouse, on Vitamin E. At first I thought his claims rather exaggerated. But now I have proved, for myself, how effective is this alpha tocopherol from natural sources. If, a year ago, anybody had told me it could steady my tachycardia, improve my circulation and enable me to breathe freely at night, I would have disbelieved them. But now I know that every word is true and I cannot, for the life of me, understand how it has such limited recognition in present times of "cardiacs" and coronaries.

Mrs. Eileen Marsh, Bermuda.
My friend, Mrs. Shelley, has just told me about her 75-year-old father who for years suffered from terrible cramps in his legs. They had known him

to wake up at night crying out with pain, so Mrs. Shelley asked her old countrywoman friend what she would recommend. "Get a block of rock-sulphur," she replied, "and put it in tissue paper and place it beneath his pillow. But don't tell him." This was faithfully carried out. After two months, Mrs. Shelley said, I haven't heard you complain about that night-cramp of yours lately."

"No," he replied. "It's strange, you know, I haven't had that cramp for weeks and weeks, I wonder what's happened? Guess I am growing out of them."

"I guess so," was all she said.

The old man has never had a twinge of cramp since.

Mr. J. E. Johnson, Weston-super-Mare Somerset.

My wife has Paget's disease, and I am told this is an incurable disease of the bone, She is 65 years, and has to be on her legs a lot, and does not want to continually take drugs for the pain. What would you recommend?

ED: *There is no easy way to relief from this distressing condition. If relief comes at all, it can be the result of combined operations: dietetic adjustment, osteopathy, and harmless internal medication with Comfrey and Biochemic remedies. First indication of something wrong may be the presence of tender, hot and aching bones, especially at night. Bones of the thighs, back and head may be affected; but a common cause may be the one where bones of the leg are deformed and bent. When the inflammation recedes, pain may disappear and the bones harden.*

Do not attempt self-medication. If your doctor has gone as far as he can go, and finds himself up against a brick wall, do not accept the "you-must-learn-to-live-with-it" chestnut. Be determined to help yourself, reading what literature you can about the complaint, and consulting a reliable, well-recommended herbalist.

Mrs. Clare Robertson, Bristol 8.

Have you ever had one of those it's-all-happening days? If so, you'll know what I mean. A precious reply to a letter was delivered next door with the result that four of the family all came trooping in together for lunch, with me knowing nothing about it. Just when I got the cooking organised, the laundryman came to the door and kept me talking for five whole minutes. By this time the soup had boiled over, ruining a cake cooling-off on the grill below. A visitor slipped and hurt her ankle, and the Witch-Hazel to bathe it was not in its usual place in the bathroom cabinet. The cat was sick, and the telephone was ringing its head off, it never occurring to anyone else to answer it.

At last, after scraping the pantry clean for a hastily improvised lunch, we all sat down expectantly. Just at that moment the front doorbell rang and a little man with a big portmanteau asked if we had any old coins for

(continued on page 66)

Carrot Juice Miracle

IN NOVEMBER 1935, an Edinburgh surgeon made an exploratory operation on Mrs. S. (Edinburgh), aged 76, and diagnosed cancer of the bowel. She was given six months to live. She was discharged from hospital to die. Sinking steadily, milk and brandy were given to allay the vomiting and the great pain Loved ones could see the approach of death and many anxious minds were being frantically exercised in an eleventh-hour effort to see if anything further could be done. Someone came along with the simple suggestion that carrot juice was cleansing and, if it did little good but refresh the suffering one, it could do no harm.

Hearts stood still as they gave her the first few sips of cold carrot juice. She could take it. On the second day the continual vomiting ceased. Nor did it return. On the sixth day the stools were free from pus and blood. Hope came with the well-formed stools which were seen to be clean and of a healthier hue. Urine approached normality. By this time they were giving over ten pints of fresh carrot juice weekly. All acid-forming foods were cut out. A new lustre entered the eyes and roses returned to the sunken cheeks. It was some weeks before pain and discomfort disappeared. We can imagine the delight with which members of the family took her out for a walk some seven weeks after commencement of this purely empiric practice. Weight increased, and a new life lay before her.

"I can find no tumour at all," said her surprised doctor when he examined her six months after the original medical verdict. Not content with this, he weighed her. She had gained four stones since commencing the carrot juice.

It is noteworthy to record cases of this nature, but we should not be too quick to believe that this simple vegetable is the answer in every case. Doubtless the potassium salts in the juice completed some as-yet-unknown chemical chain of reactions in the patient's body, and proved to be just the right remedy for her. There have been cures by other domestic remedies, including small tumours which Father Kneipp had known to disappear with the ample use of honey; but they did not work every time. However, whatever form of treatment is given for the malignant diseases of mankind it would appear that the lot of the patient would be favourably influenced by refreshing drinks of pure carrot juice to quench thirst, and for liberal quantities of honey to be incorporated in the diet.

"Human Case Book"

Nancy Walmsley

A YOUNG WOMEN, aged 38, with a lovely husband but away a lot, met someone who apparently fell in love with her. This attachment went on for some time. I had known her for years and was very distressed. I 'phoned her lifelong friend with whom all confidences were exchanged, who said that her friend was beginning to lose her love for her husband and would like to live with this other man. I arranged to call on her, had tea, and managed to put Sepia 200 (powder) into her tea. I did not mention the subject again, but three weeks later the friend 'phoned. I asked her how P . . . . was going on and she said, "Oh! that is all off. It was like a bad dream". All is now well and happy. Everyone asks what has happened to her. She's a different woman.

What incredible results some of these harmless homeopathic medicines yield. I know Christianity is the only thing to ensure health of the spirit, but these homeopathic medicines certainly work upon the mind, as Dr. Hahnemann and hundreds of other doctors have proved. My Materia Medica says of Sepia, among other mental symptoms, "loss of one's affection for the family". Warm personalities become cold and lose their emotional responsiveness. I thought this true personal experience would help other members of the "family".

Crataegus oxyacantha. Linn   *Harry Smith Collection.*

Hawthorn

ACCORDING TO old records, an Irish doctor in the last century had been obtaining good results when administering an unknown remedy to heart patients. It was years before it was discovered that he had used a medicine made from hawthorn berries. Later, many herbalists and a few doctors began successfully treating certain types of heart disorders with this herbal medicine.

In 1899, Dr Lyle mentioned the use of hawthorn in his Physio-Medical Therapeutics, Materia Medica and Pharmacy. He wrote "The fruit of this shrub is highly recommended as a heart tonic and by some is thought to be superior to Cactus in angina, oedema, regurgitation, enlargement, fatty degeneration. It influences the general system much as an alterant and is valuable in inflammatory rheumatism."

In recent years, hawthorn has come under scientific investigation. Ullsperger (Pharmazie, 1951, 141) isolated a yellow substance from English hawthorn and found that it produced dilation of the coronary vessels. It was reported by Fasshaucr (Deutsche med. Wchnschr., 1951, 76, 211) that one hundred heart patients requiring continuous therapy were given the liquid extract and the results were generally beneficial. Marked subjective improvement was noted in patients with mitral stenosis and patients with heart disease of old age. In other patients, digitalis could be either temporarily discontinued of considerably reduced when hawthorn extract was administered.

RICHARD LUCAS
Nature's Medicines

Agnus Castus
(Vitex agnus castus)

NATIVE to the shores of the Mediterranean, this fascinating verbenaceae is first mentioned in Arabian Medicine. It has taken this stream-lined scientific age to resuscitate from oblivion a remedy which was priceless to the ancients.

Physicians of antiquity were well acquainted with this plant prodigy. Their uncial writings credit it with specific healing properties, with special relevance of disorders of women. Early Egyptian gynaecologists – if such specialists were called in those days – might have known very little about hormone-balance affecting the ovaries, but they appeared to know a great deal about treatment.

When any plant components are found to be therapeutically successful in menstrual disorders brought about by a deficiency of the corpus luteal hormone, it seems reasonable to form the premise that they may actually have a related luteal effect. Treatment with *agnus castus* has, in fact, been so successful that it might be regarded as a form of substitution therapy.

A GOOD FRIEND FROM THE OLD WORLD

Millet is the most ancient food of the human race. It has been a staple diet for many countries of the world. After World War I, when food was scarce in Russia, millet was plentiful as it had been stored for use as chicken feed. When they discovered a human use for it they were surprised that their health had improved so much – even more than certain foods on which they relied for health and strength.

Animals fed on millet enjoy high-level health, which is not surprising, since we now know that it contains every essential amino acid, a complete protein superior in value to flesh foods and other cereals.

How to lick the smoking habit

Health Education Council

There is no guaranteed painless method of giving up cigarettes. The longer you have smoked, the more your body cries out for its supply of nicotine and tobacco smoke. And when this supply is suddenly cut off, the body is bound to react.

The first few days are inevitably going to be trying. Fortunately, however, doctors have now discovered several methods which will make it easier for any smoker to give up.

First of all, it helps if you can decide what kind of smoker you are. All smokers fall into one (or several) of six basic categories, and once you've discovered which apply to you, you can plan your attack.

Crutch Smokers light up in moments of stress and worry. Whenever things go wrong they reach for their cigarettes. When a crutch smoker gives up, he must be as far as possible from strain and tension. So a good time is on a Friday night before a relaxing weekend.

Habit Smokers are hardly conscious of smoking. For them there is no easy way out. Yet remarkably they're often the most successful at giving up, because once they've made the initial break they fall into the habit of not smoking.

Handling Smokers like to play around with the packet and the cigarette lighter. These are people who have the greatest success with dummy cigarettes, but a pencil or a pipe can be just as effective. After handling smokers find something to do with their hands for a few days, the rest is easy.

Relaxation Smokers love to light up after a meal, with a cup of coffee or tea. The solution: avoid such situations for a few days. Instead of sitting about after a meal, get up and do something.

Craving Smokers are psychologically addicted to tobacco. The craving for the next cigarette begins the moment the last one is put out. The solution is determination—all a craving smoker has to do is decide that he really wants to give up.

Stimulation Smokers feel that a cigarette picks them up. When a stimulation smoker gives up he looks for a substitute with a similar effect on his nervous system, such as coffee, tea, spicy foods or alcohol. Unfortunately, these substitutes trigger off the desire for a cigarette, and they should be avoided.

Once you've given up cigarettes, there are going to be many temptations to start smoking them again. Friends will offer them to you . . . you'll begin to notice the enticing advertisements . . . you'll think of a thousand excuses why you should have "just one".

There are, however, four ways in which you can help yourself to resist the temptation.

1. Give up with a friend. You'll be able to lend each other moral support. And of course the less you see people smoke, the easier it'll be for you.
2. Travel in non-smoking compartments of trains and buses.
3. Change your routine for a few days so that you avoid the situations when you really enjoyed or needed a cigarette.
4. Announce to your family and friends that you've stopped smoking. They'll see you over the worst time. And it'll also make it harder for you to go back on your word.

Finally, be prepared for a struggle. It probably took quite some time before you smoked as heavily as you do now. It may take just as long for you to give up. But even if you've smoked heavily for years, it's still worth making the effort, because from the day you stop, you reduce your chances of getting lung cancer or any of the diseases which are caused and aggravated by cigarette smoking.

65

sale. Flushed and furious I returned to dishing-up the meal. My husband reached over and handed me a copy of *Grace*, saying sweetly. "Darling, have you said your affirmation for today?"

Mrs. L. Digby, Surbiton, Surrey.
My husband has had psoriasis for years, since I have known him; and lotions and creams seem to improve it for a time, then it crops up again. especially in the hot weather. We would value your opinion on this matter.

ED: *Scientists have now discovered the part played by cholesterol in the behaviour of psoriasis. It has been found that the surface skin of sufferers contains four times as much cholesterol as in the normal person. Lecithin is a substance controlling the distribution of cholesterol, and whilst present in a number of everyday foodstuffs is not in sufficient quantity to bring about a reduction in skin cholesterol.*

When diets were augmented by supplementary doses of Lecithin, from 30 to 60 gms. daily, improvement took place and many cases were cured.

Lecithin tablets or capsules are on sale at most Health Stores.

Miss Hilda Wood, Warley, Worcs.
Dear Editor, Thank you again for *Grace*. It is absolutely wonderful, clean, pure, refreshing, inspiring. So worthy of its lovely title.

Having just read "Summer Kidney Stone Attacks" (p. 2308), I wonder if this is of interest.

My brother passed a stone with a little blood, the doctor enquired if he had been eating strawberries and said the acid from them did sometimes cause these stones, if eaten with cream or ice cream. If custard was taken this seemed to nullify the effect of the acid and no ill-effects were caused.

I, myself, had excessive vomiting (quite unusual for me) and for which there seemed no cause, but now I wonder if strawberries may have been responsible.

The season is short and people probably eat a fair amount while they are available.

If the acid from them, or caused by them, is so potent, it seems a pity that people are not alerted, when they would probably be taken more sparingly. Having read this article, it did occur to me that strawberries (eaten in the summer) may be responsible for some of the causes of stones.

Blessings on your lovely work. Sincerely.

From the Editor, Bournemouth.
After some years neglect, we have re-discovered the qualities of Luaka tea. Ever tried it? It is a pure Ceylon "self-drinking" or "original" tea, i.e. unblended, straight from the plant. We find it delicious. It is easily obtainable from your nearest Health Store, and recognised by the blue packet.

Large-leaf low-tannin tea of this quality needs to stand or "draw" for a full five minutes, to extract its full flavour and freshness. Recently tested by Public Analyst against three nationally popular teas, Luaka showed up with the lowest percentage of tannin. This fact should have an immediate appeal to the health conscious.

Mrs. Blanche E., Sask., Canada.
Have just received my spring issue of *Grace*, and have read it from cover to cover. I find it helpful and inspiring. This little book is just chock-full of hints and recipes for a healthy and a happy life.

I have proved that Calendula (marigold) flowers arrest bleeding. My grandchildren would not believe it until I pressed some petals on a cut finger. It worked.

Miss Little, Birmingham 28.
I noted your comment in the Summer issue of a member of the Family who discovered that there was nothing better than cold tea for cleaning varnished woodwork. I can quite believe it. There is a lot of value in cold tea, and cold tea leaves. After a Nature ramble I came home with a severe swelling above my eye owing to gnat stings. I tried bathing it with a number of things. But everything made it worse, till finally went to bed feeling that by morning I would not be able to open that eye at all, as the lids and all around had swollen so much.

In the middle of the night I woke and felt sure the eye would not open in the morning. In desperation I groped my way downstairs to see if there were any cold tea leaves in the pot. Fortunately there were. So I made a poultice of them and put it on my eye. By mid-morning next day my eye, and all around it was back to normal. I had quite anticipated having to rush to hospital, even though it was a Sunday.

Mrs. D. Bateman, Brighton.
Just a chuckle! Teacher, talking to her class on Temperance, said. "Today I have two tumblers, one with some water and one with some whisky, and some worms. I am going to put a few worms into each glass and we will see what happens." After a few moments she said, "Now, you see the worms in the water are all alive and squiggling about, but the worms in the whisky are all dead. I would like you to tell me what effect you think whisky has on humans when they drink it."

Timothy held up his hand. "Yes, Timothy," said teacher. "Please Miss – if you have worms, drink whisky."

Mrs. N., Upchurch, Streatham Vale, London, S.W.16
By the way, I chewed two juicy dandelion leaves and a flower going along a narrow country lane, and have not had heartburn since, and what a relief!

M. E. H., N. Ireland
I have found Chamomile good for piles. I pick the weed, put a double handful in a breakfast cup of milk, reduce by boiling to half a cup, strain and drink, on rising, for 21 days, without interval. The last case of piles cured by this means was one of such long standing that the doctor said it could only be helped by operation.

Mrs. L. Evans, Leeds 8.
Can you give me any idea what to do for my husband who keeps biting his nails down to the quick?
    ED: *Tincture of Myrrh is a harmless paint to use on the nails to discourage this practice. Paint morning and evening. Of course, if you want to be dead certain – hide his teeth!*

Mr. H. Marshall, Chingford, London, E.4.
I feel I must write and tell you how I overcame a badly sprained ankle. I was running to catch a train when I twisted my ankle. At first it didn't hurt much, but by the time I arrived home it had swollen twice its normal size and was very painful. As the evening wore on it became worse – then I remembered the Comfrey in the garden and how good it is for sprains and bruises, so I applied a few leaves in a cold water compress round my ankle. The result was astounding. After roughly 1½ hours the pain had gone considerably and I was able to walk with ease. Next morning, although the ankle was still swollen, there was no pain and I was able to get to work.
    Another time I was pruning my roses when a large thorn stuck in my thumb just below the nail. It was extremely painful, but I just picked a Comfrey leaf and squeezed the juice from the stalk on to the painful area and within a minute the pain had gone completely.
    I would never be without Comfrey, which is known as Knitbone, and I also use the tender young leaves in salads.

Mrs. Mary Robinson, Hull, Yorks.
Some while ago – last year – my husband had a nasty accident at cricket – his finger was badly split. It was bandaged up, and when I saw the finger later on at home, I didn't know how to treat it. We went to a Health Store I know of and the assistant there advised us to apply Liquid Honey on a piece of bandage two or three times daily on the wound, saying that the wound would heal perfectly without leaving a scar. We did this, and after the second application the finger was eased and cleansed and in three weeks the wound was healed perfectly, the flesh knitting together without even a scar!
    What a wonderful thing! We thought so anyway. God bless you all, and prosper your work.

Anonymous.
I am not sure about the difference between rheumatism and gout.
ED: *Suppose you put your thumb in a vice and screw it so tight you can no longer endure the pain. That's rheumatism. Now give the vice another twist. That's gout!*

Mrs. Barbara Groves, Sanderstead, Surrey.
I have been most interested in your articles on Vitamin E. I was really suffering from cold feet. After reading the first article I have taken Vitamin E. I now never have cold feet. Also, I feel so much better in myself. Incidentally, I find that a strange, cramp-like and paralysed feeling I used to feel in my toes when going to bed, and on waking up, is very much less and sometimes non-existent. I hope this will be of help to others. These golden capsules are such a simple way of coping with problems of circulation.

F. Barnes, Brighton.
When on holiday we had supersonic booms from aircraft and they were terrible. But it's an ill wind that blows nobody any good. I've heard of a woman who is cashing in on these, real proper. The first two brought down two buckets of soot from her cottage chimney. But they stopped too soon. She needed only one more bang to get her chimney swept for the winter.

Mrs. Lisa Gantenbein, Santa Rosa, California, U.S.A.
I always enjoy *Grace* Magazine. It is a special treat when it arrives. It represents the way and the spirit we were brought up in Switzerland 50-60 years ago. It does not mean that it is old-fashioned by any means; but it indicates the integrity, the honesty and the wholesomeness which was considered most important at that time. We lived closer to Nature and there nearer to the Divine. I am still thankful for it and your dear gentle magazine carries the fragrancy of the God world, the Infinity. Be thankful and blessed for your principles and for sharing them with us. With heartfelt good wishes I greet you.

L. G. Hird, West Witton, Leyburn, Yorks.
One of your readers asked for a remedy for shingles. Since then I have had this unpleasant and painful complaint and found the use of almond oil most successful and speedy. Please pass on this good news.

Mrs. W. Collett, Leicester.
How so much alike are the present packages for all sorts of commodities. Coming home very footsore one evening, I decided on a foot bath and prepared it accordingly. Plunging my feet into this the effect was wonderful. So soothing, so restful, and I enjoyed fifteen minutes of bliss. However, upon putting back the carton, I read, to my amazement, that I had been using *Stomach Powder!*

Miss O. Robotham, Stockton-on-Tees.
A recent number of *Grace* gave a cure for cracks at the end of the fingers. I was interested because I have suffered from such cracks for years. I recently had a similar crack at the back of my right heel and felt I must do something to prevent a recurrence. I started applying sunflower seed oil to my heels and fingers and have not had any cracks since.

Mr. Smart, Cardiff.
After a whole week of hiccuping all over the place, a friend of mine had had cold tea, whisky, smelling-salts, and pink gin, as well as other red-hot tips from knowledgable sympathizers he met on the bus or in the factory. He finally found relief by taking two teaspoonfuls of raw onion juice. I, too, have had hiccups (messages from departing spirits) but I just couldn't face up to his cure. He was a better man than I was – Ghunga-Din!

Mrs. M. M. Hoare, Goring-by-Sea, Worthing.
I want to say a very big thank you for putting my "S.O.S." concerning the agonising cramp which I have been getting in my ankles and legs into your magazine *Grace*. I am really overwhelmed by the kindness of so many of my *Grace* friends. I have had about 12 letters all giving me their cure for this distressing complaint. I am already getting relief from one I've tried, and if that is only a temporary cure I will try and try until I reach the one that suits my particular trouble. I have written to all those who sent their address with the cures to me, but I do thank them all so very much and I feel I have made so many new friends.

Miss E. Mallinson, South Nutfield.
I feel much better taking Comfrey. My fractured ribs have healed nicely; lungs healed likewise, and I feel stronger.
ED: *This plant (Symphytum Officinale) grows upon the banks of rivers and ditches, flowering in May and June, leaves being lance-shaped and covered with fine hairs. It has a long reputation for haemoptysis (spitting of blood or haemorrhage of the lungs), haematuria (renal haemorrhage) and for hastening the knitting together of broken bones. One of its English names is "knit-bone". The S. Peregrinum contains more allantoin than the officinalis and is now widely cultivated. The one which still grows in our countryside can, however, be relied upon to live up to its ancient reputation.*

Mrs. Mary Booker, Reading.
This will make some of you sit up! I had the most terrible pains in my left hip and leg which were worse than anything I have ever had before. Great waves of pain throbbed through my leg and I was doubled up, thinking that the end had come. I thought it was some spasm of thrombosis. It was certainly ten times worse than any cramp. I tried everything. The doctor did his best, but I got steadily worse.

70

Then a thought came to my mind. There may be something written about it in *Grace*. Why not look through all the old copies? Now, it was there that I found a letter written by another reader (bless his soul!) telling of how he lost his own pains by putting some flowers of sulphur in his shoes. In next to no time I put a dessertspoonful in the soles of my stockings and waited. It was a miracle. The pain went . . . just like that! And I want to thank, with all my heart, that unseen friend who passed on such help to me. If he still reads the magazine, I wish him well. It just goes to show that the doctor does not always have the last word, and that cure for a lot of things depends upon our own efforts.

Jimmy Gordon, Toronto, Canada.
I know a food-addict, a relation, who every night before she goes to bed casts an eye over her rows of bottles on the pantry shelf. Then she goes along the line, taking pills from here and capsules from there to supplement her meals for all the things supposed to be stolen from them. She is powerfully overweight, and is looking for a herb to peel off extra pounds and help her live longer.

There she goes. At the starting-post there is a couple of multi-energy tablets, followed by vitamin "H" or something or other. These are chased down with a cup of Bo-Fo-Fa to keep her ticking over. Ad-Vigor perles are followed by two Eternal Youth globules, which in turn are reinforced with chunks of calcium to make sure of holding on to any trace-elements which may be departed from the body after a blow-out of rhubarb and custard. She says we have only ourselves to blame if we do not tip the 120 mark. She is making sure of her three score and fifty years by weighing out her proteins and tipping her bed-head to face the north. She's bitten with this health-bug real bad.

Personally, I don't care a toss about living 120 years, but I care a lot about the way every conversation is dominated by the eternal subject of food, food, food; and this mania to keep fit, as if there wasn't anything else in life.

Sorry to bother you with all this, but my wife and I are having an argument. What we really want to know is, "Do you sleep with your whiskers over or under the sheet?"

ED: *It is good to hear from you, Mr. Gordon. Sorry to learn your relation is proving a health-nut rather hard to crack. You sure have a problem on your hands. There's a lot to be said for a balanced enthusiasm for the healthy way of life, though I'm sorry to have to say there is no herb capable of solving her problems.*

Oh! Wait a minute! I nearly forgot. There is the Mulawumpa herb, of course. This plant . . . very small, very stimulating . . . is a kind of exy-tovermintic, and grows in the heart of the Himalayas, far away from little old Toronto. Do you know! The mountain goats which feed upon it live to be 400 years. Yes, 400 years old. Of course, towards the end of

(continued on page 74)

Three Minutes a Day

C. S. LEWIS, in his book The Four Loves, said, "If you want to make sure of keeping it intact, you must give your heart to no one, not even to an animal. Avoid all entanglements, lock it up safe in the coffin of your own selfishness. But in that casket—safe, dark, motionless, airless—it will change. It will not be broken, it will become unbreakable, impenetrable, irredeemable."

How broody we become when we live for ourselves alone! We all need solitude and seasons of refreshment. But how stunted we grow until we are involved with other people! There may be some truth in the observation that most of the patients in mental hospitals are there because of their retreat from normal human intercourse Why is it that we do not want to get involved with other people?

Literature is full of stupid old proverbs advising against jumping out of the frying-pan. Some hold back through fear, missing opportunities which may never occur again. Don't you honestly think that 'security' is mostly superstition? Frightened folk running away from supposed danger find themselves no safer in the long run than by doing the thing they most fear. Fear is the darkroom where negatives are developed.

The secret of vitality and happiness is to respond to the call of life and to expect no stability where none exists. The world is one of constant rhythmical unfoldment as seasons come and go. 'Change' is inevitable. How often do we find that, where we fail to make necessary changes now, nature, with her inborn wisdom and inexorable life forces may compel us to do so later, when the shock may be greater.

Security is unknown in the world of nature. Nowhere within or without ourselves can permanent tranquillity and security be found. Great harm is being wrought on our sons and daughters by the idea that science will one day provide for all the needs of man; when 'peace and security' will be facts of life. Before it is too late we must get-over to them the truth that there is no stability in science or the most perfect government if the Creator is left out of His own universe.

Security is a willow-of-the-wisp where there is no high purpose or personal responsibility. Leaning too heavily on the long arm of the State can mean a limitation of growth. There is no security on this earth. There is only opportunity.

When life becomes too soft we lack concern for others. We lose our ability to face bravely those hurts, hardships and disappointments we are bound to encounter at some stage of our journey. By keeping ourselves to ourselves we may gain some small immunity from infection or recession, but what is life when its quality is insipid?

Let Me Do It Now

If any little word of ours
Can make one life the brighter;
If any little song of ours
Can make one heart the lighter;
God help us speak that little word,
And take our bit of singing
And drop it in some lonely vale
To set the echoes ringing.

If any little love of ours
Can make one life the sweeter;
If any little care of ours
Can make one step the fleeter;
If any little help may ease
The burden of another;
God give us love and care and strength
To help along each other.

If any little thought of ours
Can make one life the stronger;
If any cheery smile of ours
Can make its brightness longer;
Then let us speak that thought today,
With tender eyes aglowing,
So God may grant some weary one
Shall reap from our glad sowing.

Anonymous

72

Bournemouth

WITH NEARLY 2,000 ACRES of Public Parks, Gardens and Open Space, Bournemouth the 1995 Winner of Entente Florale "Europe in Bloom" and three times winner of Britain in Bloom, has firmly established itself as a premier town for horticultural excellence.

The Gardens of Excellence programme has contributed to this success, and provides the visitor with the opportunity to experience the diversity not only of Spring and Summer bedding displays, Rose Gardens and Rock Gardens, but also Arid, Italianate and Sub-tropical Gardens as well as the developing Coastal Pinetum.

The Gardens of Excellence concept was born in 1992, and developed from an idea for a Botanical Garden to further enhance the town's reputation for its beautiful floral heritage. The result has been the creation of three distinctive and diverse new gardens, and the rejuvenation of Bournemouth's existing popular Gardens.

By courtesy: Bournemouth Borough Council Leisure & Tourism Directorate, Bournemouth, Dorset.

73

that time they get a little thin. So anyone with half an eye can see that if we drink our daily cup of Mulawumpa tea we stand a good chance of living long enough to become an old goat.

Mrs. N. W. Kerr, Marie, Ontario, Canada.
While reading "A Kettle Boils Over" in the Autumn issue of *Grace* Magazine, I noticed that Mr. J. Saunders, Belfast, Northern Ireland, was troubled with sore and cracked fingertips. I, too, was bothered in that way until a herbalist suggested safflower oil, which I tried with a satisfactory result. I have not had any more trouble with sore, cracked fingertips because I take the oil regularly, internally.

L. M. Twichell, Duxbury, Mass. 02332, U.S.A.
A lady well known to me, while being treated for high blood sugar, suffered a severe haemorrhage from the bladder. Examination showed a growth. Immediate operation was advised. She refused the operation, went home and began eating grapes. She ate nothing but grapes for five or six weeks and lost about 14 pounds in weight. Several months later, after living on a prudent diet, laboratory tests show urine clear and blood sugar normal. Great gain in strength and well-being.

Mrs. Woodford.
I had a horribly painful toe that swelled and bled. It exuded pus from the nail's edge most of the time. I had this for four solid years. My doctor tried nearly everything to clear it up. But tablets made me feel bad, and ointments did nothing at all.

Also, I had from time to time, blistery swellings on my forehead and upper lip, but these have cleared after taking Echinacea tablets and Vitamin E capsules.

I felt so exhausted that, after doing everything, I had to sleep. I was so bad I felt like doing so day and night. I haven't slept in the daytime, since. I feel a different person and my husband can't believe it. He says I look so bright. I feel like skipping about. By the way. I'm only thirty-one, but I felt more like ninety!

Mrs. Joan C. D. Watson, Hastings, East Sussex.
After nearly twenty years of recurring ulcerative colitis, I underwent this operation nearly ten years ago – and what a relief! To anyone facing a colostomy or ileostomy, I would say two things: the necessary appliances are being improved on all the time so keep on enquiring until you find the type that suits you. Above all, after the operation – forget it – you are no different from anyone else; think of all the people who wear wigs and dentures and they don't think they are a race apart! So, take heart and thank God for our wonderful surgeons. Yours sincerely.

Mrs. Amy Miles, Edinburgh.
I grow my herbs in pots, sage, thyme, etc.. and they do well. Last year I took them on holiday with me and they seem better for the change of air.
ED: *Splendid . . . we hope they weren't travel sick!*

F. E. Lambert, Kingston 7, Jamaica, West Indies.
Many years ago, I think about fifty years, my father cut his hand very badly and blood poisoning set in. It did not seem to yield to treatment. The doctor decided he would have to go into hospital for an operation. One of the real old-time gipsies told my mother to get chickweed and boil it, strain, and bathe father's hand with it every one or two hours, night and day. When the doctor came next time to make arrangements for his admission to hospital he was absolutely amazed at the improvement and told us whatever it was we were doing, not to let up, but continue our own treatment. The hand healed and no operation was necessary.

Anonymous
In these costly cosmetic days, perhaps readers will enjoy this tip:
Place one tablespoonful Quaker oats or oatmeal in a square of linen or cheese cloth and soak in warm water until the cream can be squeezed out. After washing your face and neck, put on this cream and let it dry. Then rinse off with tepid water and lightly splash with cold water. Soon your skin will be like velvet.

Mr. Alfred Martinet, Lausanne, Switzerland.
We were delighted to receive our copy of Summer *Grace* with Her Majesty the Queen's portrait, in colour on the cover. We are grateful that she has gone through her arduous Jubilee tasks unscathed. We greatly admire her poise and faith under present conditions.

Anonymous, Bradford, Yorks.
For years I suffered from painful cramp. But it was in a book written by Charles Wesley, *Primitive Physic*, that led me to relief. This book was first published in 1747, and reads: "Cramp to Cure. Put out your heel". I can only speak for myself. I find it works.
ED: *John Wesley is right. Every osteopath knows that cramp follows a temporary muscle spasm, where it is not caused by intermittent-claudication, a circulatory disorder. Muscle spasm can be relieved by stretching. If you draw-up the top of the foot, or better still, have the assistance of another person to forcibly flex the foot (bending it upwards) and keeping the knee joint extended (knee not bent), you will stretch the tendons at the back of the leg which can loosen it for the night, releasing the spasm.*

Miss Enid Shaw, Littlehampton.
How about having a non-child allowance?

Mrs. M. Scott, Manchester.
Working in my garden I broke the nail of my thumb across the middle. It was turned right back over the rest of the nail, and very painful. I put it back into its proper place, came into the house, dipped it in honey, and tied it up. Next day I put on more honey. In three days it was O.K. Not even a mark where it was broken.

ED: *Thank you, sincerely, Mrs. Scott, for further evidence of the healing marvels of such a simple substance . . . honey.*

Mr. R. G. Rollinson, Hull, Lincs.
We hear it is possible to grow little pots of grass in the house, for cats to nibble. What grass is it?

ED: *It is cocks-foot grass.*

Miss Barbara Elliott, Oxted, Surrey.
I have just been reading Mr. Carmichael's letter in the Autumn issue of the magazine and also the reply, advising the use of Tincture of Myrrh mouth-rinse for two or three months. The advice does not explain the *cause* of bleeding gums.

The cause of bleeding gums is a deficiency of vitamin C. Deficiency of vitamin C may have a number of causes. A deficiency may be due to a small number of raw green vegetables in the diet, to putting soda into the cooking water with green vegetables, or not eating daily one or more of the citrus fruits. A deficiency may be due to the use of sprays, insecticides and other poisons or antibiotics, thyroid or anti-thyroid drugs.

It has been found that lack of vitamin C in a diet which is otherwise healthful, can and will also produce a fatty liver, bleeding gums, and (human) hardening of the arteries (atheroma).

The giving of vitamin C in liberal quantities immediately begins to cure, and cures very quickly. Mr. Carmichael's best course will not be only to introduce plenty of vitamin C-containing foods into his diet, but to obtain a bottle of 100 tablets Redoxon, 200 mg. tablets of vitamin C, and take for the first day, two tablets, three times a day. Suck them. After that, suck one, three times a day, *without fail*. There are no toxic side-effects. Keep it up.

Make a note of the date on which you start. You will be almost dumbfounded to notice how quickly your gums will heal. Do not be deterred by the expense. Keep it up, for your general health's sake, all the year round. Also, eat fresh water-cress daily. Remember, from the very moment of picking, a vegetable starts to lose its vitamin C content.

Avoid sugar. It is a poison. Avoid it, and everything containing it. Make the experiment, drastically. It pays.

Mrs. D. M., Sussex.

Lots of people despise jumble sales and look down their noses at what are on sale. I love them. These are my acquisitions up to date: an old copy of Culpeper's *Herball*, a Dr. Fox's *Family Herbal Physician* and, believe it or not – a bound copy of *Grace* Magazine. This was my introduction to the magazine. Once I bought a packet of peanuts which the children set in the garden. Now we have a forest of little peanut plants.

Anonymous, Men of the trees.

Never before has our concern for our trees been more urgent. The elm population has been decimated, and another specie is at risk. Many sturdy oaks are undergoing steady strangulation by ivy. All our enthusiasm for planting new trees is of little avail when hundreds, perhaps thousands of magnificent oaks are dying a slow death by this killer of the woods. May I remind country readers that they can do much by cutting through or severing the tendrils and trunks of ivy, thus safeguarding many in danger of destruction.

Anonymous.

A few years ago my doctor informed me that the swelling at the base of my forefinger on the palm of my hand was a gangrenous cyst, and would eventually require surgery, but not to interfere with it until it troubled me. I had the occasional twinge when using my hands to wring anything. Last winter I started to take Garlic capsules to help ward off winter ills – two each night.

Some months later I discovered the cyst on my hand was only half the size. I took note of this and continued with the Garlic. Now, after six months, it has disappeared entirely.

Mrs. B. M. Taylor, St. Andrews Park, Bristol.

Last winter I discovered I had arthritis in my left knee, owing to an accident about ten years ago. It got extremely painful. I had to use a stick. I was so miserable. So for three or four months I massaged with the Health Store Olive Oil, first thing in the morning and last thing at night. Also I drank two teaspoons of H.S. Cider Vinegar (no other) plus one teaspoon of Acacia Honey, in a cup of warm water. I did this for about three to four months. It is absolutely cured. No sign of it now!

Mrs. H. J., Midlothian, Scotland.

Whatever would we do without our small shops? Had you noticed how wonderful they were during the bread strike? We like those shops which sell small amounts of anything: ideal for those living alone. Two ounces of nuts, or cheese, can be a very real help when catering for yourself. In the small shops I go to, there is always service with a smile. I am glad they seem to have time for poor little me!

Anonymous.
My wife has a passion for a bird in a cage. Her friend has one that fills the house with song all day long. I would like to get one for her birthday but I remember reading in *Grace* that they may be carriers of some sort of virus.

ED: *We are glad you have raised this question which has stimulated a little research into our medical literature on the subject. It seems conclusive that viruses have been shown in laboratory birds and animals to produce valve lesions identical to those in chronic rheumatic heart disease in man. Some micro-organisms certainly play a part in valvular heart disease.*

The virus most likely to be transmitted to man is psittacosis which has been known to cause pericarditis and myocarditis. We are beginning to wonder if many cases diagnosed "rheumatic heart" (often a legacy from rheumatic fever when young) are, in fact, invasions by chlamydia psittaci (psittacosis).

Early stages of psittacosis follow a pattern of mild influenza that can easily be ignored or mis-diagnosed. Pet birds are imported into Britain by tens of thousands and it would appear that pet shop owners may be at special risk.

It would be an interesting exercise for some young B.Sc., with time on his hands, to investigate the incidence of endocarditis in those exposed for long hours to birds. One disturbing fact is revealed: that there appears to be more chronic valvular disease arising from bird-contact than in rheumatic fever. Further studies are clearly indicated.

Bedtime Story.
One night as a woman was getting into bed, a hair roller fell to the floor, and she had to crawl round the bed before she put her hand on it. Suddenly she felt exhausted. That night she fell asleep almost immediately. Since then every night she crawls round the floor on all fours for two or three minutes. It's not very elegant, she admits, but it works wonders for her.

Anonymous, Northern Ireland.
I would like to know of a good herb to take for general fitness. I am at present very fit and well but am looking for some harmless herb to daily keep me "regular", much as in the same way my grandfather made himself a cup of wormwood tea. He lived to be ninety-one. I cannot take wormwood, it is too bitter for me.

ED: *We think you could not do better than to try a good "all-rounder" for liver, kidneys, mucous membranes, bowels and heart: Garlic. Two or three tablets or the cut bulb on your salad, daily.*

James Beech, Derby.
I learned about bees from my father. It is my special pleasure to grow plenty of bee-plants in our garden. I've never felt afraid of them. I've too many reasons to be grateful. Their honey has changed my life. They have protected me from colds and 'flu for over eight years, settled my digestion, and cured my wife's discharging leg ulcer. They are more than insects – they are Nature's little miracle workers.

Mrs. Ken Dobson, Ghana, Africa.
I find it difficult to express what warmth and pleasure each edition of *Grace* brings to me. We are living in Northern Ghana and how much the Africans around us appreciate being spoken to with courtesy and "caring". We like them so much and so enjoy their friendship. They have much to give. We long to help them much more than at present we are able to. My husband is here as an adviser to the Ghanaian government on irrigation. There are some 300 small dams already built by F.A.O. and various other organizations in Northern Ghana but little use is yet being made of them. The farmers still cultivate with their short-handled hoes and oxen.
ED: *It is a real pleasure to hear from you, Mrs. Dobson, and we send greetings from members of the "Grace" Family.*

Miss H. Harris, Selly Oak, Birmingham 29.
Thank you for the Winter number of *Grace Magazine*. My friends are very interested in the items read from borrowed previous issues.
As a matter of interest, I've just read the article on hiccups and thought you'd like to hear my cure, which has never let me down as yet. Judge the time between each hiccup, then put a finger in each ear and press, holding your breath half as long again as the time between hiccups. Presto – you're cured!
It's so simple. Works every time.

Mrs. D. E. Bennett, Boston, Lincs.
You might be amused to hear about my rheumaticky friend who went blackberrying. She badly nettled her legs (more grumbles) when lo and behold, about three days afterwards, she found she had lost her "screws" and has been better since.
ED: *Bravo! Maybe one day she might wish to try the old Scandinavian flagellation treatment on the back with a bunch of nettles! Brrr . . . .*

Mrs. Gladys Cooper, Parkstone, Poole, Dorset.
In the Autumn 1967 issue of *Grace* is an article on water divining and the radiations of earth, sea and sky.
There is a recommendation that to keep fully charged with vitality, sleeping with the body lying north and south will help.

For some years we have known it to be true. Since placing the beds in this position, the improvement in sleep has been really marked. I realise that a quiet mind and orderly digestion are necessary for tranquil sleep, but by placing the body in the main stream of magnetic radiations, I believe that all of these factors combine and "work together for good".

ED: *Thank you, Gladys, for a useful tip. It seems to work dramatically on some people. We once heard of a restless sleeper losing his jitters after moving around the bedstead. An intriguing phenomena.*

Mrs. L. A. Derry, Bathwick, Bath.
I read with interest Mrs. Hoare's letter in the Autumn number of the magazine, and write to say that many years ago I read that if one puts a magnet in one's bed at night, one would not get cramp. I told a friend who suffered much from cramp and she found it very effective. So much so, that she takes the magnet with her when she stays away from home! Yours sincerely.

Mr. John Anderson, Wellington, New Zealand.
Now it can be told. My sister made us roar with this experience which happened to her many years ago.

When young, my sister was wooed by an ardent gentleman, in the traditional way – on the sofa. During the remonstration he accidentally slipped off and found himself on his knees, still holding her hand. He was so fat, he could not rise to his feet; and not having a derrick handy, the girl had to help him to his feet.

We never knew why she didn't marry him, until fifty years afterwards, when she said: "If he couldn't support himself, how on earth could he support me?"

Mrs. Emily Thomson, Edinburgh 10, Scotland.
I am delighted to let you know that vitamin "E" capsules are helping me more and more in every way. It sounds almost like a miracle. That nasty varicose ulcer I have had on my leg is showing signs of healing up. There is now very little pain, and it is reduced in size.

Mrs. Leonora Louis, Montreal, Canada.
What can I do for pyorrhoea? My dentist has tried almost everything, and I am at my wits end to find some relief.

ED: *Pyorrhoea is a disease of the gums. It may be a simple inflammation or a purulent inflammation of the dental periosteum, with progressive necrosis of the alveoli and looseness of the teeth. Sometimes referred to as Rigg's disease or gingivitis.*

It is surprising how many cases of stubborn gum and dental troubles have been cured with Apple Cider Vinegar. This is not the commercial vinegar bought at the grocer's or drug stores, but the genuine old-fashioned cider vinegar. Use as a mouth wash: tumbler of warm water in which three to four teaspoonfuls of the vinegar is dissolved. Ordinary vinegar is useless. Obtainable from all Health Stores.

Mollie Jarvis, Crouch End, London, N.8.
I think each number of *Grace* is better than the last. I pass my copies to my chiropodist, who accelerated his cure of gastric ulcer by swallowing a black olive stone, which information he said appeared in *Grace*.

For the best part of a year I had been in wearing pain – just to the right of the spine – about 6th or 7th vertebrae: deep inside, not affecting the arms at all. The pills prescribed by the doctors gave no relief. All I had been able to do was a small amount of necessary work, and rest flat on the bed. This I told him and to my surprise he recommended the black olive stone, telling me how much it had helped him. His story was most convincing – so I took the advice, with inward trepidation, but feeling that it was an extraordinary recommendation for a back pain. However, within twelve hours the pain was reduced. By evening it had completely cleared up – after months and months of wearisome days. Who said truth wasn't stranger than fiction?

Mr. T. Charlesworth, Thornton, Bradford.
I came across your *Grace Magazine* at a friend's home and would like to be a contributor. I found solace and a new dimension for living more peacefully in its pages.
ED: *A warm welcome to a new member of the "Family".*

Mrs. H. Beecroft, Scarborough.
I feel sure many people will be interested to know of how I cured a ganglion – a cystic tumour on a tendon. I believe they are quite common and if, as in my case, over the pulse on the wrist, they can cause considerable discomfort, due to the pressure on nerves and tendons. Mine was in the shape of two hard lumps. I had medical treatment for a period of over a year, including having it cut out by operation, but without success. It returned almost immediately.

I had a sudden inspiration. Having read about the beneficial uses of Cider Vinegar, I thought why not try it in this case. I soaked a pad of cotton wool in cider vinegar, over which I placed a thick wad of old sheeting and bound tightly with a crepe bandage. This I did constantly for about three months, wearing it day and night and renewing the cider vinegar several times a day. It gradually softened and dispersed.

The skin around became rather inflamed, so I included a little honey very occasionally to heal it successfully. At the end of three months I gradually withdrew the cider vinegar, the bandage and the pressure, so as not to end too drastically, or get a chill in the wrist. My doctor was quite amazed with the result. As the treatment was completed over six months ago, I feel I can now safely write to you and describe it as a cure.
ED: *Sounds very convincing to us, Mrs. Beecroft. Patience rewarded!*

Mrs. J. Johnson, Cape Town, South Africa.
Madame Schumann-Heink was preparing one evening to down an enormous steak when Enrico Caruso passed her table.

Caruso's eyes blinked. "Steena, you are not going to eat that huge steak alone?"

"No, Rico," she replied, "not alone. With potatoes."

Mr. Chalk, Bournemouth.
I always remember how my father grew a large patch of turnips every year. When mature, the tops would be cut off, packed into bales, and sent to Covent Garden Market. Why? Because in those days folk cooked them and ate them as you would greens. Besides being very palatable, they were an excellent blood tonic and kept you in good health.

William Furlong, Kensington, London, W.8.
Vitamin "E" Capsules are good. My circulation was very poor but since taking them my feet are much warmer. My general health has improved enormously, noticeable after only one week.

Mr. J. Evans, Edinburgh 9, Scotland.
"You're not looking so good!" said the milkman.

"No, I've been up all night," I replied.

"How's that?"

Can you imagine how I felt when I had to admit, "I thought I had taken a couple of vitamin C tablets, but when I woke up I found they were Cascaras."

Mr. J. Saunders, Belfast, Northern Ireland.
My doctor has tried everything he knows for my sore and cracked fingertips. They have nothing to do with psoriasis or other skin troubles or so-called vitamin deficiencies, with which diagnoses I am palmed off. I've taken nature-cure treatments, biochemics, lotions and the lot. You're my last hope.

ED: *These cracks are sometimes called "hacks". Dry the crack. Open it. Insert a piece of cobbler's wax about the size of a large pin-head. Hold the finger near the fire or gas flame. When the wax is soft, press it into the crack. Cover with a small strip of adhesive tape and don't mind if the tape gets rather soiled for a few days. We're far too sophisticated these days with our hormones and halogens for simple conditions which were no problem to the older family doctors.*

Mrs. M. Jenkinson, Park Road, Leeds.
What can I do for persistent migraine? It takes all the joy out of my life and lately, with painters and decorators in the house, they just drive me

crazy with their incessant smoking and their little portable radios filling the house with noise every minute of the working day.

ED: *We are very sorry to learn of these distressing trials, Mrs. Jenkinson, and trust all will soon be well. Too many cases of migraine are caused by eggs , coffee, and cheese. Try cutting them out. Of course, other items of food could be implicated, but first see how you get on with this simple measure.*

Mrs. S. A. Dicker, Winton, Bournemouth.
My mother swore by potato for rheumatism. She would peel one and sew it up into a little bag and wear it about her person or have it in her pocket. It seems to neutralize acidity in the body in some way. Anyrate, by the time it was as hard as a stone her acidity was better and the rheumatism gone. I found relief for my own rheumatism by wearing a copper bracelet.

Mrs. R. Wiebelitz, Illinois 60751, U.S.A.
Please have all the fennel uses in an issue soon. I have been told it is good for about 20 health needs.

ED: *Fennel seed makes an excellent infusion for colic, cramps in the stomach, and severe griping in the bowel. Care should be taken to see that these symptoms do not arise from any deep-seated abdominal trouble on which professional advice should be sought. It can be used in the kitchen for flavouring purposes. It is one of the few harmless stimulants known; good for debility and for sweetening sour stomachs. In Europe the young shoots are used as a vegetable, it was part of the one-time used Liquorice Powder. (Why bring back those memories!) Sorry we cannot get round to the whole of its 20-odd uses, but we use it mainly for flatulence or wind. For an aromatic daily health drink, try pouring half pint boiling water on one teaspoonful of crushed seeds. Drink wineglassful to start off the day. This drink is also good for slimming.*

Mr. Kenneth Weston, Sydney, Australia.
Good wishes from "Down-under". We have found neat lemon juice good for the itching of shingles, dabbed on. What else is it good for?

ED: *Good to hear from you, Mr. Weston. We warmly reciprocate greetings to your family. Lemon is such a versatile remedy that it is often overlooked for use in most kinds of severe skin irritation. Also, do not forget to take it internally for its vitamin "C" , and especially to facilitate cleansing of the liver, which organ is frequently the cause of chronic itching. Sorry we haven't space to go into certain necessary dietetic adjustments, including cutting out eggs and fats.*

Here are some conditions lemon juice has been known to overcome. These we give from our own experience in a busy practice.

Urticaria, pruritis, shingles, sycosis, warts, ichthyosis, herpes labialis, eczema vesiculorum, ringworm, and severe itching of different kinds. As

*always, the best and safest medicaments are often the cheapest. But, you
know, people will not persevere. If no immediate relief is felt, the juice
should be diluted and applied assiduously for some weeks. Don't forget
. . . chronic conditions sometimes demand chronic cures.*

Fred Clarke, Newcastle-on-Tyne.
I believe it is usually the women who complain of lapses in the memory-
box. My wife goes out to work. I stay at home to do all the chores. Ever
since my 15-year younger wife insisted on our very workable arrange-
ment, they have called me "domesticated Fred".

Today, when cleaning out the bathroom to the accompaniment of my
portable radio, I went downstairs to fetch the pail and cleaning materials.
It was not until I had staggered back upstairs, still listening to "Mrs. Dale's
Diary", that I saw I was carrying the vacuum cleaner.

After six months, this is what I say. Never leave bread being toasted
while answering the door to pay the milkman. Fix clearly in your mind's-
eye the length of your water-tap if you want to avoid an embarrassing
half-hour on your wife's return. I've briskly knocked off the spout of our
best teapot. By the hard way I've learnt never to sign for a registered letter while the milk saucepan is still on the gas, and not to tip too much
Slippery Elm powder into the soup to thicken it.

I make my own home-made bread to a recipe given in Grace magazine.
Never forget, always serve something new for tea. A man's work is never
done. Regards to the "Family".

Mrs. Foxton, Crimble, Slaithwaite, Nr. Huddersfield.
In my last copy of *Grace*, a lady, Miss I. N. Carfrae, Earlsfield, London,
asks for a herbal relief for a bronchial cough. I am glad to say I can help.

A friend came to stay for a weekend and couldn't speak six words without coughing. My husband said, "I'll cure that." He gathered a handful
of Comfrey leaves from the garden, boiled them in a quart of water, then
added the juice of a lemon. After straining, he asked her to drink a cupful of the liquid every few hours. By the time she went home she was
greatly relieved and could speak without coughing. Hope this remedy will
help your readers.

STANDING BY
When troubles come your soul to try . . . You love the friend who just stands
by . . . For just to feel you have a friend . . . Although there's little he can
do . . . And so with fervent heart we cry . . . "God bless the friend who just
stands by."

Miss M. Green, Brighton, Sussex.
At different times I have tried to cure myself of biting my nails. Painting the nails with a little Tincture of Aloes was good, but somehow I drifted back. Now, I have been free from this habit for five months. How have I done it? By forcing myself to wear gloves, every minute of the day until bedtime, for three days. What a chore ! But it cured me.

Leo T. Pivirotto, Massachusetts, U.S.A. 02764.
In the Autumn issue of *Grace*, the last sentence in the narrative of Mr. Hickman of Rose Cottage, struck a truly responsive chord. I wonder how many readers grasped the profound significance of "It is my belief that, if the whole truth were known, roses can occupy an intermediate station between heaven and earth, being a vehicle for some subtle mysterious power, maybe celestial, for the comfort of men and women in their extremity."

A number of years ago I had a part in two experiences which up until now I would not make public. However, the readers of *Grace* are evidently in a class who would find the same inspiration that I did.

A friend of mine, a family man, purchased an old house in the country. It needed a lot of work and when October came, with its crisp nights, it was discovered that the heating system was completely useless. They could not afford a new one but after a long search a used one was found that was apparently in fair condition but was priced quite high for their pocketbook. It meant going into more debt but the cold nights made it imperative that they act soon.

One evening, before retiring, Mrs., in praying her Rosary, asked to be given the affirmative sign of a white rose. The next morning after breakfast she had to go out in the back yard and suddenly she became aware of a very large white rose in full bloom on a bush that had not borne even a bud all summer. She had passed that spot every day at least once and had not seen even a bud. They bought the system and her husband installed it himself without encountering even the slightest difficulty and it proved most efficient.

The following summer, I found myself in a deep quandary over a decision of great personal importance. The more I struggled with it the more indecisive I became. One night, before retiring, I asked for enlightenment through the sign of a white rose. Early next morning I went to church. At the top of the steps the six-year-old daughter of my friend was waiting for me. As I greeted her, she smiled and said, "I brought a white rose." Her statement failed to register in my mind. After entering a pew, I instinctively raised my eyes to the altar, and there in direct line of vision was a beautiful white rose in full bloom and a bud.

Later in the day I visited my friend. She informed me that the rose was the only one that had appeared on the bush that summer. It had come as suddenly as the one in October, and that immediately after cutting, the plant withered and died. It never showed any sign of life thereafter.

I wonder if our Saviour's Crown of Thorns was taken from a rose bush?

Secret life of Plants

TOUCHING the subject of plants, did you know there is such a thing as mutual regard between them? Can there be good and bad relationships between all growing things? Science can confirm certain "lore" traditionally held by earlier generations, is now correct.

Test controls have shown why strawberries do much better in the presence of the weed, borage. German Chamomile, in small colonies, increases the oil content of the peppermint plant Cauliflower is known to grow better where there is celery, nearby. It is claimed that white cabbage butterflies are kept away from cabbages by celery plants. The culinary herb, chervil, and radishes are mutually helpful to each other's growth. Have you ever seen a bed of chives attacked by disease or insects? Near apple trees, they initiate health and prevent "apple scab". And so we could go on.

Do plants possess senses of which we know nothing? Animals respond to instincts. They can foresee natural or domestic disasters and escape before they occur. Birds migrate. It would appear that plants exhibit what can only be called "emotional responses" to people and situations. To pray over, or talk lovingly to plants is now an accepted therapy. Scientists can monitor, by means of electrical apparatus, sounds of "pain" emitted by plants when maltreated. Is it possible there is a mysterious "something" in the atmosphere to which they respond?

Luther Burbank, horticultural genius, created many new strains by loving them and letting them know his wishes by talking to them. You might have heard of the species of edible cactus which in its original state was bristling with murderous prickly spines. Burbank set to work on it. After three years the plant responded and a variety was propagated all soft and succulent, with no spines. Planted at strategic points in the Arizona desert, this new source of food provides nourishment for untold desert animals and beasts of transport.

How can we take a wider interest in our native plants, birds and small mammals? We can lend our moral support to what is being done to conserve the accumulated knowledge and wisdom of centuries of observation. The earth is a great mystery. We discredit a beneficent Creator when we ignore Him, shutting Him out of His universe to give pride of place to the scientist.

Ecology starts in our own garden. We can resist every new move towards pollution. A nettle-bed is still a place for garden birds to find the black, hairy caterpillars of the common tortoiseshell butterfly. Let us keep it so. Ladybirds, red or orange with black spots, methodically search our rose bushes for greenfly. Even the wild dog rose spares some of its pollen to the hoverfly for food.

When did you last watch humble bees creeping into foxgloves or go bumbling over the clover? This is the time when hundreds of tiny frogs leave ponds they lived in as tadpoles and make their way to the meadows . . . even our own gardens.

Man is not the only creature of consequence on planet Earth. We should all have a thoughtful regard for the "rest". We, ourselves, and all living creatures are bound up together in the web of life. What affects one directly or indirectly affects another. We live in a wonderful world.

Human Case Book

Nancy Walmsley

ONE Sunday morning I had decided not to go to Church but to sit in my garden but I was not allowed to do this. I have heard many people say, "I didn't really intend to, but somehow my mind wasn't at rest and so . . . " That is exactly what happened to me. An inward voice repeatedly told me to go to Church and, of course, I did. On arriving, I saw a stranger sitting in the back row, weeping. I immediately asked her to come forward and sit with me (feeling certain within this was "the reason"). All through the service she wept silently. I couldn't question her much so asked her to come to tea the following Tuesday. She came, still weeping, saying she had a wonderful husband, good and kind, and three grown-up children. All were good to her. Then what was the trouble? She could not do any cooking, housework, nor find interest in her family or life.

I went to her home and talked to her. A very sad case. Doctor's treatment was of no avail and she had no hope at all. She was willing to have my treatment. I summed-up her trouble as being "in the mind", which is so often responsible for many illnesses. I gave her Anacardium for the mind at night; Ignatia 6x for nerves three times daily, and Sulphur 30 once a week. In less than three weeks I phoned her and to my great surprise she was laughing, telling me she was having her lounge re-decorated, and that she was sitting on the floor phoning. Of course, I went along to see her. The change was so great that I could hardly believe it possible. Smiling, she was full of ideas for improvements to her house.

In the evening her husband came to see me, and with tearful thanks said he could only call it a miracle. Also her children came. My "weeping" patient had no return of the depression for years and has now left Bristol.

Mr. E. Britton, London, S.E.9.
Asthma is the most serious of allergic diseases and is responsible for thousands of deaths every year. In my case, irritation started in the nasal passages and over the years, worked down to the chest. This is what causes the constriction and difficult breathing.

The new sprays can give immediate relief, but nobody likes to use them indefinitely, especially after hearing of some of the dubious side-effects they may leave. Is there anything in your line of country you feel can help?

ED: *One has only to read through medical literature of the past to discover that asthma remedies run into hundreds. Ultimate improvement usually depends upon the removal of certain foods from the diet; to spinal adjustment, and intelligent medication.*

Whilst not wishing to unduly raise hopes in chronic cases, we respectfully submit the following bit of information from which some might derive benefit. Old Dr. Blunt, homeopathic physician, considered Natrum Mur (obtainable in the form of the Biochemic Salts of Dr. Schuessler) as almost specific. He said he cured more cases of asthma with this, than with all other remedies put together. We are making no promises, but we feel we should say that many sufferers have been helped thereby.

Mrs. W. E. Hay, Corrie, Shoreham by Sea, Sussex.
As usual *Grace* gives pleasure to so many and makes us say "For what we have received". I wonder if readers would be interested to know that there is also obtainable, Slippery Elm for poultices, in case of septic wounds. I had a badly poisoned finger, turning septic. Two doctors declared if it were not removed I should lose my hand. When a friend who was a clever herbalist saw it she asked "if I had a fig". She removed the seeds, pounded it in olive oil, then filled it with slippery elm powder mixed with a little olive oil to prevent it sticking. She bound it round the finger and renewed it three times during the week, after bathing in warm water. It soon became quite well, to the amazement of the doctors.

"Rutin tea" (1 teaspoonful added to the tea) prevents hardening of the arteries. Periwinkle is a useful herb for Glucosuria (sugar in the urine).

ED: *Readers will doubtless remember how, from their bibles, Hezekiah cured his boils with a clump of figs.*

Mrs. M. Bedwell, Battle, Sussex.
A friend fell and hurt her leg, and had to have 16 stitches in it. She attended hospital each day and it did not heal, so they tried honey and a marked difference was noticed directly. It soothed and healed. I know our grandmothers' remedies were sure and safe. The new painkillers are so dangerous and have side effects. They are tested on animals and animals cannot tell you how they feel. What is proven in animals is not always true for the human species. Yours sincerely.

Mr. J. M. Watkins, Ojai, California 93023, U.S.A.
In my 88th year I send readers the following definition of grace by Dr. John Jowett:
"Grace is more than mercy. It is more than a multitude of tender mercies. Grace is more than love. It is holy love in spontaneous movement going out in eager quest toward the unholy and the unlovely. By its own sacrifices it redeems the unholy and unlovely into its own strength and beauty. The grace of God is holy love on the move to you and me. It is God unmerited, undeserved, going out towards the children of men, that He might win them into the glory and brightness of His own likeness."

Mrs. M. Stievenard, Millbrook, Jersey, C.I.
We very much enjoy a reader's tip of putting several washed rose leaves fresh from the garden into the teapot with a little tea before pouring on the boiling water. The flavour is so mild and pleasant. This is such an economical way with tea.

Mrs. E. Lewis, Woking, Surrey.
I would like to pass on something that happened to my grandmother many years ago. She had a poisoned hand, and was to go into hospital to have it removed, as it did not respond to the doctor's treatment but got steadily worse. My grandfather, going home one day, met an old countryman who begged him to collect Ragwort and make a poultice of it for the poisoned hand. This he did, and kept it up for two days or so, and when the time came for the operation, the hand was quite healed. My grandmother used to show me her hand and tell me this story when I was a small child, and she always remembered how nearly she had lost the hand, and felt grateful all her life for the "miracle" that saved it.

John Fawcett, Riding Hill, Northumberland.
Perhaps you might be interested in my experiences in the use of Chickweed, for it seems this humble plant does not receive the recognition it deserves.

Some years ago, I suffered from wet eczema behind the knee which resisted all the doctor's efforts, and applications of various ointments and lotions bought from chemists. This complaint persisted for three and a half years. In desperation, I looked up an old herbal, and found Chickweed!

SUFFERING is a kind of repairing process, so make it so. Try to learn the lesson it teaches. Life is a mystery. The fearful pain will fade. Turn to work. And put your agony into something and change it. "Sorrow shall be turned into joy." Try to lose yourself more utterly, to love more deeply, to feel oneself a part of life, not separate. Life Accept Me.

KATHERINE MANSFIELD.

The procedure was simplicity itself. I gathered a handful, washed it, chopped it up as one would with mint, placed it in a pan with pure lard, and allowed it to simmer for about fifteen minutes. It was then strained into a jar. When cool, I applied it to the affected area, and bandaged. This treatment was continued each day for four days. Result – complete cure. There has never been a sign of a return.

Since this experience I have used it very successfully for dermatitis, skin troubles of all kinds, cuts, wounds. I have never found it to fail. I have even supplied it to Hospital Superintendents who have found it satisfactory when allopathic preparations have proved useless.

Perhaps this might be useful to other members of our wonderful *Grace* Family. I hope it will. In any case, I would like to pay homage and respect to this wonderful herb and if possible have it placed where it belongs – in the "Honours List" of herbal medicaments.

Mrs. Joy Luton, Cranbrook, Ilford, Essex.
For about two years I suffered a nasty, ugly wart on the first finger of my left hand, which became quite painful. Treatment from the doctor did nothing, he then sent me to the local hospital, where they performed on it with the knife and I had to keep it bandaged for a fortnight. To my horror, on removal of the bandage, the wart was still there ! I then went in search of an old friend whom I knew to be an expert on herbs – he took one look and said, "Oh ! thuja will get rid of that for you in no time!" I infused the herb and took a wineglassful morning and evening, also dabbed the wart twice a day with a concentrated essence of thuja. It worked like magic – in three weeks the wart had completely disappeared without sign!

Mrs. L. Whitton, Weston-super-Mare, Somerset.
Reading suggested cures for ulcerated varicose veins, may I tell you how my mother was cured? She was in agony for three years, then was advised to use Peroxide of Hydrogen. This she used by letting drops of it pour into the open ulcer. Result, a complete cure in two weeks, with no further trouble. She lived to 85 and her legs were perfect. Just in case this helps someone.

Mrs. E. Boult, Hixon, Staffordshire.
Reading the letter by Mrs. W. Fisher I am reminded of my own dear mother and her mother, too. They lived by herbs and could find one for almost every ailment, from "mousear forget-me-nots" for whooping cough, parsley tea as a lotion for bathing nettlerash; groundsel for Granny's age-old eczema (which the doctor couldn't cure but mother did!) and barley-straw and sweet cream made into a salve to cure Grandad's shingles. Why, I could fill a book with 'em !

Miss Herapath, Bournemouth.
Some years ago my sister was injured when in a queue while waiting for a trolley bus. When the bus arrived she was the next person to mount the vehicle when it swerved, knocking and injuring the front part of her leg. It was very painful for a long time and later on developed into phlebitis which was most distressing. It spread rapidly and she found scratching only made it worse. She tried rubbing on Cod Liver Oil and it improved from that hour. After a short time the skin healed and the trouble disappeared.

ED: *Thank you, Miss Herapath. In the same way as the best things in life are free, the most effective cures are the simplest and the cheapest.*

Mrs. Stefni Dawn, Monrovia, California, U.S.A.
Dear Friends: Recently I met a man here at Ferraro's, in Monrovia, California. He comes often to buy the Ferraro's fresh carrot juice. I assumed he was about 80, at the most. I admired his perfect posture, as well as his excellent general health appearance. He is actually 99. His is an interesting story.

When he was about 12, his parents died of T.B. He, too, had been sickly all his life. Then, he made up his mind he was going to learn how to keep well. He began to study books by Bernard McFadden. It seems to me he learned McFadden's ideas well and also got some ideas of his own.

When he was 97, he was riding his bike some distance from his home. He came upon some gravel in the road, skidded and fell off his bike. One of his legs was badly bruised and swollen and made it painful for him to walk home. When he got there, his 67-year-old daughter insisted that he see a doctor. The doctor found no broken bones. (That's remarkable at that age by itself.) The doctor told him that it would be necessary for him to sit with his leg propped up in an elevated position, for about two months. He said:

"Doctor, don't you know what would happen to me at my age, if I sat for two months? I'd never be able to walk again for the rest of my life. Who are you kidding?"

So he rode a stationary bike at home. He said it was very painful at first, but it was necessary to keep the blood circulating. In two months, he was riding his bike around town again, and still does. He also loves to walk.

His name is Richard Marshall. His birthday, Nov. 7th, 1866. With best wishes.

ED: *Doesn't it make you feel good to read of men like this? They certainly breed 'em tough and full of honest-to-goodness common-sense over the border down Monrovia way!*

91

Close Hauled.   *Photo: A. Tanner.*

Anonymous
My father, at 21, was blind for six weeks in one eye – with cataract. He used to tell us how, after trying one professional man after another, a gipsy told him to use Elder Flowers from the hedges. He did so, following her instructions, and the thing cleared completely. He was nearly 61 years when he died and never had it all those years.

Mrs. D. B. Isaac, St. John's, Newfoundland.
I am a Canadian reader of *Grace* and I enjoy all the articles and help of this dear magazine. Frequently I notice readers asking for help for high blood pressure – where medication has failed.

What about trying belly breathing, which is not deep breathing – it is only natural breathing. After one has learned how to use one's bellows, that is how to breathe naturally, one can take a few inflations at any time or place, but I advise the morning and evening routine for the first several months.

After getting into bed at night – lie on the back with knees flexed and mouth open. Let one hand rest on the abdomen as an indicator. Disregard the chest, and draw a long breath through the open mouth, to inflate the bellows. This is indicated by the rising hand. When the hand has risen to the top of your capacity (without straining), relax, closing the mouth, so that by the elastic reactions of lungs and breathing muscles the air, which inflated the bellows, will be quietly blown out through the nose. The descent of the hand indicates this. Do six inflations night and morning, the success being to keep consistently at it, as it could be a year before one feels real benefit, but it is so simple as it takes only one minute night and morning.

People who adopt this B.B. routine generally find it has a calming, soothing influence, and helps restless folk to get pleasantly relaxed to fall asleep. It serves as a natural massage of the liver and bile apparatus and benefits many ailments associated with the inactivity of these organs. It tends to bring down high blood pressure and keep it down.

Mrs. M. Cumming, St. Peter Port, Guernsey.
I had two very painful boils under my arm, which had contracted the muscles and were most obstinate.

I applied a fresh green leaf of the Common Water Betony (which grows profusely by canals and rivers in England, but not so much here, so many Guernsey people cultivate a plant in their gardens) and felt cool relief at once. As the leaf dried I continued replacing with a fresh one, until, after three or four days the boils had disappeared, muscles relaxed and, eventually, no scars. My husband had a bad whitlow on his finger which he treated with equal success.

Another thing that may be of interest. I, normally, suffer from chilblains on my feet every winter and start taking my (hitherto effective) remedy at the first signs of itching and swelling – about early October.

Earlier this year I bought a pair of Dr. Scholl's wooden-soled sandals and wear them about the house continually. THIS winter – no swollen feet – no itching chilblains – no chemist's remedy ! So I concluded from that that my toes needed more exercise. I admit all the family can now 'hear me coming" but who cares !

Mr. F. T. Newnan, Camberley, Surrey.

When you bring flowers into the house some of them may affect you in various ways. You may find that you are allergic to some, that others stimulate, that some appear to relieve anxiety and depression; and in many cases the seemingly inexplicable mood changes we all experience at times can be traced to the odorous particles circulating in the atmosphere – as in hay fever. A friend of the writer who suffers from severe periodic headaches finds that the proximity of broom disperses even the worst bouts.

Mr. J. Leach, Huddersfield, Yorks.

Somewhere in *Grace* I read of honey used on the skin for carbuncles, and when I did this mine cleared up quickly. I told another man about it and he was amazed how it took out all the pain, and how quickly it healed. I also heard of somebody else using it for boils.

ED: *Thank you, Mr. Leach, for a useful letter. Pass the word on. I reckon we shall have to have a Carbuncle Party. It should be a great gathering, and a swell affair.*

Mrs. H. Baker, Keymer, Hassocks, Sussex.

Your magazine is especially comforting to me as besides being "elderly", for many years now I have been more or less a prisoner to my room with painful rheumatism and a bent spine, It is so exhausting struggling to walk at right angles to myself! I do not have a doctor as I don't want drugs. My husband and I live alone in our cottage and coping is quite a problem as you can imagine.

I have happy memories of Boscombe, Bournemouth, I lived there in my youth. In those days – so long ago – it had an aura of romance and beauty – always music everywhere – in the Arcade, the Gardens and Dan Godfrey at the Winter Gardens where for sixpence one could promenade the "top shelf' and listen to that heavenly orchestra.

I must not waste your time with my nostalgic rambling. All blessings on your work.

ED: *Lovely to hear from you, Mrs. Baker, though we are sorry to learn you cannot walk down your lane in the warm spring sunshine. What's it like in the garden? We hope it will be possible for you to inhale the fresh, clear air of spring and find pure joy in the throstle's song. God bless you and keep you.*

Miss C. L. Johnson, Farnham, Surrey.
One hot summer day I was driving rather quickly along a country road when a bee flew into the open window of my car and dashed itself heavily on my eyebrow leaving its sting in a point close to my eye. I pulled out the sting and saw that the bee had been killed by the force of the impact.

My eye was swelling rapidly and was very painful – I felt it would very soon close my eye, so I turned into a nearby school where I knew the Head Master kept bees and our conversation took the following trend:

ME: "Look what one of your bees has done to my eye."

H.M.: "Put a penny on it."

ME: "Don't be silly."

Then he took a penny from his pocket and pressed it on the painful and swollen eye. Immediately the pain was relieved and the swelling began to go down. After half an hour the inflammation had gone completely and I could hardly tell which eye had been affected. I have since used this method for wasp stings and it has always worked.

Miss Jessie Robinson, Hazel Grove, Stockport.
I read in the last issue of *Grace* that Mr. Smart of Cardiff could not face up to taking onion juice for hiccups. Few people seem to know that it is quite pleasant if a little honey is mixed with the juice. Also, if a large onion is sliced and put into a basin with honey spread over each layer, and left to stand, covered-up, over-night, the liquid is pleasant to take. Two teaspoonsful two or three times a day can relieve chest colds and some forms of asthma.

I always have a teaspoonful of honey after eating spring onions in salad. It removes the after-taste and odour.

Mrs. Marjorie Dale, Elmstead Market, Nr. Colchester, Essex.
I note a Mrs. G. Woodrow, Hitchin, gave a remedy for cracked finger tips which is very interesting.

Myself I have found Olive Oil very good; rubbing a little well into the hands at bed time, also rubbing the oil well into the skin at the top of the fingers around the nail.

Olive Oil is also very good for keeping out the cold – a teaspoonful taken two or three times a week keeps me warm against the cold weather.

Miss L. A. Wright, London, N.W.10.

War-time, mid-winter, a precious week's holiday and sciatica! Anyone who has had sciatica can well imagine the agony endured on my train journey from Oxford to Torquay.

At dinner at the hotel, during which I could hardly remain sitting, I debated what I should do. Should I call in a doctor who, I knew, would order me to bed for perhaps a fortnight? This would inconvenience the hotel-people and I had not travelled so far to spend my precious holiday in bed! Should I 'do a Coué' and tell myself it was all in the mind? I had little faith in this method!

Suddenly, there flashed into my mind an idea, from where I knew not to this day, I can only think I had heard it or read it long before and the subconscious had stored it until needed. It was this. Thirty-six hours in bed fasting, taking only cold water will cure an attack of rheumatism.

I knew that rheumatism and sciatica are not the same but in my extremity I determined to try it. On the Saturday night I went to bed with a jug of cold water by me on the table. The pain that night and the next day was hard to bear and as P. G. Wodehouse would say, a corkscrew could have taken my correspondence course in twists and contortions!

All kindly-offered food, aspirin, coffee, tea, were refused and I kept to the cold water only. The second night I slept well and the next morning the pain had quite gone just thirty-six hours since the beginning of the fast. I did not exactly leap from bed with a gay snatch of song, but how thankful I felt to be free from pain.

After a little toast and tea and later, an ordinary lunch, I was able to walk three miles by the sea. A slight weakness was felt in the leg for a few days, but I enjoyed my holiday after all.

Mr. A. Poulter, St. Stephen, Cornwall.

I see that Honey is at last being re-discovered as a wonderful cure. A few years back, when driven nearly frantic by skin inflammation and shingles, after getting no relief from Calamine, I suddenly thought – why not apply a little smear of Honey? (Try anything when desperate enough!) To my relief, it left a coolness behind in place of the hot irritation, and reduced the intense itching.

Moreover, it cleared up the spots quite quickly – wasn't I thankful? It is very sticky of course, but after applying it, a light cover of some sort can keep the skin away from clothes. Alternatively, a diluted application, say 50/50, with warm water, is just as effective – Spreads easier, and not so sticky. Best wishes to all.

CLOVELLY . . . not far from the beauty of the wild moors, river valleys and picturesque harbours of North Devon.   *Roy Westlake.*

Mrs. I. Kinscott, Salisbury.
Reading through the *Grace Magazine* brings back memories of my child-hood home on the edge of the New Forest at Marchwood. I can still recall the scent of our orchard, of daffodils and sweet apple blossom on the wind. How well I remember those hot afternoons of summer when the smell of hay floated through the kitchen window; then the autumn with crisp frosty mornings when we would step out into the clear morning air. I can never forget the winter evenings when father gathered from the woods those huge crackling logs which blazed in our hearth with friendly warmth. We used to cut our own mistletoe which grew on an old russet apple tree. I would go into the loft where the odour of the Blenheim apples was almost over-powering.

We never needed a doctor. My mother believed in plenty of fresh air and good simple food. We ate honey and gathered young nettles which were cooked as a vegetable and they had excellent blood-purifying prop-erties. We drank elderberry wine and sometimes used parsley as a poul-tice for injured fingers and boils.

St. Luke the Beloved physician, in a book I have recently read, used many herbs for his healing of the sick. Like other physicians of his day he must have used medicinal barks which, since the beginning of time, have been known to possess healing properties.

Mrs. Gladys Bunker, Ilford, Essex.
I wish to thank you for the many pleasant hours I have spent with your lovely little magazine. I shall never be able to give it up. I look forward to it so very much. It has helped me in so many ways – and whatever problem I may have, I completely forget it while reading your pages within which I have sometimes found the answer to my problem.

Mrs. L. J. Picton, Pinelands, C.P., S. Africa.
I wonder if you know of this gargle, which helps my husband so much in the winter. Simmer a packet of dried sage for ten minutes and allow to cool (in a pint of water). Strain and add a good tablespoon of honey and a tablespoon of vinegar or lemon juice. We call it the 'witches brew' as with the vinegar it brings up so much dirty muck. This came from an old Swiss gentleman and we would not be without it. Unfortunately, it does not keep very long, at least out here, maybe in cooler England it would. I have also found that the same amount of sage and water made into a drink is a great help if you do, as I do, a lot of public speaking. A tablespoon just before you go to your meeting will sustain and strengthen your voice.

(continued on page 100)

Flowers of the valley.   *Duncan McEwan*

DIAGNOSIS FROM THE TONGUE

MOST unregistered practitioners do not operate an X-ray apparatus or enjoy access to up-to-date laboratory techniques. They must therefore be "as sharp as a needle" when it comes to detecting objective symptoms and clinical signs by careful observation.

There is a world of diagnosis in the tongue, frowned upon by present-day physicians. The old doctors knew that the tongue was an excellent indicator of the condition of certain organs hidden from view, such as liver, stomach, bowels. From it can often be read the state of the blood and brain. The following clinical aid can prove valuable to the busy practitioner and often enable him to pick up the real cause of a patient's trouble, which might have been overlooked by previous investigators.

1   A heavy white-coated tongue with or without elevated papillae indicates . . . *gastric derangements.*

2   Brown coat in the centre and white at the sides . . . *derangement stomach and liver.*

3   Tongue very dark brown like gingerbread, or even a deeper brown . . . *malignant bilious fever or typhus.*

4   Charcoal hue at the root . . . *blood poisoning.*

5   Fur on the tongue . . . *catarrh of stomach.*

6   Transverse fissures on tongue . . . *intestinal irritation.*

7   Longitudinal tracks . . . *irritation of the kidneys.*

8   Sharp pointed tongue . . . *evidence of nervous irritation.*

9   A large flabby tongue . . . *glandular disease.*

10   Smooth raw beef tongue . . . *inflammation of the stomach.*

11   Red tip and edges, sharp pointed, with white coat or fur on other coat in the centre . . . *chronic inflammation of stomach.*

12   Tongue large, tremulous, creamy . . . *delirium tremens.*

13   If patient thrusts or darts the tongue out of his mouth and it is tremulous . . . *chorea.*

14   Tongue buff colour, or like new leather, very deep sharp pointed or may be patchy, or papillae elevated . . . *typhoid fever.*

15   A thick coating white or brown . . . *malassimilation.*

16   Aphtae, or ulceration in patches on the tongue . . . *malnutrition very great.*

17   Strawberry tongue, perhaps surface slightly coated in streaks, papillae projecting greatly . . . *characteristic of scarlatina.*

18   Tongue very bright red, moist, with or without coating . . . *hysteria, nerve tension.*

19   Extreme dryness, shining, glazed dirty white or brownish, without either usual dryness, enlargement or redness . . . *the derangement involves rather the lining membranes than the nerves of the stomach and that not to a too serious extent.*

20   Tongue shining and glazed or chapped . . . *ulceration of the bowels.* Warts on the edges near roots . . . *syphilis.*

21   Tongue is furred with shiny matter, with vivid red tip on margins . . . *affections of the lining membranes but of a more serious character.*

22   Yellow tongue qualified by one or more of the last named conditions . . . *implicated* liver.

23   Clean tongue, of bright redness, naturally moist, but the papillae unnaturally prominent . . . *derangement of the nerves of the stomach*

24   Tongue dry red, glazed . . . *similar affections of the last but more severe and of longer standing.*

25   Swollen red tongue with white fur . . . *a degree of nervous derangement of the digestive organs as to react congestively upon the brain and implicate that organ.*

26   Tongue cracked, furrowed, fissured, swollen . . . *nerves of the stomach.*

27   Swollen tongue thinly coated, white but bright red at the tip and margins . . . *complications of both varieties of indigestion, that of the lining of the membrane and the nerves.*

98

Torre Abbey Gardens, South Devon.   *Roy Westlake.*

TORQUAY

DO YOU believe the best things in life are free? I do. Are things difficult with you? If so, I'm sorry. But let me tell you about Elizabeth.

Elizabeth had everything a woman could wish for: a smart car of her
own, a fine house, an adoring family, and an able husband who was a
whale for work.

But after four years, coronary thrombosis claimed another victim and
she found herself with the children on a very reduced income. What did
she do then? Why she pitched straight into a job selling cakes in the shop
next door to the bakery, and mother was game enough to look after the
children.

A determined and resolute outlook soon took the sting out of that burden of grief and life gradually became worth living. She attacked with
faith and hope those eroding thoughts of self-pity when they invaded her
inner citadel. Her re-habilitation has been perfect. The weekly purse
does not permit any luxuries, but with mother and the boys she is as happy
as the day is long. One of their chief delights is to get away to the hills
of Blandford Forum kite-flying on Sunday afternoons.

So, you see, if things are rather trying to you, remember Elizabeth and
how the best things in life are free. (*Entre nous.* I hear tell of a thirty-
five-ish bachelor barrister making frequent trips to the shop from his office
across the road. I'll bet it's not for wholewheat biscuits!)

ED: *Thank you, Mrs. Picton, down there in sunny South Africa. Say, when are your lovely juicy pineapples coming on to the London market? We shall remember your advice for the next meeting of the local Debating Society and wet our whistle with Witches' Brew. Hey ! Can you hear me at the back of the hall?*

Stephen, aged 14.
I suffered from Migraine for years, and it could not be cured. A copy of *Grace* was sent to my family in which Vervain was mentioned for the relief of Migraine. I insisted on trying it. After the first few cachets of dried Vervain in my tea the migraine pains left me and have not been felt since.

Miss K. Harris, Milton-under- Wychwood, Oxon.
May I ask a question that rather worries me? In a back number of *Grace* I read how harmful aluminium cooking utensils were to cook in and I am wondering about kitchen foil. We are advised to wrap food in it and to cook food with it wrapped around.
ED: *We are not quite clear on the use of kitchen foil ourselves. We feel it cannot be good but lack convincing evidence.*

John Richardson, London, S.E. 11.
Overheard in a conversation between two London surgeons: "We operated just in time. Another two days and he would have recovered without us!"

Mrs. I. Weaire, Romford, Essex.
For some years I have been taking honey daily. Some days as little as a teaspoonful. It has suddenly occurred to me that for some years now I have not been troubled with the chilblains I used to get in the winter months.

Mrs. G. L. Cave, Victoria, British Columbia.
Sometimes, when I have only myself to make lunch for, I don't want a whole pot-ful of soup. So I concoct my own brew. Other members of the Family in a similar position may wish to hear of it.
I cut one small onion and fry it in butter or margarine till lightly browned. Then I add one cupful of milk; sprinkle with parsley, salt, pepper, and a teaspoon of wheatgerm, I simmer for fifteen to twenty minutes, and serve. Try it, and see how tasty it can be. It's bang full of vitamins, too.

Mrs. C. W. Daniels, Kidderminster, Worcs.
Although keeping to health foods, I still suffer from flatulence and heartburn.
Regularly I had to take Nat. Phos. to counteract acidity. I have now discovered what was wrong. I was mixing starches, proteins and alkaline foods all up together. No wonder my poor old tum was in a state of ferment ! On holiday in the Lake District someone recommended the Hay Diet. Dr. Hay has three principles:

1. Starches and Sugars must not be eaten with Protein and acid fruit.
2. Fats, Starches, Sugars and Proteins should only be eaten in small quantities. Vegetables, salads and fruits should form 80 per cent of the diet. These are essential to maintain the alkaline reserve.
3. All refined sugars and starches should be avoided.

Now I no longer eat potatoes or wholemeal bread if I am having meat or fish. Result: no blown feeling. These two foods are reserved for a starch meal. I never use brown sugar or honey on acid fruit, just cream. Sugar and honey are only compatible with starch fruits such as bananas.

There are certain foods, though, that are compatible with all meals, viz. mushrooms, nuts, oils, raisins, cream cheese, butter, cream, milk, egg yolks (the white is highly indigestible and one of the most acid foods known).

If any other *Grace* readers suffer from indigestion or other troubles, I can strongly recommend this diet. And it is so simple. Life should be enjoyed, not endured. All good wishes.

Mrs. A. Foster, Liverpool 4.
I have been suffering from anaemia for the past two years. This is made worse by heavy periods. I have just finished a course of injections but do not feel at all well. The doctor nor the hospital ever mention diet, and I feel it is important. Can you name some iron-containing foods?

ED: *Here are a few. Cheese, spinach, onions, dried peas, eggs, oatmeal, beans, cabbage, dried fruits, red meats, leeks, turnips. Fowler's black treacle, Crude Black Molasses.*

Mrs. L. Plowright, Sunderland.
Can one eat stinging nettles?

ED: *Yes. Nettles are delicious when eaten like spinach. They should be gathered in spring, when young and tender; washed, and placed in boiling water, salted. Boil until tender, strain; and chop up small. Delicious, warm, with a little salt and butter. At this time of the year nettles may be a little woody and fibrous but I know of a hardy old ash-tree man who eats them at any time when available. No need to zip yourself up with vitamin pills when serving nettle-spinach.*

Mrs. Eileen Marsh, Hamilton P.O. Bermuda,
I'd like to share a little story with you that happened to our friend Mr. Ritchie Smith here, a beekeeper, a few months ago.

Mr. Ritchie Smith had just started his lunchbreak and he was preparing to sit down and rest his tired legs from standing behind a counter all morning. Suddenly he had a "feeling" he must go across the road, but he did not want to do this. However, the compulsion was so strong he finally crossed the road. He walked along the edge about 300 yards. By now he was beginning to wish he was sitting down enjoying his sandwich lunch, but the urge was so strong he continued walking and when he came to a place which was a "dead end" he looked around, could see no reason why he was there and said to himself, "I am an idiot – wasting my time like this." He turned to retrace his steps, THEN he saw it. Three motor assisted bicycles leaning against a wall, and on the engine of one bike was a huge swarm of bees! THEN he knew why he had been nudged, and quietly said, "Thank you, GOD." He rushed back to the shop, got a cardboard carton, picked up the bike and shook the bees into the box which he took back to the shop and tied the lid down, When he left work that evening he cycled home with his treasure.

These bees now produce the most perfect honey I have ever tasted. It is just like velvet and cannot be bought. Truly those bees are something special. It shows how we must "listen" and respond to God's loving guidance. He always knows what is best for us.

I found a very dear "pen-friend" through the magazine and may God bless all the Grace Family.

Mrs. J. V. Clarke, Horam, E. Sussex.
While I am sending you my subscription I am writing to say that readers might like to know that Chickweed (*Stellaria Media*) is a very pleasant and nourishing salad ingredient and plentiful in most gardens. When growing in good soil, it is tender, and some children like it better than lettuce. It has similar healing properties as Slippery Elm (for internal irritation, indigestion and ulceration) and is so kind to "tummies". A healing ointment is also made from it.

Wild garlic (ramsoms) (*Allium Ursinum*) can be found in damp places, with a leaf something like Lily of the Valley, and balls of white flowers, in spring. It has a strong onion smell. My family love it. It can be used in cooking, or dried for use in winter instead of expensive garlic capsules for those who do not mind its pungent smell and taste. My husband is fond of garlic herb mustards.

Mrs. I. M. Cawker, Clacton, Essex.
I feel constrained to tell you of a charming little incident which I recently experienced.

My husband and I had visited our daughter and family for an hour or so and were on the point of leaving for home and waving goodbyes from our car. Just as we were starting, my son-in-law dashed into his front garden and came running towards us. In his hand he had a lovely rose-bud, which he had just plucked, and with shining eyes he thrust it into my hand, through the car window.

It was just a small, spontaneous action, which I am sure sprang from a loving thought, but it meant so much to me. No words were spoken, except my "thank you".

At home on my kitchen window shelf, in a little black vase, this lovely rosebud has opened, so beautifully, into a perfect bloom, and I have watched and enjoyed every phase of its opening, over these last three days.

Today, as I was watching, and still admiring its colourful shape (I believe it is called "Opera") and still reflecting the thought behind it, the rose shed its first two petals. As it did so it quivered! I have never seen this happen before. Could it be that my lovely rose and I were loath to part?

As I write this sweet anecdote to you, I am surrounded in my garden by roses of all shapes and colour, but none can quite express what my gift rose has meant to me. Truly, only a small action, on the spur of the moment, but what pleasure it has brought. Such gallantries today are rare, but so acceptable in this matter-of-fact world. Thank God for sons-in-law!

Thank you and yours once again for *Grace* and for all the loving care that goes into its publication. God bless you all.

Miss Gertrude Loveless, Ohio, U.S.A. (101 years).
As I listened, after a hard day, to the evening "Symphonic Varieties" programme with Beethoven's 7th Symphony, I thought of the picture in Spring *Grace*. The Turner picture, "Crossing the Brook" is so beautiful, too. The Summer issue is just as beautiful.

Grace helps me to try to be quiet and I suffer less pain when I am not too harried or worried.

Mr. Arthur Spencer, Cape Town, South Africa.
I enjoy your magazine. Your readers might like to hear what happened to a man prescribed bifocals, down here. He says:

"I've just got my new glasses. I've never had it so good. Since wearing them I've fallen downstairs; stumbled upstairs; bitten my left thumb severely while eating bread rolls; stabbed my wife while reaching for the cheese; crashed the left wing of my car against the garage post; had my office in a 'flat spin' through setting my alarm clock an hour too late; adorned myself with odd socks; drew blood on right thumb of self trying to pin papers together; been chased by a newsvendor to whom I gave a cherished old threepenny-bit instead of a sixpence; and set all this season's beans in staggered formation. What wouldn't I give for a pair of simple, plain bore, country style spectacles – the sort you could pick up on the market place for 30p. I'm advised to persevere until my eyes get used to the glasses."

GET BUSY

ALTHOUGH generalizations are dangerous, I venture to say that at the bottom of most fears, both mild and severe, will be found an over-active mind and an under-active body. Hence, I have advised many people, in their quest for happiness, to use their heads less and their arms and legs more—in useful work or play. We generate fears while we sit: we overcome them by action. Fear is nature's warning signal to get busy.

– Henry C. Link, Ph.D.

Are We Playing With Fire?

A WOMEN in her early forties writes: "I wish I knew what was wrong with me. I have a good home, a good husband and a lovely family. But I am always tired, depressed and irritable. For a long time I have been told this is natural and normal. Not to worry. I must learn to live with it."

In a woman's life we blame the "change" for so many things. It is taken for granted that all sorts of other physical and mental complaints can be blamed on oestrogen deficiency.

Hormones are the "in" thing, today. They are as fashionable as Freud. They have edged their way into every department of Medicine, into animal feeding stuffs, and into the beauty business. Of the 1,500,000 women in Britain on the "Pill" no less than 120,000 suffer from depression. Are we playing with fire?

Then there is that cloud which can form over the spirit from a congested liver. It is possible we may have eaten too many eggs, too much chocolate, an extra hunk of cheese? A deranged liver has always been associated with melancholy. There's something to be said for this notion. A key factor for a healthy liver is an adequate intake of that versatile vitamin B group. He is a brave and kindly physician who halts completing his prescription pad to offer advice on diet.

Where depression has an anxiety background, sleep may be a problem. We spend a large part of our income feeding, exercising and entertaining the body, often to the neglect of sleep. Two teaspoonfuls of honey in a hot relaxing drink at bedtime is still one of Nature's gentlest soporifics. Isn't it amazing how many common complaints clear up after deep and satisfying sleep?

Today it is fashionable for Freudian psychologists to belittle the role of guilt. A guilty feeling, after known wrong-doing, is bound to manifest as depression. A lot of people suffer from "delayed-shock depression" which is nothing more than a guilty conscience festering away in the vaults of the mind. Has anybody ever ridden rough-shod over his conscience and got away with it – scot free?

Our doctor's anti-depressants have little real effect upon the moral fabric of our mind – the area from which most mental unrest emanates.

Malignant thoughts have children. They beget chemical changes in the blood. It has been proved that a virulent jealousy and gnawing bitterness are capable of inducing biochemical change in the white blood corpuscles, deranging the natural immune system. In a remarkable way this confirms the truth of the Old Book which equates disease with wrong thinking and powerful destructive emotions.

The Avon Bridge, Christchurch, Dorset.   *Photograph: Ronald Goodearl*

Leslie Parker, Clapham Common, London.
Though late in the season I still get Hay Fever. Can you help?
ED: *Have you tried chewing honeycomb? It has proved curative in many cases, and certainly seems a good preventive. Try chewing the comb like chewing-gum. It is a good plan to do this in good time another year – before the season begins. Chew a lump about three or four times daily when an attack is on.*

Mrs. E. McPherson, Calling Lake, Alberta, Canada.
May I tell you of my experience with the sulphur mentioned in *Grace* for arthritis? You will remember it recommends putting some flowers of sulphur in one's socks. It is the most miraculous experience I've ever had. In less than two days all pain was gone. I stopped taking it because it kept coming out of my shoes and tarnished all my silver ware. Do enjoy *Grace* so much.

Alice Richmond, 48, Denver, Colorado.
Greetings from an appreciative reader of *Grace*, across the broad sea, for your uplifting magazine. I am a displaced New Englander, born near Canada in Maine, now living in the lovely state called Colorado, in the midst of the Rocky Mountains. I read *Grace* until the print is worn off the pages: well, almost. And you will never know how many countless blue, sick, young, and old Americans you are cheering-up with *Grace*: no-sir-ee Sir! Do you want to hear how one copy can do this? I shall tell you. I clip, I type poems, I telephone, and I mail all the fine articles that I know some friend of mine will be delighted to know about. I know their drooping spirits are again lifted heavenward, dear kindly Editor. You have also inspired me to write poems and stories. All these thoughts of mine get published in other magazines and newspapers, all having been inspired by reading your articles. Imagine, dear Editor Bartram, how the goodness of *Grace* takes root in hearts of my countrymen. Friends are sustained through bedridden hours through the extracts I type and send them. The enclosed small donation is a mark of my appreciation, and to help to publish your great-little magazine. Keep well. Keep smiling.

Miss A. M. Jackson, Bramley. Guildford, Surrey.
I have found Honey (the pure) excellent for chapped hands and even for oven burns.

Mrs. S. Busby, Burton-on-Trent, Staffs.
I have a son aged nine years who has been successfully treated with the use of goat's milk for a strong allergy to cow's milk. This took the form of severe digestive upsets resulting in debility and a great deal of pain, and also asthma and eczema. He found great benefit from using the milk as a beverage.

Mr. L. Jackson, London, N.W.4.
There's far too much of this telling people they will never walk again, or that they are chronic cases. How come the doctors to be so cocksure? The experience of myself and some others I know tell a very different story. For too long we have been dictated to by the representatives of only one opinion – the orthodox opinion. It is time they woke up to the fact that in spite of their depressing verdicts some people are in fact getting cured, elsewhere. All you hear in some quarters is: "It's chronic – you-will-have-to-learn-to-live-with-it." There are lots of new discoveries which the orthodox man has not yet caught up with. It is a tragedy today that there is too much of the "closed shop" mentality, in which the job of healing is regarded as the property of the favoured few who have passed the official examinations. Sometimes in hospitals the specialists are worse – we're not fit to breathe the same air as they – they are looked up to as a kind of rather "exclusive brethren" who can be as autocratic as they please,

I spent four years helping to fight dictators. Another bunch of them have grown up since the war. Why do they think they are the only ones who know anything about sickness? A scientific education is only part of the job. When I lay in bed with a bad stomach pain and couldn't move, a little "pip-squeak" stumped up my path, came straight through my front door (with not so much as a by-your- leave), stalked into my bedroom, and before I had told him anything, his Prescription Book was in his hand and he was writing out the tablets. We pay for these men. What kind of health service are some people getting?

If they cannot cure certain things for which there are other methods, they should be honest enough to admit it, and send patients to others who have proved they can do the job. Here is what cured my wife's arthritis.

One tablespoonful cod liver oil. This is now sold mint-flavoured. Two, three or four tablespoonfuls orange juice. Emulsify them by shaking up in a jam jar with a screw cap. If you do not want to contaminate a cup, drink straight out of the jar, last thing at night. Do not eat or drink anything else before or after it. My wife's knees and shoulders used to be very stiff. Walking was painful, but now her walking is so good that she can do all her own shopping.

Mr. H. J. Irwin, Barons, Alberta, Canada.
If any of your "family" should come to you about albuminuria, and who are despairing over the possibility of a terribly expensive kidney machine, just suggest bean-pod tea – a sure remedy to dissolve the amyloid and albuminoid substances clogging the glomeruli of the kidneys, a condition resulting from a lifetime of eating a high protein carbohydrate diet.

Mrs. L. Clegg, Oswaldtwistle, Lancs.
I was very interested in the article of *Ground Ivy* in the Winter edition. I would like to tell readers how it cured me of a dilated stomach nearly

forty years ago. My stomach began to swell and was pressing upwards on the heart, causing dreadful palpitation. I daren't lie down as I was afraid my heart would stop.

I sent for a doctor who told me it was a dilated stomach, and gave me some medicine. He also put me on a diet of dry brown toast; nothing else. I was on this diet for two years and still didn't mend; losing over two stones in weight, and getting very weak. Some new people came to live next door and the lady asked me what was the matter. I told her. She said, "Get some *Ground Ivy* from the herbalist's, put it into a teapot and brew it as ordinary tea. You cannot drink too much of it."

Well, I did this. Within a few weeks my stomach was normal. I found I could eat anything and have never had any trouble since. The same lady told me it had cured her son of gastric ulcer that had bothered him for months. I have taken *Grace* since it was first published and look forward to its arrival. It's a great help to enable us to live.

Mrs. Lena Feick, St. Jacobs, Ontario, Canada.
Several years ago my uncle came to our home and he had pricked his finger with a rose thorn. The finger was swollen and throbbed with pain. He gets blood poisoning quite readily, so he was concerned, especially as my cousin kept urging him to go to a doctor. I put a chickweed poultice on while he was there, and another when he went home. He told me later that the pain soon left and the finger healed in a short time.

Mr. L. James, Brighton. Sussex.
Dr. F. G. Banting, who discovered Insulin, warned in 1929 that diabetes had "increased proportionally with the per capita consumption of cane sugar". He called refined sugar a "dangerous foodstuff". Other noted medical men have agreed with him, but still nothing is said about it on a national scale. A vigorous campaign was set in action against smoking as a cause of cancer, but nothing is said about slow breaking-down of the body through white sugar and white sugar products.

The only satisfactory alternative for sugar is honey. I am not mentioning dates or other dried fruits rich in sugar and which are very good. Sugar oxidizes quickly in the stomach, being a shock to the nervous system and organs. It is not good nourishment and can even bring about faulty nutrition.

Honey is assimilated naturally and easily. It does not affect the kidneys as too much sugar does. It enables you to recuperate quickly and is not acid-forming. And for those who want it, it is the gentlest laxative in the world. I'm for honey every time.

Elizabeth E. Williams, Southbourne, Bournemouth.
Have you ever thought, as I have, of the effect one has when presented with a gift? Take flowers, for instance. Suppose someone offered you

the choice of a bunch of woodland primroses or a few choice carnations grown in a hot-house. Which would you choose?

Perhaps I would hesitate in my choice. But not for long. As I gaze at the beauty of the carnations, with their delicate colouring and delicious perfume, I'd sense the hot-house in which they were grown with its moist, warm air; sun shining through the glass roof; shelves of pot plants, debudded at the right time, carefully tended with artificial manures, and the rows of exquisite blooms reaching to the sun.

Then my gaze would fall on the bunch of primroses. Immediately I'd be transported in thought to the woods. There, are the gnarled oaks with lichen- covered trunks; slender birches; silent beeches, and, at their feet, cushions of velvety moss luminous in the golden sunlight. In the thicket, protected by last year's dead leaves, primroses would be peeping, fresh and moist in the damp cool earth. Between the trees a spring sky would be blue with traces of cumulus cloud. It would be mating time for the birds and all the world be young again.

Yes, I have made my choice. Have you?

Mary Wilcox, U.S.A.
I have invented a new breakfast and have found it so inviting and wholesome. First, I slice a dead-ripe banana on a plate and add two heaping teaspoons of sunflower seeds previously soaked in water overnight. Then a little amount of each of the following: ground sesame seeds, ground nuts (any kind), and ground coconut. Next a sprinkle of powdered nettle, and top it off with five or six nice soft prunes with their own juice. I think it is "dee-licious".

Miss A. M. Burt, Froxfield Green, Petersfield.
When my sister was a baby she was rather delicate and used to have wind very much. My mother used to make mint tea for her and sweeten it with brown sugar. A few spoonfuls gave her ease, and she was able to sleep soundly.

"Anonymous". Joliet, Illinois, U.S.A.
I believe in herbs. I have had some good results. Here is one.

Prostate Gland trouble. Horsetail grass and pumpkin seeds. Equal quantities. Cook in water for half an hour. Take wineglassful of the liquor three times daily. This cured my 85-year-old brother. Horsetail is a grass that grows a lot around here.

Miss Lois Beechey, Pencoed, Nr. Bridgend, Glam.
I live in the country but of necessity I have to earn my living in the city. The pace, the noise, the superficiality is sometimes rather frightening and I am glad to get home in the evening to the peace and tranquillity of the countryside. I consider myself to be in a very fortunate position to be able to do this and to me the simple life is the real way of living.

Mr. Percy Barker, Sutton Coldfield.
After reading in *Grace* of people who have been cured in a natural way, without drugs, I feel I ought to tell you this. My father suffered from muscular rheumatism and pain for years until he was recommended to cut out of his diet all animal fats, salt, sugar and alcohol. Only one cup of tea to be taken a day. Instead of tea and coffee he took the juice of half a lemon in a glass of warm water on rising.

He bought a juicer, and during the day took as much carrot juice, celery juice and beet juice as he wanted. He said carrot and celery juice was the nicest. He had only about half teacupful beet juice daily as in large quantities this can increase blood pressure. He wholly got over the rheumatism and never again complained of pain.

Dr. T. de la Torre, Santa Ana, Costa Rica, C.A.
We eat bananas twice a day and do not get tired of them. It is our main article of diet. I believe it is superior to bread, more delicious and alkaline. Fat content of bananas is low, but compensated by the higher content of carbohydrates, as the body can convert starch and sugar into fat. Combining bananas with almonds, peanuts, walnuts, sesame seeds and especially coconut makes an ideal and almost complete food. Whenever possible we eat sun-dried bananas with nuts or peanuts.

Mrs. L. M. Smith, Stanton Caundle, Sturminster Newton.
You have asked for it Mr. Editor, so here it is.

Two winters agone I was smitten down with metal poisoning, feeling very ill for two days, with violent vomiting and diarrhoea. Lay prostrate for two days and nights, with neither bite nor sup. My only desire was to be left alone and lie still. I tried all sorts of things to bring me back to normal. Nothing did the trick until I suddenly bethought me of some Parsley Wine I had made. I reached for the bottle, warmed it gently on the hearth and kept drinking an egg-cupful at intervals of two hours. It did the trick, when other things failed.

Since then I have read in *Grace* that parsley is good for biliousness. In case any reader would like the recipe, here it is:

Parsley Wine

Ingredients: 1 quart Parsley Liquid with
               1 lb sugar (brown), 1 teaspoonful
               Allinson Dried Baking Yeast

Method:
Press as much parsley as you have available firmly into pan, and cover with water. Simmer tor 20 minutes. Strain, pressing leaves to get all out. Add sugar, stirring all the time until dissolved. When liquid is lukewarm, sprinkle yeast on the top, cover with a cloth and leave in a warm place overnight. Strain into clean bottles next morning, cork lightly until fermentation ceases. Then cork tightly and leave for six months.

Mrs. M. Latchett, Salisbury, Zimbabwe.
My daughter has had diarrhoea on and off for two years, with frequent passing of watery motions. Everything possible has been done. She gets rid of it for a time, then it comes back. She is 18 years.
ED: *We are sorry we have not space to go into the dietetic aspect. Slippery Elm Food is helpful. Obtain four ounces Raspberry Leaves. Place one ounce in one pint cold water. Bring to the boil. Simmer for two minutes. Add a pinch or two of Cinnamon Powder. Strain when cold. Give one wineglassful after meals, three times daily.*

Mr. J. Walters, Toronto, Canada.
Please give me a simple food good for gout and for very acid urine. Also one for skin troubles, please.
ED: *Rice and water only. Boiled rice. Drink all the water. For skin troubles have you tried "All Bran" for breakfast?*

Mr. Aspinall, London, N.W.4.
I do not suffer from ill-health generally, but I do get very irritable and my family seem to think I'm snappy.
ED: *Irritability can often be due to shortage of Niacin, one of the B vitamins. Try Brewers' Yeast tablets.*

Cyril Scott, Eastbourne.
The following concerns an acquaintance of mine,
A gentleman in his sixties was in great distress because unable to pass water. The doctor was called in and a catheter had to be used several times. The doctor told him that he was suffering from "prostate" and would have to undergo an operation, But it was then discovered that he had sugar in his urine, and it would be dangerous to operate while the diabetic condition was present. In consequence injections of insulin were given. Finally the patient's osteopath advised him to try parsley tea. The result was astonishing. Not only was he able to urinate freely, but in a very short time all trace of sugar had vanished from his urine. After first drinking the parsley tea, a lot of offensive substance came away in his urine. But the latter soon became normal, and the erstwhile patient is now in fine fettle and able to play his rounds of golf with enjoyment. Though the doctor wanted him to continue with the insulin, he refused, and feels much better without it. There is no more any thought of an operation.

Mrs. L. Chambers, Spalding, Lincolnshire.
Here's a tip for the old codgers. If your clock is running slow you can sometimes save the clockmaker's repairs by putting it in a warm oven overnight. It loosens clogged-up oil and its heart can be ticking away merrily in the morning.
ED: *Wad d'ye know about that!*

111

Mr. L. Mitchell, Fife, Scotland
Greetings to the *Grace* Family. You ask for cures of complaints without the aid of drugs. This was my experience. I suffered for years with psoriasis, a skin rash which must be the most stubborn to heal. I tried everything. I wondered if it would ever be cured.

One day, a man told me of somebody who had been cured by honey and cod-liver oil. It took me some weeks to get round to the idea. Then I tried it. It took the redness out, and soon it ceased to get flaky. Though it remained red for weeks I kept at it, and my skin trouble has now completely disappeared.

ED: *Honey and cod-liver oil is an old German combination known as Desitinsalve. It is used as a wound-dressing, results being obtained in infected wounds, ulcerations, carbuncles, fistulas, boils, burns, felons, etc. It has even been known to heal deep necrotic tissues. It can stimulate granulation in chronic leg ulcers, and readily eases pain and tension. The change of dressing is not painful because the wound exudes a thick exudate of lymph which prevents adherence. Many cases of psoriasis have been cured. Almost all have found some relief. Place four ounces cod-liver oil in a glass jar with a screw-cap. Add four or five teaspoonfuls fresh, or this season's honey. Shake vigorously until honey is dissolved. Apply to affected skin surface and change dressing every twenty-four hours. The quality of honey is important, as "creamed" or processed honey mixed with inferior syrups would minimize its healing effect. Make sure your honey is just as it is when it leaves the hive, and not heated or pasteurized.*

Miss E. Taylor, Henley-in-Arden, Solihull, Warwickshire.
I am a fairly new member of the Grace Family, being in my second year. And how delightful I find it! The magazine is so handy to take on a bus or short train journey when reading time is short. I like to keep it beside the bed for late reading.

I am most interested in the readers' letters. One can always learn something from them. May I pass on my method of getting to sleep? After something has upset me during the day, events churn over and over in my mind, and sleep does not come. It is then that I forcibly "about turn" all my thoughts and focus them on all the things which give me most pleasure in seeing, hearing and smelling. First coming to my mind's eye is a newly-ploughed field, the soft brown earth turned in long, straight furrows and resting awhile until the miracle of spring. Then I see my first violet in the hedge, almost hidden by the leaves. How this always gives me a thrill! Soon, I am searching for cowslips along railway banks. Can you recollect the smell of boiling jam; and of sheets and "washing" stiff with frost? There are so many things to re-live in this way. It is surprising to realise how so many small things mean so much. Sleep comes. They never seem to fail.

Mrs. M. Chapman, Winnipeg, Canada.
How shall we ever be able to thank you for the wonderful improvement
in my varicose veins, and for help for my husband's "nervous exhaustion"
and bad circulation. All due to your Vitamin "E". There ought to be a
packet in every home.

Mrs. C. Nelson, Braintree, Essex.
I want to tell you of a villager of over 90. She said, "There, that's a wonder.
I'm still alive. When I wake up in the morning I say to myself; right often
I do: 'Dearie me, here I am still. The Lord has forgotten me again.'"

Madeline King, New York, U.S.A.
I enjoy the magazine very much. May I say a word on Homoeopathic
Medicine; it has helped me greatly.
    Ferrum Phos. for Diarrhoea (4 tablets 3 times daily) – a bad case, and
it sure put me back on my feet. Also, Kali Sulph. (4 tablets 3 times daily)
for Eczema – on my hands. It was itchy and red, watery fluid would ooze
out of it. They are fine now.

Mr. L. R. Stewart, Ark, 72740, U.S.A.
Some time ago I read in *Grace* that Kelp tablets taken over a long period
of time will cure prostate gland trouble. And I found it so.

Mrs. Pennyfeather, Hertfordshire.
I use a great many dried herbs in soups and stews and I like to raise and
dry my own, cheaper, better and compost-grown. Marjoram, Lemon Balm
and Thyme I raise from seed. Sow in March or April, thinly in the open
in a shallow drill in full sun, and thin the plants to about 3 inches wide.
You get a small crop the first year, but the plants are much bigger (move
them wider in the autumn) the next year. You can buy plants to put in
now, but it is easy to raise them from seed and the Thyme comes in such
nice little bushes compared with divided ones.
    I cut my herbs with scissors just before the flowers open, which is when
the flavour is best. I put each bunch in a paper bag and put them in the
oven last thing at night while it is still hot and they dry very easily.
    When I have them dry and crisp, I put them through the mincing
machine, which cuts up all the stems and makes them look exactly like
bought mixed herbs, but greener. I keep them in screw top jars until they
are wanted. Mint can be done this way, too, but separately: let it just start
to flower and do it the same way; it makes quite good mint sauce even
in the depths of winter.

Lady Halsey, Hemel Hempstead.
So many people have written about painful rheumatic cramps. My father
suffered badly all his life and I got to spend sleepless nights till being rec-

ommended the Bio-chemic tablets – Mag. Phos. Four tablets when necessary. It really worked wonders for my own father and if I get even a twinge now it seems to cure it at once. I find one is much more inclined to get cramp from tiredness or driving long distances – so always take this with me. It works wonders. Obtainable from Health Stores.

Mrs. Lisa Gantenbein, Santa Rosa, California, U.S.A.
Thank you for the *Grace Magazine*; it is grace, it is dignity, it is gentleness, it is beauty, it is peace! It is natural and most helpful.

May the celebration of Christ's Birthday renew and revitalize your love and devotion that enable us to have the privilege of getting your magazine.

Miss Gladys Bowden, Saltdean, Sussex.
You ask for any 'tips" readers may have. One I find a great help is to take nearly a dessertspoonful of pure olive oil (from Health Stores) before breakfast. I have a very dry skin and used to have very rough hands which no amount of various hand creams seemed to keep soft, also my hair was dry and simply lapped up brilliantine. Now I have none of this trouble, so I pass on the tip in case any other of your readers suffer in this way.

Mrs. S. Ellis. London Road, Brighton, Sussex.
I hadn't been sleeping well at night, and got tense. Then I went off my food after seeing a television picture on mental health. I have always wanted to be slim, so I did lots of cuts with my food. Then I cut out smoking. That made me really irritable. In the end I wondered if I was going crazy. I needed reassurance that I was not going schizo-something-or-other.

My husband sent me to the doctor and I asked him. "How do you tell if you're nuts?"

What do you think he said? He looked me over, and chuckled, "Don't worry about all that psychiatric terminology. Just give yourself this simple test. If you think you're crazy, you are not. If you think everyone else is crazy, you are.

Miss F. E. Bellingham, Tonbridge, Kent.
Regarding your suggestion for natural remedies, may I suggest one for *Psoriasis*? As you know this is an exceedingly stubborn complaint. In the first place, on the return of oranges to the market after the war (during which time I first developed Psoriasis) I found that a daily orange caused the gradual disappearance of the sores. Subsequently I found I could not digest oranges and on ceasing to eat them, psoriasis gradually returned. Then, quite accidently whilst taking yeast tablets, I discovered these had a similar effect to that of the oranges, presumably both of them supplied some vitamins lacking in my food, or in short supply through

through poor assimilation. I have tested the yeast 'cure' by leaving off the tablets and then starting them again. Later on, I tried a combination of yeast tablets and Rose Hip (vitamin C) capsules and the two together proved to be more rapidly effective.

Mr. A. L. Taylor, London Road, Leicester.
If readers have an opportunity they should hear Dr. Hugh Sinclair, D.M., F.R.C.P., Fellow of Magdalen College, Oxford, at one of his public meetings in connection with fluoridation of our water supplies, Here's what he says:
"Dental caries (dental decay)", he says, "is a very severe and increasing problem in this country, but this condition was not due to fluoride deficiency. There is a great deal of evidence that the teeth of our ancestors were much better than ours today, but so far as we know the fluoride content of their diet was the same, I have studied the perfect teeth of dogs and found no fluoride at all."
"How much fluoride delays caries in children is not certain; probably about three years. There is no question of fluoride completely preventing dental caries. It does not."
Many scientists now believe this condition to be due to a dietary fault. What folly it is to feed the body with neat chemical by adding fluoride to our drinking water. The obvious thing is to correct the fault rather than try to mask it while allowing the dietary fault to continue.
My own opinion is, that neither scientists nor parents are prepared to stand out against the excessive consumption of sweets, soft drinks, white sugar products, lollies and all the chemically charged candies and cookies on the market these days. Children grow up slaves to the confectionery industry.

Mrs. Wendy Wisdom, Clontarf, Dublin 3.
You may like to pass on this recipe to your readers. It is my own invention and a nourishing, health-giving accompaniment to any meal.
Special Salad: 1 lettuce; 1 head of chicory; juice of half a lemon (or orange); 4 tablespoons of olive oil; 3 tablespoons of wheat germ; 2 cloves of garlic.
Crush garlic and rub round bowl and mix with olive oil. Wash and shred lettuce and chicory, and toss in dressing. Add wheat germ and mix and finally pour lemon or orange juice over all. It's delicious.
ED: *Absolutely top hole.*

Holidays are here again

A COMPLETE break from the routine of everyday life is surely the basis of an ideal holiday. Some, like these children, enjoy a holiday with father on the beach. For them, it will be paddling in the sea while mother relaxes in a deck chair.

What is it about England that makes it such a great place for a holiday? England has such a wealth of excellent seaside resorts . . . large ones like Scarborough, Blackpool and Torquay, or the quieter more elegant ones like Cromer in Norfolk and Hove in East Sussex.

Our beaches have a special place in the sun-tan possibilities available during summer-time for the sun-hungry. This is the time to top-up our reserves of vitamin D. Ultra-violet rays of the sun manufacture vitamin D in our skin. We need it for sturdy muscles and firm bones. True, we can get this vitamin in milk, butter, eggs and oils, but not one of us can afford to forego an annual holiday in the sun. Don't leave it until too late. Listen to what Leonardo da Vinci said about going away:

"Every now and then go away, have a little relaxation, for when you come back to work your judgement will be surer. To remain constantly at work will cause you to lose power of judgement . . . Go some distance away because then the work appears smaller and more of it can be taken in at a glance and a lack of harmony and proportion is more readily seen."

What about getting that travelling bag down from the attic?

TIME TO PLAY

IF YOU want to enjoy one of the greatest luxuries in life, the luxury of having enough time—time to play; time to rest; time to think things through, time to get things done and know you have done them to the best of your ability, remember there is only one way.

Take enough time to think and plan things in order of their importance. Your life will take on a new zest. You will add years to your life—and more life to your years.

Benjamin Franklin

Childhood – a time for golden hours in the sunshine . . . a time to disregard time . . . a time for fun on the beach, when Dad has time to spend with the family.

J. H. Johnson.

Mrs. H. A. Sturt, Wappenham, Towcester, Northants.
I have discovered the wonderful 'solvent' quality of beetroot. Boiling a couple (oldish ones I admit) in an enamel saucepan completely furred up from using it to boil water for a long time, in place of kettle, I found the 'fur' so softened that it could be easily rubbed off – or scraped off when not easily rubbed. Our water is very hard. Beetroot must be a good solvent for one's internal plumbing system? I know this vegetable is highly recommended as an internal cleanser when taken raw in salads.

Mrs. Gladys Brown, Bradford on Avon, Wilts.
You may like to know how I cured a wart I had had for years. It also removed ugly protruding pin-points of flesh growing on my throat. I applied apple-cider vinegar and honey. Equal parts, twice a day.
ED: *Congratulations Mrs. Brown. It just goes to show how we should first try the harmless homely measures, before resorting to toxic lotions and cauterization*

Mrs. E. Wright, Lauderville, Florida, U.S.A.
I am very much over-weight (15 stones) and have a diet to follow, but it cuts down on fluids. What can I drink which will not help to put it on?
ED: *One of the best drinks for obesity is a natural well-water from France – Contrexeville water. Good for slimming generally. Rich in minerals, and with an absence of chlorine and fluorides. Obtainable all over the world. Good for habitual hyperorexia, nutritional imbalance and slowing down of the lipidic "turn over"; and for hydrophilic increase in adipose tissue. Plethoric obesity.*
You wish to be a sprite? Then make sure your fats don't fight.
Careful how you bite, and you'll soon be stepping light, Mrs. Wright.

G. E. Ashby, Bunts Lane, Seaton, Devon.
I should like to tell you that my Poodle of 12 years has had a Vitamin "E" capsule daily for the last 18 months. It has arrested the cataract in his eye, and certainly filled him with renewed vitality.

Miss Joan Hill, Dinton, Aylesbury, Bucks.
There is something I discovered, last year, which I would like to pass on to the 'Family'. Dried elderflowers are a marvellous addition to an apple dish. They bring out the apple flavour. The taste is simply exotic. Just add quarter teaspoonful elderflowers, finely rubbed through a sieve, which will be sufficient for six people.
I myself gather the flowers when in full pollen. I think it must be the pollen which gives the piquant taste. Best wishes to you all, from yours sincerely.

Mrs. J. V. Clarke, Oakroyd, Horam, E. Sussex.
As you ask for readers to send in reports of help from herbs, etc., here is mine. Comfrey is not often mentioned, but I would not be without it. Years ago, Mother injured her finger in a car door, and it refused to heal in spite of all the usual treatments. A herbalist told her to use a Comfrey poultice, which she did, using fresh wild Comfrey. It healed in a few days. We have used it many times since for bruises, sprains and "nasty" wounds. A friend broke a small bone in his foot. We gave him Comfrey for a compress, and he said that in half an hour the pain and swelling had gone. If I prick my finger on a rose or hawthorn, it is usually painful for hours, but if I immediately rub the place with the juicy stalk of Comfrey the pain goes almost at once.

I have both the wild, Officinalis and the Russian. The wild is said by some to be best for medicinal use, the Russian being mainly used for fodder and compost as it is very prolific in growth.

It is in fact a very nourishing human food. We often use the very young leaves in salad. They have a slight cucumber flavour, and when short of greens I have cooked them like a spinach. They have been tinned; I am not sure if they still are. They are very high in protein and used as a medicine for healing internally, varicose veins, gastric ulcers, etc. I have used both kinds for all purposes and not found much difference except in the quantity obtained from each plant.

Anonymous, Hitchin, Herts.
The undergiven treatment has proved to be a most effective remedy in curing the excruciating pains, and locked joints, associated with the various forms of rheumatism. I speak from personal experience, which is apart from

(continued on page 122)

Hay Fever

HAY FEVER is one of the best examples of a mucous disturbance due to allergy. Some cases may arise from sensitivity to pollen when its concentration in the air reaches a certain level.

As strange as it may seem, all allergic diseases are inter-related. Many are due to heredity. For instance, a person with asthma may have a child or grandchild suffering from eczema. A victim of migraine may pass on the same tendency but it may take the form of nettle rash. Any one of these can be carried through birth and result in a strong predisposition to hay fever. Some allergies are known to work out of the system over the years. Others disappear at puberty or adolescence; or at the change of life.

A simple, safe medication is garlic. Garlic capsules are very popular at the present time to allay the acute distress of hay fever. Some folk find no difficulty in eating a slice of garlic straight from the corm at mealtimes and ignore any embarrassing halitosis (onion breath) which might follow. Others are content to wipe the inner surfaces of their salad bowls with a slice of fresh garlic and enjoy a continental flavour with their green meals. Some have found this priceless vegetable a harmless alternative to injections and drugs.

Try it also for catarrh.

Look Good and Feel Good
on the Grant Loaf

DORIS GRANT is a renowned nutritionist and author of several books on nutrition: Dear Housewives, Housewives Beware, Your Daily Food, Food Combining for Health (co-authored by Jean Joice), and last of all, Food Combining for Life – the health success of the century.

She is a strong supporter of natural food diets after having re-discovered the Dr Hay System of healthy eating. Doris says, "Bread made from whole-wheat grain is the only bread for health. Its value has been known for over 2,000 years, but never, in the history of the world, has it been so valuable or as necessary as it is today.

Because of the important vitamins and minerals it contains it acts as a powerful protection against the many substances that adulterate and contaminate the food, air and water in our brave new chemical world. (Your bread and Your life – Faber & Faber).

"The milling of our white bread removes the greater part of 8 vitamins and 12 minerals. This results in a distortion of the natural balance of the nutrients in wholewheat and the totally inadequate restoration to white bread of four statutory additives (B1, niacin, iron and chalk) compound this distortion."

"The subtle relationships between nutrients – which are only now being partly understood – are particularly vunerable when the nutrients are in any 'inorganic' form."

"Vitamin B1 is part of the Vitamin B complex and one of the body's best safeguards against ill health," she says. "It stimulates the hydrochloric acid in the stomach, which promotes digestion and acts as a natural antibiotic. The whole Vitamin B complex has miraculous qualities, in fact, fairy-tale like powers. It has such a brightening effect on the mind that it has been called the happiness vitamin. It looks after nerves and muscles, particularly of the heart, stomach and colon; it helps the matabolism of carbohydrates (that means the digestion of starches) and the more starches we eat, the more B vitamins we require. Lack of Vitamin B complex leads to tiredness, nervous exhaustion, intestinal trouble, poor appetite."

"Never make the mistake of thinking," she say, "that supplements are a substitute for right nutrition. Unless your diet is a sound one (as sound as possible in this age of factory-made chemical fertilisers, and chemical food additives) vitamin and mineral supplements will not be very effective."

White bread cannot truly qualify as the staff of life. No one can pretend that it is equal to wholewheat food for health-giving values. Doris is still healthy and active at the ripe old age of 97 years and is regarded by many as one of the foremost women of the 20th century.

You can take the Editor's word for it . . . it is so nutty and delicious. Real yummy!

THE GRANT LOAF
The loaf which has held its ground over the past 50 years.

Metric (Imperial)	American
1.35kg (3lb) stone ground wholewheat flour	12 cupsful stone ground wholewheat flour
2 teaspoonsful or less sea salt	2 teaspoonsful or less sea salt
1.2 litres (2 pints) water at blood heat (98.4°F/37°C)	5 cupsful water at blood heat (98.4°F/37°C)
3 level teaspoonsful dried yeast	3 level teaspoonsful dried yeast
2 level teaspoonsful Barbados sugar, honey or black molasses	2 level teaspoonsful Barbados sugar, honey or black molasses

1 Mix the salt with the flour (in very cold weather warm flour slightly to take off the chill).
2 Place 3 tablespoonsful of the water in a cup, sprinkle the dried yeast on top and leave for 2 minutes.
3 Add the sugar, honey or molasses. Leave for a further 10-15 minutes by which time there should be a thick creamy froth.
4 Make a well in the centre of the flour and pour in the yeast mixture and the rest of the water.
5 Mix well – by hand is best – for a minute or so, working from the sides to middle until the dough feels elastic and leaves the sides of the mixing bowl clean. Flours tend to vary in how much water they take up – the dough should be slippery.
6 Divide the dough into three 1 litre (2 pint/5 cup) bread tins which have been warmed and greased.
7 Put the tins in a warm (not hot) place, cover with a clean cloth and leave for about 20minutes or until the dough is within 1 cm (½in.) of the top of the tins.
8 Bake in a fairly hot oven, 400°F/200°C (Gas Mark 6), for 35 to 40 minutes. If the loaf sounds hollow when the top is knocked, it is done.

Quantities for One Loaf:

Metric (Imperial)	American
450g (1lb.) stoneground wholewheat flour	4 cupsful stoneground wholewheat flour
½ teaspoonful sea salt	½ teaspoonful sea salt
360ml (13-14 fl. oz.) water at blood heat (98.4°F/37°C)	1¼ cupsful water at blood heat (98.4°F/37°C)
1½ level teaspoonsful dried yeast	1½ level teaspoonsful dried yeast
1 teaspoonful Barbados sugar, honey or black molasses	1 teaspoonful Barbados sugar, honey or black molasses

By courtesy: Thorsons Publishers

(from page 119)

the cures I have witnessed in others who tried it, at my suggestion. The only disadvantage it has – by present-day standards – it is simple, and cheap.

Procure some Flowers of Sulphur from a chemist (8 oz.) and sprinkle, say, two level dessertspoonfuls in the boot or shoe. Instead of in the shoe, it could be distributed in the sole of the sock or stocking. I have found the wearing of a second sock over the first to have some advantages. Continue daily, but effects ought to be noticed after a few days. The virtue of the sulphur works through the whole system of the body, as will be evidenced from any perspiration on the body, and also by turning black any silver articles worn.

Sulphur should not be taken orally. It is a compound, and does not get into the system this way. Abstain from alcohol. With every good wish. Yours sincerely.

John Tobe, Ontario. Canada.

In a sober and meditative moment I reached the conclusion that when that enlightened day dawns that we as a society can separate "money" from the "healing arts" we will have progressed a long, long way towards the eradication of disease in human beings.

I say this without any desire to cast reflection on any of the many noble professions connected with the healing arts. But I repeat, as long as millions of pounds and billions of dollars can be made out of sickness and disease and the suffering of humanity, there will be no great effort on the part of anyone to spread knowledge about the right way to live and thus avoid ill-health.

Anonymous:

From pills and bills, from ills and chills . . . From cures that do not mend us . . . From beatniks, bombs, and juke-box stars . . . From rates and taxes, scorching cars . . . From interference by the State . . . From gossips who exaggerate . . . And boasting men who think they're great . . . Good Lord, from these defend us!

Mrs. F. Glenna Hills, Logan, Ohio, 43138, U.S.A.

Every time I pick up *Grace* I wish I were living in England.

Mullein leaves are the reason for this letter. My father fell and injured his leg. Medical attention did not heal it. Neither did treatments at a Turkish bath where it was oven-baked. A neighbour suggested hot fomentations: Mullein leaves wrung out of hot vinegar. After a few days, the leg was completely healed.

Mrs. E. D. Saberton, Waterbeach, Cambs.

I would like to pass on a poem. I do not know who wrote it but I hope I have remembered it correctly. It's about 18 years since I saw it written down, a friend had it on a calendar and kept it hanging in her kitchen long

after it was "out-dated" as she liked its message, as I do. Our sincere acknowledgment to an unknown author:
Take a step at a time
And you'll cover a mile.
Without any haste or hurry.
Lay one brick at a time
And you'll finish the pile,
Without overworking or worry.
Do one thing at a time
And whatever you do,
Be sure it's the best that you're giving.
Live one day at a time
And your whole life through
You'll find that your life is worth living.

Mr. D. F. Richardson, St. Leonards-on-Sea, Sussex.
My wife was told by the doctor she was incurable and that she would not be able to walk again. A herbalist told her to try a simple treatment at home. When I asked his advice, the doctor scoffed at the idea. Well, in spite of him, she did it, and is now completely cured of her arthritis. This is what she did:
Ingredients. 3 Grapefruit, 3 Oranges, 3 Lemons, 2 ounces Epsom Salts, 2 ounces Cream of Tartar.
Method. Squeeze all juice from fruits and set aside. Put all skins, pith and seeds through a mincer. Pour two pints boiling water over it. Add juice and allow to stand overnight. Next day extract all the juice by squeezing through a fine cloth or sieve a little at a time in order to extract as much as possible. Dissolve Cream of Tartar and Epsom salts in one pint of boiling water, add juice, bottle and keep in a cool place.
Dose. One wineglassful before breakfast. Take only one dose each day. My wife's case took over eight months, but it was worth it. Her joints soon improved. Stir well before drinking. I hope this may do somebody good.

Mrs. E. A. Bickers, Ongar, Essex.
What can I do to help my poor circulation?
Dear Mrs. Bickers, we hope the following will assist your circulation.
You can always remember that dates, figs and raisins favour a rich flow of blood to the extremities (hands and feet). That is, if they are taken every day. Do not overlook or grow tired of them if you wish to keep warm during the chilly winter months ahead. For icy mortals, the Biochemic salt, Silicea 6x, can work wonders. I discovered this some years ago when prescribing this versatile little tablet for split broken-down nails. A patient returned saying, "Since taking those tablets I don't feel the cold so much," Being a little sceptical I tried it on a number of frigid folk (just feel their feet when giving them an osteopathic adjustment) and was surprised to find this is reasonably true.

123

Another discovery I have made from seven years' study of the metal copper in relation to disease. Presence of copper on the body appears to stimulate the red corpuscles and heighten the haemoglobin level of the blood. That's why I believe a copper band worn on the wrist can have a dramatic effect upon some people's health. I am sure you will not overlook the "some". It does not work in every case. Readers of this magazine will be aware of many cases of cramp in the legs and arms being relieved by copper.

Now I am telling you that a number of wearers have quite by chance noticed they no longer feel the winter's cold so acutely. I know there will be a lot of thinkers who will find that too much to stomach. But we have to follow facts to wherever they lead, and must not be ruled by prejudice or superstition.

To get back to the subject of circulation. Those who can stand it should start the day with a cold-water-sponge-down of the whole of the body, followed by a brisk rub-down with a coarse dry towel. Too many hot baths are enervating and are the reason why so many folk feel the cold. Except in cases of heavy perspiration and other troubles, never take one more than twice a week. Some can get along quite comfortably on one.

A little self-massage with the palm of your hand on trunk, arms and legs, on rising and on going to bed can prove helpful. For the back of the legs use upward strokes, thus assisting the return of venous blood to the heart. Liberal helpings of a good honey may be taken for breakfast an cold mornings.

Agnes M. Burt, Petersfield, Hants.
When I was a girl my father used to gather Plantain leaves from the fields and hedgerows, and poured boiling water on them. They were left to cool and he used to steep his feet in the warm infusion when his feet were tender.

Mrs. J. Martin, Adelaide, Australia.
A friend is believed to have cancer and she does not seem to improve. Someone said that electrical treatment might help. Our doctor is against it.

ED: *Your doctor is quite right. Electrical treatment should never be given in the presence of benign or malign swellings. Electrical vibrations stimulate cell growth in normal and in abnormal cells.*

John Tobe, Ontario, Canada.
A most interesting case presented by Dr. Eugene Foldes in the Medical Journal of Australia (31st May, 1958) claimed that baldness is caused by salt intake. Dr. Foldes conducted an experiment in which, under closed environmental conditions, he actually counted the hairs falling from the head of a subject taking heavy quantities of salt. Under conditions where the salt intake was noticeably reduced, the number of falling hairs

decreased. To lend emphasis to his experiment, the doctor tried enlarging the salt intake. The number of falling hairs increased in two days.

Is this the reason that so many men today are bald or balding? Is loss of hair considered an hereditary condition because we inherit our taste of salt from "mother's home cooking" – the same cooking which feeds our balding father?

Mrs. L. Gordon, Harrow, Middlesex.
When I was a little girl my mother was a great sufferer from rheumatism, and her face would often be writhed in pain. When her doctor came he did not prescribe any drugs at all, and at first we thought it rather queer. He said. "Change the whole of your underclothing to best quality wool – no cotton or silk." Also, she was told to dispense with sheets and pillow slips. She had to sleep between flannel sheets. She had to make this a life-long habit.

Reluctantly my mother tried it. We thought what happened to be a miracle. After a few months all her rheumatism had gone. She never had any more pain through the rest of her 87 years.

Mr. W. G. Butler, Boxford, Newbury, Berks.
In the Autumn issue of *Grace*, 1964, I read about the good things brought about by drinking Sage Tea. For years, as long as I can remember, I always had a large haemorrhoid which was exceedingly painful at times. Within days of having started on my daily drink of Sage Tea all the pain went out of it, and it entirely disappeared.

ED: *Thank you very much, Mr. Butler, for your experience which we know will help many others. For the benefit of new readers, this daily good-health drink is one teaspoonful dried sage to a teacupful of boiling water. Allow to infuse. Strain when cold. Drink small teacupful in the morning, or half teacupful morning and evening. Sage for age – that's the adage.*

Mr. J. P. Beach, Coalmont, Tennessee, U.S.A.
Back in 1913 and 1914 I sold aluminium cooking utensils to help pay my college expenses. I delivered several thousands of dollars worth, thinking I was doing people a favour as well as helping myself through school. Twenty years later, I learned what a fool I had been, and what a mistake I had made. I went back to my old aluminium territory and told the remaining few people I had unwittingly deceived them. Was it too late? Many were crippled with arthritis. Several had kidney, heart, liver and bowel complaints. Now I know it was aluminium which brought on their troubles and my own. I, of course, had a complete aluminium culinary outfit in my kitchen. I, too, was suffering from almost everything in the book, including very bad varicose veins. After dropping the use of all aluminium I now have better health at 60 than I had when I was 20, and my veins are much better.

Why should this metal not be used with foods? When food leaves the stomach it enters into the duodenum. This organ supplies alkaline juices which combine with the aluminium in the foods, and which is not neutralized by the saliva. So the gas-making (wind and flatulence) or leavening process is continued throughout the whole tract, changing the character of the living tissue of the alimentary canal. These taints can also affect liver and kidneys and produce symptoms of metallic poisoning.

A most important thing is that aluminium destroys vitamins in foods. It can induce a pellagrous haemorrhagic condition of the intestines with ulceration of the duodenum and stomach. I believe many duodenal ulcers are caused in this way. It can be a common cause of constipation and colitis.

Alum, which dissolves from aluminium cooking vessels, when taken with foods cooked in it, is believed to be a specific cause of cancer. This belief is supported by a number of authorities.

Baking-powders and pickles should be avoided as they contain alum, a product of aluminium. They have a hardening effect. They are found in some commercially baked goods, and in some products to cause bread or pastry to "rise-quickly". Try this simple experiment. Don't laugh ! Just try it.

Boil ordinary drinking water in an aluminium kettle or saucepan for half an hour. Pour into a glass container. Aluminium compounds can be clearly seen with the naked eye. They are not calcium deposits precipitated from the water. These are on the sides of the kettle. Just try to drink that glass of water the next morning. It is aluminium hydroxide.

It is in this form that the metal enters the body and is absorbed into the blood circulation, It is a catalyst. That means that it acts on all living tissues it contacts. They are now dumping powdered aluminium into city waters besides other chemicals such as fluorine and chlorine. God help the people! One day we believe Science will prove these to be poisons. Yes, I said "poisons".

ED: *An alternative? There's nothing like a good quality enamel. And, of course, if you can afford it – stainless steel.*

Alpenlandische Beinenzeitung.
    . . . I heated a boiler of about thirty-five gallons of water. When I opened the cover, it flew with great force against the ceiling. The vapour and hot water poured forth over my unprotected head, over my hands and feet. Some minutes afterwards I had violent pains and I believe I would have gone mad if my wife and daughter had not helped immediately. They took large pieces of linen, daubed them thickly with honey and put them on my head, neck, hands and feet. Almost instantly the pain ceased. I slept well all night and did not lose a single hair on my head. When the physician came he shook his head and said , "How can such a thing be possible?"

Mr. C. H. Thompson, Dorking, Surrey.
We know that both Nature Cure and Spiritual healing can do some wonderful things. It must be difficult at times to know just how long one should persevere with them. Their healing can be very slow. What would you say would be signs to tell us when to go for a specialist's opinion?
ED: *A very interesting question, Mr. Thompson. After having taken any kind of medicine for three weeks without apparent benefit it would be wise to consult your doctor or health specialist. Better to be sure than sorry. The following signs are by no means exhaustive, but should be regarded with some concern, and a second opinion can often be invaluable.*
1. Unusual bleeding or discharge. 2. A lump or thickening in the breast or elsewhere. 3. A sore that does not heal. 4. Persistent hoarseness or cough. 5. Persistent change in bowel or bladder habits. 6. Persistent indigestion or difficulty in swallowing. 7. A degenerative change in a mole or wart.
Leave not thing to chance.

C. Keith Denny, Lilydale, Tasmania.
I think there is a risk that this period will go down in history as the time when man upset the balance of Nature. I have grown honeysuckle here for 40 years without spraying. Last year they were ruined by Aphids, and would have been this year, if I had not sprayed four or five times. The scientist will take credit for the spray. But I think he may have done something which killed the natural enemy of the Aphids! I have recently been told that there are now no swallows in Perth, West Australia, and I remember them there in hundreds! It seems to me that in this, *Grace* and I are not far apart.

Mr. J. L. McD., Marion. Indiana. U.S.A.
I began beekeeping because I had rheumatism, and it has disappeared, but I consider it due more to the fact that I ate honey than to bee stings. Nearly four years ago, I had rheumatism in my knees. I finally went to Dr. K. . . . for advice. He put me on a citrus fruit diet, allowing only honey. In a week, he allowed breakfast food sweetened with honey. It did the work, and I liked honey so well that I bought a few hives of bees to supply my family, and now – I want everyone to know honey and to like it, as Nature's own health-sweet, full of pep and vitamins that God gave us, pure as snow. My growing son is developing into a healthy, sturdy ten-year-old since the use of honey, egg and milk drinks. My rheumatism never returned.

Miss Elizabeth Sparrow, Bridport, Dorset.
What time is it?
Time to do well . . . Time to live better . . . Give up that grudge . . . Answer that letter . . . Speak the kind word . . . To sweeten a sorrow . . . Do that kind deed you . . . Would leave to tomorrow. .
It's always that time, folks.

Mr. E. Irving, Marsh, Huddersfield.
Lakhovsky has shown us how sickly plants have been cured by surrounding them with a spiral of copper wire; is it possible for human tissues to be regenerated?
ED: *I do not know. But some evidence is strongly in favour of it. We have had a number of letters from readers reporting the disappearance of warts and moles after wearing a Copper Bracelet. This is something quite new. We were aware of how it can often take the pain out of cramp, and lessen the burden of rheumatism and arthritis, but the vital role played by copper on the human body is only just beginning to dawn upon us.*

Miss H. M. Legg, Walthamstow, E.17.
I pray I shall always be able to have *Grace*. I'm an old age pensioner, 89, and always enjoy *Grace* because I know it keeps me near to the eternal Laws of God, and must help many to get back to nature and simplicity.

Mrs. Feick, St. Jacobs, Ontario.
I have received many helpful hints from the pages of your magazine, and would like to give the following, which we have used with good results: Use warm milk to wash inflamed eyes, especially infants' eyes. We use raw milk. This treatment is also good for "Pink Eye".

Mrs. Prosser, Boscombe, Dorset.
When we were farmers near Manchester we used to gather Comfrey Herb to make a mash for bathing the cows' udders when they were inflamed or irritated from milk fever. It worked everytime, and was most successful. There's a lot to be said for the old remedies.

Miss C. Parnell, Gorleston-on-Sea.
Many thanks for *Grace*. Reading its pages is – to me – like wandering through a leafy lane in the heart of the country on a sunny Spring day. One gets just that satisfying, peaceful feeling. Quite a remarkable little magazine – I've never ever found one quite like it. I like "While the Kettle Boils" with everyone having a little "say". May its life be a very long one!

Mrs. R. J. Wright, Missouri, U.S.A.
I am having so much trouble with my arms. They have no feeling. As the old saying is: they go to sleep. I can't sleep at nights. They bother me so much. What can I do?

THE HEALING CRISIS

Inflammation is a reconstructive process and should not be suppressed with drugs. Every acute disease is a result of a cleansing and healing effort of nature.   DR. HENRY LINDLAHR

Photo: Roy Westlake

STRAWBERRIES, and only strawberries, could now be thought or spoken of. "The best fruit in England–everybody's favourite–always wholesome. These the finest beds and finest sorts. Delightful to gather for oneself–the only way of really enjoying them. Morning decidedly the best time–never tired–every sort good–hautboy infinitely superior–no comparison–the others hardly eatable–hautboys very scarce–Chili preferred–white wood finest flavour of all–prices of strawberries in London . . . only objection to gathering strawberries the stooping–glaring sun–tired to death–could bear it no longer–must go and sit in the shade." Such, for half an hour, was the conversation.

–Jane Austen

ED: *This could be caused by a number of things – possibly by an impacted lesion of two upper dorsal vertebrae of the spine, resulting in pressure on the nerve roots. In order to be sure there is no degenerative nerve condition, visit your doctor. If he rules out the latter, consult an osteopath.*

Also try the following: Obtain two or three ounces Cramp Bark (Viburnum Opulus). It is readily obtainable in America, where it grows. Take half an ounce and simmer slowly for 15 minutes in one pint water. Strain when cold. Drink one wineglassful after meals three times daily. Is also just the tonic to jolly you up when down in the dumps!

Cramp Bark tablets should be available from your Health Stores.

Mr. S. Blyth, Nottingham.
Can you recommend a good herb tea?

ED: *A good combination is equal parts: Raspberry Leaves, Agrimony and Wood Betony. It can be made in the same way as for ordinary tea, to which it is often preferred from a health point of view. Infuse one or two teaspoonsful in a teapot. Step up if you like the flavour.*

A Cup That Cheers
A woman with a history of over 15 years chronic acidity and indigestion found surprising relief when she discontinued Indian tea and took to an occasional cup of English Chamomile tea. Within a few months her life was completely changed. Nervous irritability gave way to perfect gastric harmony.

"I've never felt so well for years," she confessed. "I can now eat anything and my nerves are much calmer. What's more, I no longer lie awake at night thinking I've got an incurable disease. I sleep like a top. I put three to six flower-heads in a teacup and fill with boiling water. I let it infuse for five or six minutes and drink it warm. I have one or two cups a day. It has made a big difference to my life."

Sister L. B. Snook, Victoria, British Columbia.
Your magazine is read from cover to cover many, many times and it's the remark I hear from folks who borrow it. They keep wanting to go back and pick it up, even though they have read it all once over. I enjoy reading 'While the Kettle Boils' and thought I would like to add something that may help other readers.

It has cured many cases of rheumatism. It is also very useful for sore throats. Take five drops Eucalyptus Oil, on honey, on rising for three mornings. Stop for three days, Then take five drops for three days. Stop for seven days. Take five drops for seven days. Stop for two weeks, and

Checking the map and cooling feet at Upper Slaughter, Gloucester, England.
Photo: Dennis Mansell

repeat if necessary. This treatment also cured a patient of mine who had been under the doctor for her throat with loss of voice. Of course, if you are treating a serious throat condition it has to be taken once every day.

Miss G. E. Arthurs, Stroud Green, London, N.4.
Since wearing a copper bracelet for my arthritis an amazing thing has happened. I thought you might be interested to know that it dispersed a mole I have had on my wrist for years.

Mr. C. Chapman, Wistaston, Nantwich, Cheshire.
I have always had psoriasis. It goes away for some months but always returns for no reason at all. Nothing I do to it seems to drive it away. It is dry and scaly, but I keep it moist with olive oil. It irritates badly.

ED: *Always bear in mind the liver when dealing with skin diseases. Old Culpeper knew a thing or two about herbal healing: he linked the liver with chronic skin diseases. Consider jaundice, for instance; the skin goes yellow – and it itches. Much chronic skin irritation can be brought on by a surfeit of eggs, sugar or onions. Some may have observed the dry skin which accompanies chronic liver troubles. I am convinced that liver damage is a fact in most cases of intractable psoriasis, eczema and urticaria. So put the liver on the reins. That is why I always include Barberry (Berberis Vulgaris) in my medicines for this complaint.*

I have known cases of nettle-rash aggravated by Brewer's Yeast, an elixir of life when used in its proper sphere.

Radishes . . . now, there's a fine liver/skin food/medicine for you! They regulate the function of liver and gall bladder, and are good for skin diseases generally – execpt acne. which has an endocrine origin.

Olive oil can feed psoriasis. Replace with cod-liver oil?

Mrs. E. Eaton, Skegness, Lincs.
I am taking Sage Tea as prescribed in the last magazine and am finding tremendous benefit from it in my 80th year.

HONEY, OR YOUR LIFE

"IN HEART weaknesses I have found honey to have a marked effect in reviving the heart action and keeping patients alive. I have further evidence of this in a recent case of pneumonia. The patient consumed two pounds of honey during the illness; there was a marked early crisis with no subsequent rise in temperature and an exceptionally good pulse. I suggest that honey should be given for general physical repair and, above all, for heart failure."

– Dr. G. N. W. Thomas, Edinburgh, *The Lancet.*

Harold J. Irwin, Esq., Alberta, Canada.
I have found that tea made of Mullein leaves very greatly improved the cold circulation in my hands. This is the only thing I have found to help. I cannot trace this use in any of the herbals. A cold circulation can be due to a malfunction of the exocrine gland, the pancreas. This controls upper and lower blood levels – a recent discovery of physiology – which now considers the pancreas to be a dual gland.

John Tobe, Ontario, Canada.
As I go about my busy way I feel I hear some people say, "How can that loony nut be healthy? He does such crazy things! He eats of herbs from the fields and does not spray. He does not take the shots or pills, vaccines, innoculations or immunizations. Yet he is healthy. I do all the right things and I and mine are ill.

"It is certain, because of his blasphemy, he is undeserving of fate's protection. He will be punished for disregarding science, for paying no heed to all the modern drugs and wondrous potions such as tranquillizers, barbiturates and other glorious benefits of seience. Surely the fates will not allow that renegade to be healthy to spite us."

Readers of *Grace Magazine* may think this is a bit of exaggeration, but I know for a fact that that is often thought and spoken by people when they meet one of us so-called "health nuts" and they resent so much the fact that they are sick and we loony nuts are healthy.

Mrs. F. Thompson, Manchester.
My doctor says I have anaemia. I am told I have had all that is possible with injections and iron medicines but I am getting on so slowly. My life is a burden, no appetite. I feel more dead than alive and at night I cannot sleep for a tiring cough.

ED: *You need a herbal medicine rich in vitamin B.12 on the one hand, and which is an astringent-demulcent on the other. There is a powerful plant meeting these requirements, and that is Iceland Moss (Cetraria Islandica). People of the Shetlands call it Staghorn Moss. It is a true lichen which grows among grass and heather in parts of Scotland and the Outer Hebrides. Before the advent of British Medicine the native folk of Iceland used it as a medicine. It is a first-class demulcent, and the etheric oil it contains would be helpful for your cough. Its most ancient name in Saxon medicine is Lung-Moss. It is highly recommended for chronic catarrh and chronic bronchitis, and is one of the most versatile of lichens you would meet in a day's march. Mode of preparation: ½ oz. to 1 pint cold water. Bring to boil. Simmer for two to three minutes. It can be poured through a strainer or drunk as it is: one wineglassful after meals three times daily. Quite overlooked in modern medicine. Quite safe.*

131

"An Indian", Cook School, Phoenix, Arizona.
Born here ages before the White Man came, my people had the entire country to ourselves, its lakes, streams, forests, mountains, and game of all kinds. We were a happy and carefree people. Our school was the great out-of-doors, and Mother Nature was our teacher.

We saw the Great Spirit in the starry heavens – His painting in the sunset, we loved the green carpet of the plains decorated with colours of countless flowers. We worshipped Him in the majesty of rugged mountains topped with snow, in the sun and moon, and in great animals like the bear, and birds like the eagle.

We wondered about Him when lightning flashed. We trembled when we heard His voice in the boom of thunder. We were touched when a star fell, and bewildered when meteors sprayed the sky with fire and even once we saw a long-tailed comet which we did not understand.

I am an Indian and I want all my people to know Him who is the light of the world. We thought perhaps you might like to help us.

Mrs. L. T., Battle, Sussex.
I feel I must write and tell you about some of my family who have taken Lignum Vitae. Well, since my husband had a swollen rheumatic knee for a long time, after taking the remedy it is now completely gone and he can walk miles now. Also, his sister's husband had an accident three years ago and could not put his arm up at all well. He can now get his arm right over his shoulder and is delighted about it. I hope you do not mind me writing to you as it is nice to be out of pain.

Mrs. O. Williams, Breconshire, S. Wales.
I am taking an infusion of violet leaves as an aid to slimming. Last week I pricked my finger with a large thorn from a rose bush and before I washed it, I picked up some potatoes with the wet earth still on, a few hours later my finger began to swell twice its normal size. I had taken the tea but still had the violet leaves, which I soaked in hot water and held the leaves to the finger several times, and after a few applications my finger was quite normal. I never saw anything work as quickly. How wonderful nature is, I believe the Bible says that God gave the herb of the field for the healing of mankind. *Grace Magazine* is such a blessing, may God reward you for all the labour you so graciously put into it and may you experience renewed physical and spiritual blessing during the coming year. Once again, a big Thank You.

ED: *Thank you, Mrs. Williams, for sending this useful account of your experience. We hope other readers, too, will share their cures with other members of the Grace Family. It is not generally known that before the days of A.T.T.S., violet leaves were used for tetanus. We welcome letters from those who have overcome their illnesses by natural means. Please let us hear from you, letting us know herbs used, and by what means cure was effected.*

Mrs. Cooper, Bedford.
I am in my early twenties and have tried everything for acne without success. Please advise. Something simple, please.
ED: *Here is a quickie. Save the water in which you cook the cabbages. Use no salt. Add a teaspoonful of yeast and vegetable extract. One teacupful once or twice daily, at any time.*

Miss H. Ashington, Birmingham 5.
My teeth are dull and however much I clean them they don't seem to improve.
ED: *Have you tried fruit and vegetable juices? Try juices of carrot, celery and spinach, which should bring back the sparkle not only to your teeth, but to your hair and eyes.*

Mr. Edwin Davies, Swansea, South Wales.
I don't want you to leave me out of this tea business. I see men have sent in about tea. A perfect cup of tea depends on two terminal leaves and a bud. The young two leaves and the new bud give the best quality. I've known a tea estate in the middle of the jungle where hyena call in the night. I've drunk tea in many countries. In Afghanistan they take it weak and very hot, with lemon in it. I've had it in little bowls – beautifully decorated. Ceylon tea is black and grows up high.
It is called Buddha's best gift to his followers who drink it with butter in it. A nice cup of tea does more good than all the politics and religions put together. People are different all over the world; but one thing remains unchanged – their love of tea and the good cheer that goes with it.
ED: *So, you harassed housewives and weary workers, now you know!*

Miss E. Nesbitt.
I have for many years had this trouble of a stuffed nose – usually not much bother in the daytime – but tiresome at night.
. . . On one occasion I managed to scrape off enough capping from a section of honey I had for a good chew. A little later (actually I'd forgotten I had been chewing the comb) my nose started to stream, and for about a day thereafter my nose was quite clear. At night it made a wonderful difference.

133

Grace Post, Chicago, Illinois, U.S.A.
Since I have taken Lignum Vitae for rheumatism I have been able to hold a fine needle in my fingers and do sewing again. Also it makes me happy to be able to use my typewriter again.

Miss A. Crossley, Grasmere, Westmorland.
Cashew Nut Roast. 2oz. Cashew nuts milled. 1oz. breadcrumbs (wholemeal). Approx. ½ cup water, vegetable stock or tomato juice. ¼ teaspoonful marmite or pinch of mixed herbs. Mix all well together and add a pinch of salt and teaspoonful chopped parsley. Mix to soft consistency. Steam ¾ hour in greased basin or cook in moderate oven for ½ an hour. A real treat!

Mrs Mary Booker, Reading.
My father, Mr Jackson, was a supervisor on the railway in the early days. He was a man of spirit and was responsible for sinking the Edale to Chinley Tunnel in Derbyshire. While laying part of the Derbyshire line (which runs up to Darlington) a heavy wagon ran into him and his ankle sustained a severe mauling. So badly was it broken that the doctor said it would not be possible for him to work for months.

"We'll see about that!" said my father when he arrived home from the surgery. "Go and gather me some Comfrey from the hedgebank and we'll see who's right." Every day he washed the foot with an infusion, and applied hot poultices made from the roots and leaves of comfrey. Within a very short time he turned up for full duties with a foot that had healed up beautifully. Which just goes to show that God's own remedies are quite capable of standing on their own feet.

A. Southwood, Heythrop Grove, Moseley, Birmingham.
Sometime ago I read a letter in *Grace* stating that a friend or relative could not have a certain operation, but it was performed successfully after drinking parsley tea. No mention was made as to its preparation, but later on it was mentioned again, stating that the parsley was placed in half pint of water, brought to boil, and allowed to simmer for a time before cooling and straining.

I have been doing this for a friend who is a diabetic. As a result, her urine is now always negative.

Mildred Hatch, St. Johnsbury, Vermont, U.S.A.
Aspirin is known to cause gastric irritation and bleeding. Medical sources have noted that it is particularly likely to cause trouble in patients with peptic (gastric) ulcers. It is also reported that a large number of patients with chronic dyspepsia are chronic aspirin eaters.

Mrs L. Cooke, Melbourne, Australia.
My husband has severe nerve and stomach trouble and cannot eat solid foods. I am at my wit's end to know what to give him to build him up. The acidity is bad.

Potassium broth is what he needs. This is strongly alkaline and eliminative. It has relaxing properties for nervous tension and internal troubles, and can be prepared and taken as desired.

1 cup finely grated carrots, 1 quart cold water, 1 cup finely grated cabbage, ½ cup shredded spinach, one tablespoonful chopped parsley stems and leaves. Place the vegetables in the cold water and bring to simmering point. Keep at this heat for 5 minutes. Cool, straining and squeezing through muslin. A little yeast extract improves the flavour.

John Tobe, Ontario, Canada.
I know doctors won't like me for what I'm going to say. I have many dear people close to me who are doctors, and I am not speaking from malice.

But tell me, does this make sense?

Whenever someone has the slightest glimmer of an off heart-beat, the slightest sign of arterial trouble, or anything to do with the old-ticker –

YOU KNOW YOU ARE OVERWEIGHT WHEN:

- people you used to think were overweight begin to look thinner
- you want to enter a lift carrying three people but they shout, "Full up!"
- you board a plane and the passengers make the sign of the cross
- your friends say you used to be taller
- your clothes shrink inside the cupboard
- in restaurants, waiters show you the list of desserts first
- after a bath you take longer than usual to dry yourself
- an empty taxi passes by and the driver pretends he doesn't see you.

he's urged and practically compelled to consult a doctor – an M.D. Why an M.D.? Why not a Hygienist or a Herbalist? Or any of the other healing professions?

Is it not an accepted fact that M.D.s have the highest ratio of heart disease of all the professions? Shouldn't they have the lowest death rate from this trouble? Why not have the doctors and others so afflicted consult those who have managed to get to the age of 70 or 75 without a heart attack? To my simple mind, this would make sense!

Mrs I. Weaire, Romford.

When I was a little girl of under ten years old and living in the country, I discovered quite by chance a lark's nest containing, I think it was, five little brown eggs. Oh! the thrill it gave me, and still does – after nearly fifty years, when I think of it.

Mrs S. Higginson, Lisburn. N. Ireland.

I have some Comfrey growing in my garden and am just wondering if you could help me in suggesting ways it could be used. I use the leaves for salads. What good properties does Comfrey possess?

Ed: *All members of the Family might like to know that besides the young leaves being cooked as a vegetable similar to spinach, comfrey is now being used as a meal in soups, mixed with flour for bread-making, and mixed with tea for a sustaining beverage. This latter is good for those*

Mr. Nobody
Anonymous

We know a funny little man
    As quiet as a mouse.
He does the mischief that is done
    In everybody's house.
Though no one ever sees his face,
    Yet one and all agree
That every plate we break, was cracked
    By Mr. Nobody.

'Tis he who always tears our books,
    Who leaves the door ajar.
He buckles the zip upon our skirts
    And scatters pins afar.
That squeaking door will always
        squeak –
    For prithee, don't you see?
We leave the oiling to be done
    By Mr. Nobody.

He forgets the lop in the gas,
    That kettles will not boil:
His are the feet that bring in mud
    And all the carpets soil.
The papers that so oft are lost —
    Who had them last but he?
There's no one tosses them about
    But Mr. Nobody.

The fingermarks upon the door
    By none of us were made.
We didn't forget the bath-tap
    When rooms below were sprayed.
A ball-point pen we never lose! The
        Shoes
    That laying round you see,
Are not our shoes — they all belong
    To Mr. Nobody.

136

who are thin and cannot put on weight and flesh. It has fine health properties, including vitamin B.12 in traces. It has a curative effect on duodenal ulcers, some lung troubles, asthma and has always been used for purifying the blood. Leaves may be made into a mash and applied as a poultice to old ulcers and sores which refuse to heal.

It is excellent for promoting the union of broken bones and fractures refusing to heal.

Mrs Haddon, Ringwood, Hampshire.
My sister's fingers were swollen and painful. One was so enlarged that she could not move her wedding ring and was about to consult her doctor to have the ring cut. I persuaded her to rub it well, every evening, with hot olive oil. After perseverance she was able to remove the ring and felt more comfortable. By continuing with the oil the swelling subsided and the finger returned to normal.

Miss Smith, Fife, Scotland.
I am glad to read in the papers of Hayfield Drink. We had it when working at haymaking and harvest. It is made with honey mixed with lemon juice or apple juice. It used to put new life into us after a hard day's 'stooking' in the fields. Love to all the readers.

Miss Weeks, Monmouthshire, S. Wales.
. . . I have had good results to date for insomnia. Also, if I am wide awake and restless and can't go to sleep at night, hitherto I have had to take a phenobarbitone pill. Now I just pick up my Copper Bracelet and hold it. In about 5 to 10 minutes I'm away and asleep.

Mr L. J. Slaugenwhite, Jersey Shore, Pasadena, U.S.A.,
Last September while I was visiting California and Arizona, a growth the size of a marble developed on my neck near the Adam's Apple. Apparently caused by unaccustomed use of water treated with fluorine and other chemicals. It was painful and caused interference with breathing. I took teas steeped from red-root, gentian root, blue violet and yellow dock, and drank plenty of pure unsweetened grape juice. In just three weeks it was gone.

Mrs Enid Ashley, Vancouver, Canada.
They must be a funny lot of people who read your magazine. That's why I'm sending you this reminder of the hot 'sarsaparilla' days in Blackpool before I left the old country.

A shy little man stepped up to an old-timer herbalist just off the seafront. "Is it possible to have castor oil so it can't be tasted?"

"Yes," said the herbalist, "and while you're waiting, have a glass of sarsaparilla on me at the soda fountain."

The man moved to the counter and gratefully accepted the drink. "How did it taste?" asked the Herbalist.

"As nice a drink of sarsaparilla as I ever had."

"Well, the castor oil was in it. That proves you can have it without tasting it."

"But it was my wife outside in the car who wanted the castor oil," said the man.

Mrs Hardiman, Oakdale, Poole, Dorset.
I was converted to the use of herbs when a girl in my teens. I suffered from a severely ulcerated leg for which no usual treatment did any good. Then I was told of an old Welsh cure of stubborn leg ulcers and boils by placing over the painful area a cabbage leaf. This was the inner white leaf. In despair I tried it, binding it over. The amount of pus which came away was amazing. I let it continue to discharge until it all drained away. Soon my leg was completely better and I've never had it since.

I've recommended it to several people with good results. But once, a friend did it on my recommendation, and as expected, the discharge of poisons increased. Unfortunately her doctor grew alarmed and told her to stop it. This she did with no conclusive results.

Mrs Moeder, London, W.2.
I am recovering from a painful ear infection, and during the feverish nights your tranquil magazine brought me such peace of spirit. How can one express gratitude for such a rare publication? It must take a tremendous amount of work to collect so many lovely things.

Mr John Preston, Adelaide, Australia.
I read somewhere of a man who paid £700 to be stung by bees to cure his arthritis. I give you my own way. When the doctor can do no more for you and you feel like crawling up the wall, and down again, crush-up carrots into a poultice and wear for a week or two. Mine disappeared after six weeks, and the trouble has never come my way again.

SESAME SEED SAVOURY

Ingredients: 6 oz. Sesame; 6 oz. Linseed (ground); 1 onion; 1 garlic; 2 eggs; Vesop to taste.

Method: Mix both seeds (ground) with 1 cup boiling water, adding other ingredients. Bake in oven as sesame seed savoury. This savoury is very nourishing and an excellent tonic for a weak stomach and digestive system.

– EMILE JUST

Mrs Norman V. Habberfield, Alberta, Canada.
We are always pleased to receive your wonderful magazine. As you write a lot about honey, we would like to say we are beekeepers, and agree that honey is one of the most curative foods known. Our honey is produced in the foothills and meadows of the Canadian Rockies from wild flowers and clovers, etc. Our bees are never fed sugar.

Lady Eve Balfour tells this story which she heard when travelling America.
A Texan cotton-grower made the discovery that if he turned geese into his cotton fields they ate the weeds but did not touch the young cotton plants. So, instead of spending the usual large sums on labour for hoeing (this is one of the major items of expenditure in cotton growing), he turned geese into the plantations. The result was that not only were labour costs drastically cut, but none of the erosion occurred that so frequently follows loosening the soil with the hoe. In addition, the geese manured the fields, consumed all the weeds, and fattened in the process. So the farmer had two crops (cotton and fat geese) instead of one. I hope other cotton-growers will explore the possibilities of this seemingly admirable plan.

ED: *Was Texas ten years ahead?*

Miss N. Stott, W. Sussex.
Readers will be pleased to learn that both arthritis sufferers to whom I gave Feverfew Essence have reported spontaneous improvement. Also, Mrs Hall's dog has benefited. He's an arthritic. too.

Anonymous.
Is there any treatment for cystitis? I can't hold my water properly.

ED: *Although men do have this condition, it occurs more frequently in women. The sufferer has to pass water frequently, not that she passes a great amount, but even with an empty bladder the urge may be persistent. Urine may be cloudy and with an unpleasant smell.*

Plenty of barley water should be drunk, which dilutes strong urine and washes out the bladder. There may be tenderness in the loin with shivering, nausea and vomiting. Good hygiene and the avoidance of synthetic underwear are helpful.

Parsley water will deal with minor inflammation. Place one handful of fresh parsley into an enamel saucepan (never aluminium) *and cover with one pint cold water. Bring to boil. Simmer for one minute. Strain when cold. Drink: half teacupful two or three times daily, half hour before meals.*

A number of drugless agents are available for stubborn cases; each may be taken singly or in combination with others. These include Cranesbill (geranium maculatum), *Marshmallow* (althaea officinalis), *Chamomile* (anthemis matricaria), *Horsetail* (equisetum arvense) *and* Burr-Marigold *(bidens tripartita).*

(continued on page 141)

10 reasons to see your GP

Use this checklist to decide whether you should visit your GP.
If you answer yes to one or more questions, you may need
tests or treatment.

1 **Do you look paler than normal?**
You could be anaemic.

2 **Are you more thirsty or passing more urine than usual?**
You could have diabetes, but these symptoms could also suggest bladder, prostate or kidney problems.

3 **Are you suffering from stomach pain? Have your bowels become more constipated or loose, or have you noticed blood or mucus (phlegm-like fluid) in your stools?**
This may be due to something more than piles, so don't be afraid to tell your doctor.

4 **Are you suffering from sweats – especially during the night?**
The most common cause of night sweats is the menopause, but you may have a chronic infection of blood disorder.

5 **Have you noticed any palpitations, shortness of breath, cough, chest pain or ankle swelling?**
These don't necessarily mean trouble, but you'll need to have your heart, lungs and blood pressure checked to be on the safe side.

6 **Have you recently lost or gained weight, eg, more than a few pounds for no apparent reason?**
Significant loss or gain could mean thyroid disease, depression, diabetes, or serious disease in any part of the body.

7 **Are you sleeping badly? Do you feel tense, anxious or depressed?**
Stress and depression are the commonest causes of TATT (tired all the time), partly because they interfere with restful sleep.

8 **Are you taking medicines that disturb your sleep?**
Beta-blockers, cholesterol-lowering drugs and even Prozac may be the culprits.

9 **Have you recently suffered from an infection or had an operation or accident?**
Your body may simply have slowed down in order to concentrate on recovery; ask your doctor when you can expect to get back to normal.

10 **Do you smoke, eat badly, drink too much or exercise too little?**
Your GP or practice nurse can suggest ways to help you improve your lifestyle.

Do not overlook reliable vitamin C. One 1 gram tablet, twice daily, can effectively deal with many bladder infections, especially E. coli the most common cause of urinary tract infection.

Nothing irritates a sensitive urinary tract more than coffee, tea, alcohol and hot spicy foods (curry, etc). *At the time of infection it is advisable to discontinue all sugar products, except honey, which is soothing.*

Miss Thelma Burnett, Bromley, Kent.
When recently in hospital for an operation I was sent the following verse which I found most helpful and comforting.

'In the rainbow see His promise . . . In the sunshine see His love . . . In your trial hear His whisper . . . Coming from the realms above . . . In your weakness know His power . . . In your pain, His healing balm . . . Just to know He will not leave you . . . Will produce the perfect calm."

Miss R. V., Exeter, Devon.
While sitting in the garden sunbathing, I put my jar of vitamin E cream (which I use to protect my skin) on the lawn beside me, and must have dropped off to sleep. When I woke it had vanished. For months it was a mystery, until a neighbour dug it up in his garden where the dog had buried it.

Mr Jim Galbraith, Ayrshire, Scotland.
I am writing to give you a first-aid measure against cramp. The best thing is to move the leg in the direction opposite to that in which it is being pulled by the cramp. If the calf muscles are pulling the foot and toes down, try to move your foot and toes up. When you do this, the muscles in front of the leg contract, and those at the back (in the calf) automatically relax.

"Lone Pine", Lone Pine Drive, Ferndown, Dorset.
Some years ago I was almost fatally electrocuted in the bath. Quick action on my husband's part saved my life. Thereafter when in the presence of thunder storms (possibly because of the air charged with electricity) I felt as if I was painfully crushed under heavy weights.

One day I had a plain copper band fitted to my arm. Since then, if thunder comes I feel completely normal. A fracture of the thumb left the joint painfully arthritic. This too has completely gone. How grateful I am for this help.

Mr H. Patterson, Dinnington, Sheffield, Yorks.
I am a sufferer of arthritis. Is there anything you can recommend me to do to my knees, apart from taking things internally. I am all right on diet.

ED: *For swollen joints of arthritis a fomentation of Castor Oil can sometimes prove helpful. Wring out a cloth or guest's hand-towel in hot water and spread a layer of Castor Oil over the surface. Bind around the affected joint at night and allow to remain on. Remove in the morning.*

An Epsom Salt bath can assist in eliminating toxins and poisons. Add to your bath water, at about 100 degrees temperature, two to three pounds of commercial Epsom salt. When in the bath rub the joints vigorously. Do this before bedtime once or twice weekly. Always go straight to bed after a hot Epsom Salt bath, as it is easy to catch a chill if one goes out into the cold,

Miss M. Jenkinson, Sarisbury Green, Southampton.
I have tried everything for blood pressure. I have seen my doctor and also a Nature Cure man but still it is too high. I have bursting headaches and pains at the back of the neck.

ED: *Lime Flowers are helpful for high blood pressure. They should be infused in the teapot as ordinary tea. Slightly aperient. Drink one or two teacupfuls daily. Remember that yeast can string-up B.P. cases, and is best avoided. Heard of Rutin?*

Mr E. Crowe, Beccles Road, Gt. Yarmouth, Norfolk.
My rheumatism is worse with every change of weather. My stiff neck is painful at nights, and seems to be worse from sitting in a draught. The bottom of my back aches something chronic when I wake in the morning. It is true when I say that every time I blow my nose my bones give me an extra "squeeze" just out of spite! If I sit long my buttocks go to sleep. I love my garden; but Oh, these weeder's knees!

Can you tell me what to do for shootin' through my elbows, cramp in my calves, little bony molehills studding my finger joints, and ants creeping where I daren't mention, soreness in the thighs and little demons in my legs held up by a pair of icy-cold feet.

I know this is a tall order. I'm no longer any good at taking tablets. My wife says I've had more than a bucketful. When I was a boy my mother gave me dock-root for boils, Bless her! Wish she were here now; she would know what to give me.

ED: *Dear Friend, We are very sorry to learn of your line of vexations in the flesh. You nearly flummoxed us. Usually we hear of a person having one, two or possibly three of these symptoms but, jumping rattlesnakes, you seem to have got the lot!*

There is so much we could say, but space forbids. Have you tried Crude Black Molasses dissolved in hot water? Not everybody's "cup of tea". Worth trying. Dissolve two teaspoonsful in a teacupful of hot water. Drink once daily. Twice daily if you relish the stuff. Good for bowels needing a little gentle persuasion. Some find relief in Lignum Vitae. Some swear by Yerbama tea. Then, there's Maté tea which is said to render the population of Paraguay immune to rheumatism.

Homoeopathically speaking, your symptoms appear to add up to Calc Phos. Four pellets after meals three times daily could prove helpful. These together with the above teas should be obtainable from your nearest Health Food Stores.

A summer's day, St Paul's Cathedral, London.   *Dennis Mansell.*

Mrs P. Long, Orpington, Kent.
For almost three weeks I have been taking Agnus Castus and Dolomite tablets. I am pleased to say I feel 100% well. The pain in my back has almost disappeared. I have suffered from lumbago which has left my back very weak and painful. I am only 40. I am very glad to be free from pain, nothing else has ever worked.

Barbara Huttmann, with 35 years' experience as a nurse.
Most people are not willing to take responsibility for their own health. They often eat too much, smoke and drink heavily and then expect their doctor to work a miracle on their diseased bodies.

So, the doctor is put in the position of having God-like powers, according to our expectations, and often, if he is willing to answer, we don't want to listen. We just want to go to him childlike, and say "fix it". The point made is that most patients need to accept more responsibility for safe-guarding their own health.

Mr R. B. A., Leicester LE8 3YA.
We have found that Hawthorn has had a dramatic effect on my wife's high blood pressure. Together with a salt-free diet we feel that we have achieved results that ten years of drugs have failed to do.

I feel the use of Hawthorn has saved my wife from a slow, lingering death. Side effects of the drugs have been too frightening to put into words.

Ellen Poole, Florida, U.S.A.
Sometime ago I read in *Grace* of a lady who cured herself, entirely, of a long-standing case of bronchitis, by eating Garlic and Parsley dipped in vinegar.

All my life I suffered off-and-on with bronchitis, and could never get cured. So I tried the garlic and parsley and am amazed already at the wonderful results. I can never thank you enough for printing her letter. I am so much better . . .

Mr B. Cunningham, Reading.
What refreshing drink can you recommend when the thermometer is well up into the 80's, in place of tea.

ED: *Make this thirst-quenching Orange-Lemonade for that afternoon tea-break in the garden.*
Ingredients:
Juice of 2 or 3 lemons. Juice of 2 or 3 oranges. Two dessertspoonsful of honey. One quart of water.
To Prepare:
Bring the water to boil. Allow to cool. Stir in honey when warm. Add the juices when cold. Store in an ice-box, refrigerator or cold place. Serve as desired. Ice may be added.
Talking of blowing the thermometer, did you hear of the time when Dr. Albert Schweitzer played host to several European visitors at the hospital at Lambarene in French Equatorial Africa?
"This heat is unbearable," one visitor moaned. "What's the temperature?"
"I don't know," said Schweitzer. "We don't have a thermometer here."
"No thermometer?"

144

"No," replied the doctor. "If I knew how hot it was, I don't think I would be able to endure it, either."

Mabel Lambros, Maidenhead, Berks.
I believe Hephzibah Menuhin (Yehudi Menuhin's sister) is deeply interested in the healing power of music, She has done much good work in that direction. I would like to give my own experience.

An injured knee, with a displaced bone and a clot of blood, gave me 5½ months incessant pain. Manipulation was given, but it took some time for the clot to disperse. One Sunday evening while attending a Salvation Army Service, I was inspired to ask God that the stimulating vibrations from the band's music might course through my knee and heal it, This DID happen. Instantaneously, I slept that night free from pain. The knee has given no trouble since. Thanks be to God.

Mr B. J. Bailey, Maidstone, Kent.
I wouldn't have thought it! After my friends had tried to persuade me to wear a copper bracelet, for weeks, I eventually gave in. I have now worn one for five months and can say that my painful hip is not so bad, and the cramp has gone entirely from my right leg (sciatica). Don't ask me how it works . . . all I know is that in the place of painful restless nights I can now sleep. I also feel better during the day. Copper has certainly done something for me. I hate superstition, but there must be some good reason why.

Mr C. Burrell, Salisbury, England.
I see I am not the only man who looks forward to a sit-down with *Grace* magazine during the break for tea. My brother was a tea expert, and it occurred to me that readers might like to know how the experts make tea. This is what he told me.

Be sure that fresh water in the pot is fiercely boiling. Warm the teapot. It is not an old wive's tale that you should take the teapot to the kettle, and not the kettle to the teapot. In this way the water in the teapot remains nearer boiling point for a longer time than if the boiling water had been poured into a cold teapot. It is no good if the water is off the boil.

This is where my brother and I disagreed. He said that professional tea-tasters allow five or six minutes for the tea to infuse. He used to scold me for not allowing more than three minutes! For the average tea lover five minutes is usual. But I guess I just can't wait that long!

Miss C. Pettitt, Bridge End, Sheffield.
They say, as the spring approaches we need more vitamins, especially C', to keep fit. How can we get it?

ED: *You will find it in the young shoots of herbs – chives, parsley, dandelion leaves, watercress, mint. Chop them all, and take raw.*

Mary Vincent. Na. Ferrisburg, Vermont, U.S.A.
Here is a song of praise to *Grace* for all the splendid good for both mind
and body. I am a nurse trained in the school of medicine. Since retiring
am doing my little service for mankind and *Grace* is perfect with my ideas.

I am most happy to be a member of your group. With best wishes and
blessings enclosed is my Love offering. My finance is low, but my
spirits are high. Am most eager to spread the good news. I correspond
with over a hundred, all over the world. Ever yours in fellowship of
goodwill.

Mrs S. Robinson, High Wycombe.
I found the article on Honey very interesting – have always used a lot.
My baby never had sugar. I have used it on burns, when the pain has
gone instantly, and no blister. Also used it on my eyelids when they were
affected by the cold weather. A teaspoonful at night, taken in a tiny glass
of apple-juice does help one to sleep.

I am 78 years of age and live alone, but very busy in the garden, etc.,
so the days are never long enough; but if I do feel at all depressed, I open
a *Grace* at random, and always find something to help – for which I say
Thank you . . .

Mr T. Lemon, Aberdeen, Scotland, writes:
I look forward to the arrival of *Grace*. Here is my tit-bit:
Prescriptions come from poor and rich . . . The druggist has to make
'em . . . Sometimes they go in bottles which . . . Gives him a chance to
shake 'em . . . Some go in capsules, bitter things; . . . In powder oft his
stuff he brings . . . No wonder, while he works, he sings . . . He doesn't
have to take 'em!

Mr L. P. B., Netherseal, near Burton-on-Trent.
I have a lot of heartburn, with tenderness of the stomach, and wind rising in my throat. What would you recommend?

146

ED: *You have a large choice of herbs, Dandelion Root is good. Two teaspoonfuls of the dried root are boiled in one pint water for ten minutes, and allowed to cool. Strain. Drink one wineglassful after meals, two or three times daily, according to severity of the case. We know old codgers who chew a nob of the root to keep stomach and liver sweet and clean. Others prefer two teaspoonsful of Meadowsweet Herb, to a teacup of boiling water, and allow to cool; drinking one wineglassful after meals, when necessary. Some savour a few drops of Oil of Peppermint.*

Then, of course, there is the Biochemic approach. It is amazing how four tiny tablets of Natrum Phosphate 6x can deflate that bursting inner-tube. Natrum Phosphate splits up lactic acid into carbonic acid and water. In this way it alkalizes the blood and cancels out the acid tendency.

We sometimes forget that potatoes are non-acid forming, and can be eaten freely for stomach acidity. They have a large amount of vitamin C but being alkaline this is easily lost if boiled without the skins and then mashed, thus exposing the cells directly to the air. You have noticed how flat mashed potatoes taste only a short time after they are mashed.

Mrs S. A. Dicker, Winton, Bournemouth.
I had rheumatism so badly that I could not lift my hand to the back of my head to comb my hair. The pain was terrible. In a very short time all the pain disappeared after wearing a copper bracelet. To me this was marvellous. Two more things copper did for me. It took down the rheumatic swelling of my knee. My left arm was always cold before wearing the bracelet, now it is always beautifully warm. The doctors could do nothing for me, so you can tell how pleased I am.

Mr M. Mace, Grimsby, Lincs.
I hear that two hundred miles of tooth-paste is squeezed on to toothbrushes every day in Britain. This means fifteen million pounds worth a year – four and a half tubes per person. Also, most tooth powders contain acids and coarse grit which can wear away the enamel coating on the teeth. This is without talking about dentifrices consisting of precipitated chalk mixed with alkalis, astringents and antiseptics, perfume and colouring matter.

In the face of all this, how can we avoid some of these poisons?

ED: *This IS an indictment upon the modern dental industry, Mr Mace. We know readers who use simply Lemon Juice, and others who swear by salt. Powdered Orris Root is sold for this purpose. Cider Vinegar and honey (or Honegar) is finding some use for this purpose at the present time.*

Some American readers like Papaya tooth powder made from the milky juice of the papaya. It has a solvent action on vicious little deposits which can occur in gums or teeth not approachable by ordinary brushing. It contains the milky juice from the skin of the unripe Papaya melon which grows in the tropics.

Whatever did they do in the past before the glamour-strip advertisements? Until the 18th century they polished their teeth with a cloth dipped in salt, pumice, or ashes of nettles. But we draw the line at the man who starts off his day with a mouthful of soot. "Leaves them sparkling like little glow-worms," he grinned.

Mrs Perry, Bournemouth.
I had eye trouble when in my teens which caused me a lot of distress. Our doctor was one of the old school, sympathetic and was not afraid to recommend simple medicines. I was advised to place one single chamomile flower in an egg-cup and fill it three-quarters full with boiling water. When cool the flower was removed and the infusion used as an eye-douche. This was a great comfort and helped me to overcome the trouble.

Mr Harry Freeman, Grove Road, Manchester.
At last we have found the ideal cold-cure. My wife and I have had to work with others dripping with nasal colds and snorting wheezy chests all day long and in all sorts of draughts. Is it a miracle we haven't caught anything? I say it isn't! We have a teaspoonful of honey (or two) in a glass of hot milk before we go to bed. Readers should try it.

Mrs Taylor, Bournemouth.
I once had piles which bled so badly, and the pain was such that I had to sit down. It was more than I could bear. Then I was told to insert small ice cubes into the rectum. Taken from the refrigerator, they can be shaped to a convenient cone. Cold water strengthens the walls of the veins in that part of the body. The result was a wonderful improvement and no pain.

Miss A. M. Jackson, Bramley, Surrey.
In *Grace* for Winter 1960 Miss Helen Wilson of Preston told us how inflamed and swollen toe joints have been cured with Fuller's Earth. She tells how an aged mother found wonderful relief from the great pain in her big toe joint.
   Well, I did the same thing for my swollen big toe joint, and it is now better. I have used herbs all my life and can recommend Parsley tea for passing through the Change of Life. It is good for the sweats and discomfort of that time.

Miss A. Crossley, Grasmere, Westmorland.
What simple lunch recipe can be made up for one person?
   ED: *Here is an uncooked Nut Savoury for use with salad. Take half a Weetabix or Shredded Wheat, 1oz. milled nuts, 1 teaspoon water or vegetable stock or tomato juice. Mix all well together. Add a little yeast*

extract if desired. If on the dry side add a few drops more liquid. Make about an hour before mealtime.

Miss Margaret Dunlop, Co. Armagh, N. Ireland.
I am sending Postal Order for *Grace* to be sent to myself and my three friends. I want to tell you how much I enjoy *Grace* and how much it helps me to live. Yes, and I'm still going strong . . . and know how to be jolly and lively. I have just come back from Canada having gone alone – by jet plane! Visited nieces and nephews in Winnipeg and Calgary. Had a marvellous time. Wherever I went I was known as Aunt Margaret from Ireland. They showered on me hospitality to an overwhelming degree, nearly killing me with kindness. They took me to Banff, and I ascended a peak of the Rocky Mountains in a gondola lift and walked about on the trip, 7,500 feet up. My, that WAS an experience. I was sorry for all the family back home; we had 80 degrees of sunshine all the time . . . nearly killed me. Yes, I'm alive and kicking all right. I can walk two miles. Love to all the dear readers.

Mrs Winifred Hare, Poole, Dorset.
I shall never forget the dramatic effect of honey on a violent bout of palpitation. It happened at night. The heart was hammering away, and when I lay down I could feel it pulsating. This went on for nine hours and in the end I thought my last had come. "This is it" I thought. We had sent for the doctor and he was on the way. My husband did not know what to do. Suddenly we thought of honey: dissolving teaspoonsful of it into hot water. What followed was a miracle. Within three minutes that terrible palpitation vanished, and I felt better. I was all right before the doctor came.

Mr John Piner, St. Clements Hill, Capetown, SA.
I have tried all ways to cut out smoking. You are my last hope. What can I do?

ED: *Smoke as much as you like on the first day – but start smoking one hour later than your usual time in the morning. On the second day, delay your first puff by two hours. Continue on ensuing days – every day, start smoking one hour later than the previous day . . .*

This will spare you the grim and dreary prospect of being faced, suddenly, with an entirely smokeless day. Besides, too abrupt a halt may prove harmful. So if you must stop the pleasurable habit, why not do so by degrees? It will enable your nerves and body to adjust themselves to the switch-over, and you will take things serenely in your stride without suffering from shock and irritability.

Then, even if you don't succeed in stopping to smoke altogether, you will, at least, no longer be smoking more than is good for body or budget. Gently does it! – together with an earnest endeavour to stick to your time-schedule.

149

Mr R. J. Richardson, Ontario, Canada.
I would like to send a helpful hint proved by experience. You can rely on it.

For Gall Stone, fast 24 hours, and on retiring take 4 ounces Olive Oil and 4 ounces Lemon Juice. Give yourself an enema of warm water in the morning. If the oil is hard to keep down after swallowing, don't think of it, or up it comes. Regards to the *Grace* Family.

Mrs Margaret Nisbet, Colehill, Wimborne Minster, Dorset.
Four years ago! How quickly time has passed since he shared our picnic lunch in the garden of our thatched cottage. Of all our feathered friends he became our special pet because of the tousled feathers on his back, which would not lie down. At the sound of his name "Robbie" he would come flying towards us and perch on the trellis. Every morning, early, he would pipe at the front door until we let him in. Hopping his way through the sitting-room into the dining-room he would wait patiently for the biscuit tin to be opened. He had his own tiny brass tray of crumbled biscuits under a chair. He became so tame that he ate from our fingers.

He lost all his feathers on neck and head. This called for a change of diet. We gave him brown bread crumbs, whole-meal biscuits and little bits of butter and cheese. He thrived on it. His feathers became quite restored. When weather was wet he would ask to come in, and sit until his feathers were dry, unafraid and completely at home. In December his visits became more frequent; it seemed to be a full-time job to keep opening and shutting the door. He loved warmth from the coal fire. He loved to be talked to as one would hold a conversation with a pet dog. During icy blasts and torrential rains he visited the open bedroom window for his daily rations.

The very cold spell proved too much for his frail form. We found him in his last sleep behind the grandfather clock. It was a wonderful feeling to know that we were loved by a red-breast. We recall with joy the great happiness his presence brought to our home.

Mr J. D. Curtis, Brisbane, Australia.
We like your pictures of the way osteopaths work. Do you know a simple manipulation which the ordinary person can do, quite safe, for headaches.

ED: *Any layman can apply the following neck-stretching movement. The person with headache or migraine sits on a low stool. Let the helper stand at her left side. Apply the thumb and first and second fingers of the right hand firmly to the base of the skull. Place the left hand under the jaw. Gently lift the head and stretch the neck upward and backward. Heavy people require a good strong 'lift'. Approach the job as if you were trying to lift the person off the ground by the head. Hold him or her on the stretch from 30 to 60 seconds. This movement unkinks the arteries and straightens and drains the veins, thus relieving congestion in the brain.*

150

Salad Days

BY FRANK NEWMAN TURNER, M.N.I.M.H.

FOR A CHANGE, make a salad using cooked new potatoes and peas (either cooked or raw, if very young and fresh). If you decide to use cooked peas, add a sprig or two of mint to the small amount of cooking water. No bi-carbonate of soda *please*—it is bad for the stomach, and personally I think that if peas are fresh enough to eat they do not need artificial aids—either for colour or tenderness. New potatoes cooked with mint are, of course, also delicious.

An alternative salad, in addition to potatoes and peas you will need: spring onions, radishes, celery sticks, cheese.

Grated raw turnip or carrot, if liked, could be added.

Cook the peas and potatoes ahead of time, so that they may be drained and cooled. When cold, slice the potatoes and heap the peas on them. Add the grated turnip or carrot juice to taste.

If a dressing is wanted, use orange juice.

Clean the spring onions and radishes, leaving as much of the leaves as possible as these contain valuable elements which are lost when—as so often happens—the greens are cut off. Arrange onions and radishes in clusters on either side of the bowl, leaving the salad mixture easy to serve.

Serve with block cheese and celery sticks.

Slowly lower the head and release pressure. Finish off by firmly stroking the neck downwards along the course of the main arteries and veins, on both sides. It may be followed by what is sometimes referred to as magnetic treatment. Take the head of the patient between your hands and with your thumbs stretch the skin of the forehead outward, half a dozen times. Then make regular magnetic strokes from the forehead downward and outward along the neck and arms.

R. M. Gale, Hales, Norwich.
My grandfather used to tell a story of a farmer which concerned an event supposed to have taken place near Woodbridge many years ago.

Londoner's relaxing ground, Queen Mary's Rose Garden, Regent's Park.
British Tourist Authority.

The farmer was driving home from market with his grown-up daughter in their horse and trap. At one point of their journey they were held up by robbers who demanded their money. After searching the pair and finding nothing, the highwaymen appropriated the horse and trap and drove away, leaving the farmer and his daughter standing by the roadside.

Father and daughter looked at one another and finally he said:

'What did you do with the purse?" to which the daughter replied by producing it from her mouth and said, "You often tell me that my mouth is too wide but it's bin useful today." Father was silent for a few minutes, then he said:

"Pity your owd Mother warn't here, we could have saved the hoss and cart."

Eva Breakstone, Oklahoma City, Oklahoma, U.S.A. (Dr. A Wigmore's Study Group).
I have been a victim of an awful case of arthritis for many, many years. My nephew suggested that a possible change in my mineral make-up might

be achieved if I stopped all tea and coffee drinking. I have been a devoted follower of the "coffee break" and a "tea cosy". As he is a professor in the Missouri University at Columbia, I followed his advice. It was hard work drinking herb tea but after a week I sort of got used to it, and by the end of eleven weeks my arthritis had actually disappeared. The relief from pain after eleven years – as I write this I notice the connection between eleven weeks and eleven years – was like being born again. It is my hope that other folks suffering from arthritis will try this.

Ezra Rubinstein, San Francisco, U.S.A.
I want you to tell me the best thing to eat. I work at account books all day and have to use my head in the evenings. Been doing this for years. What can be done to strengthen the brain?

ED: *Parsley, my dear Rubinstein, parsley. Nothing like it for stimulating those jaded cerebral cells. How? First take it raw in salads or with your hot meal. A refreshing summer drink may be made by bringing to the boil in a saucepan a handful of fresh parsley in one pint water. Remove saucepan on boiling. Do not simmer. Strain. Drink one wineglassful two or three times daily. Also safe for nervous troubles, trembling hands, and general jitters. Big husky men can take a teacupful as frequently as desired. Just the thing to make the Trial Balance come right, first time.*

Mrs T., Missouri, U.S.A.
What is good for Hay Fever? For Anaemia?

ED: *Homoeopathic medicine, Allium Cepa (red onion). Four tablets three times daily, between meals, until relief is felt, for Hay Fever.*

For anaemia, a knowledge of the blood picture (microscopic examination) is necessary. Severe anaemias are the province of the specialist. For simple anaemia, equal parts of these safe and harmless roots may be tried with profit. Blue-Flag Root and Yellow Dock Root. Take one ounce of each. Mix. Place half an ounce of the Mixture in one pint cold water and bring to boil. Simmer for 15 minutes. Strain when cold. Drink one wineglassful after meals three times daily. Biochemic salts Calcium Phos 6x (four at night) and Ferrum Phos 6x (four on rising) are helpful auxiliaries. Attention to diet is important.

Margaret Mackenzie, Kensington, London, W.8.
What is a weed? A plant whose virtues have not been discovered – *Emerson.* To create a little flower is the labour of ages – *Blake.* I believe a leaf of grass is no less than the journey-work of the stars: and the running blackberry would adorn the parlours of heaven – Walt Whitman. Wherever there is life, the storehouse of infinite energy is behind it – Swami Vivekananda. To know God is to live – Tolstoy.

From one member of the Family to another. Greetings.

Mr Francis Tucker, Tunbridge Wells.
I am glad you are not a sober-sides, Mr Editor. "Give me a sense of humour, Lord . . . Give me grace to see a joke; . . . To get some happiness from Life . . . And pass it on to other folk."

Crossing over to the chemist's drug counter, we asked the pharmacist, "Do people get all mixed-up when they come in here'?"

The old pharmacist smiled, "I'll say they do. They ask me for paralysed gauze; aspiration tablets; polluted water; Scott's emotion; cynical thermometers. But the prize of the lot was the woman who came in the other day and said she wanted a box of exorbitant cotton wool. You know, son, looking at today's prices, maybe she was right."

When a pharmacist made-up a prescription for his old friend he said, "Fred, let me know if this stuff does you any good. I've got rheumatism myself."

Mr Jack Smithson, London, N.12.
I have angina pectoris and get a sensation of my chest being in a vice. It goes numb all down my arm, and I am out of action for the rest of the day. I was once cured of measles by Homoeopathy many years ago by my mother. Can you tell me any of these tablets I could use?

ED: *Tiger Lily and Cactus are good. Cactus (Cactus Grandiflorus) is better for pains which point or move to the left. Tiger Lily (Lilium Tigrinum) is better for pains which tend towards the right (upper right arm).*

The 'Cactus' patient cannot bear lying on the left side, while Tiger Lily is better lying on the left side, and "worse lying on the right side". Tiger Lily is specially suitable for women who suffer from heart symptoms during menstrual periods.

If angina is accompanied by anguish, restlessness, and fear of death, Aconite 6x may be taken when necessary. This is a sovereign medicine for heart spasm. It is also of value in 'Agoraphobia' (a nervous dread of open spaces), or 'Claustrophobia' (a morbid dread of confined spaces). A most useful help where psychic disturbances always dominate cardiac phenomena, or where a racy heart has been touched-off by fright or emotion.

For angina cases, generally, Liquid Extract of Cactus grandiflorus takes a lot of beating, but this is herbal, and the homoeopathic law of Similars does not apply. It is safe for all when taken, 3 to 5 drops morning and evening, in a little water.

Miss I. Edgington, West Bournemouth.
Heard in passing . . .

Three adult elephants played on the sloping grass. One rolled over the edge into a gulley. After recovering from the shock he stood on his feet and was surprised to see a small animal.

"Who are you?" he said.
"I'm a mouse."
"Why are you so small?"
"I have been ill."

Mr I. W. Clark, Rayleigh, Essex.
I feel the following will be of interest to readers. While cooking the Sunday lunch, my wife sustained a severe burn on her wrist, about four inches in length.

"She was in considerable pain. We immediately applied honey thickly over the affected part, and covered with dry lint and bandage. Within ten minutes she was free from pain. She did not disturb the application for twenty hours. Upon removing the bandage you can imagine our surprise to find no sign of blistering or damage to the skin. It was remarkable. This might help other readers should they be faced with a similar experience.

Mrs C. M. Irvine, Mealsgate, by Carlisle.
I find the articles on food most interesting. I cured myself of overweight and rheumatic pains by a fruit-salad and raw vegetable diet. At 75, I feel energetic, well and happy.

Latest health news from Health Conference:
Eminent surgeons say that sufferers with kidney stones should avoid tomatoes and take no lemon juice.

Miss L. N. Candlin, Brighton, Sussex.
Juniper is not used today like it was in my childhood. Near my grandmother's home in Sussex there were some juniper bushes. I well remember my grandmother picking and eating one or two berries when she passed that way "because they were good for her kidneys".

It can also be taken in infusion. Four to six berries to teacup boiling water. Drink the fluid when cold, wineglassful after meals, three times daily.

Anonymous.
I have tried all the cures for smoking without results. What do I do next?

ED: *Without being unkind, I know of only one sure and certain cure. Visit the cancer ward of any hospital. Never fails.*

Mrs R. Kennedy, Co. Antrim, N. Ireland.
Your magazine has a place in lives of people who try to relax. I have a way of relaxing which sends me back to my work revitalized. I play a disc of Chopin's famous Nocturne in D flat major, Opus 27, No. 2, by a well-known concert pianist. I take care other items on the same side of the record don't jolt me back to reality too soon. The exquisite velvet texture of the music lifts my mind upwards towards the friendly cosmos.

I find half an hour in the presence of beauty during my afternoon sit-down does as much for my mind as a hot-bath does for my body. The companionship of good music means very much to me.

Mrs S. Elmington, Victoria, Australia.
My daughter has had anaemia for two years and cannot 'take' iron and the usual tablets. It is pitiful to see her drooping around the place. No energy. No interest in life. We have been driven to distraction. What do you advise?

ED: *Space does not permit detailed reply. Breathing exercises, Hot Epsom's salts bath, once weekly. Rest, sunshine and fresh air essential. Vitamin B.12 daily: when this is deficient the red cells are deformed and immature and cannot work efficiently. This vitamin is the missing factor said to have been discovered in Comfrey, which root grows wild and free in the countryside almost everywhere. This plant also contains trace elements of calcium and phosphorus, builders of solid bone and flesh. Raw, uncooked fresh fruit and vegetables. Apricots, carrot juice, honey, No frozen foods, chocolate or salad dressing.*

A blend of simple herbs of value for enriching and improving the blood, complexion, body tone, containing no harmful drugs is: bogbean 1oz: comfrey leaves 1oz: holy thistle ½oz: wormwood ½oz: hops ½oz. If constipated senna leaves may be added.

To prepare: Infuse one heaped tablespoonful in one pint of boiling water in a teapot. Allow to stand for one hour. Take wineglassful after each meal, with an extra one before retiring, if desired. For children: Dilute with half the volume of water again. Sweeten with honey.

Mr L. Percy, Edinburgh, Scotland.
What can I do for cracks at the side of my lips which do not heal?

ED: *These can be caused by a number of complaints. In many cases, they can indicate a deficiency of Vitamin 'B'. An excess of salt has also been known to be a cause. Avoid salt. Cut down fats. Steady with starches. Plenty of raw, fresh, uncooked vegetables and fruits in salads. Wholemeal bread. Three or four Brewer's yeast tablets at each meal.*

HEALTH IS AS INFECTIOUS AS A CONTAGIOUS DISEASE. I WILL AFFIRM IT.

"Know, then, whatever cheerful and serene
Supports the mind, supports the body, too.
Hence the most vital movement mortals feel
Is HOPE; the balm and life-blood of the soul."
RALPH WALDO TRINE

Holidays are here again.   *Jane Miller*

From a member of Grace Family who wishes to remain anonymous:
I wonder if the following will help others.   I often think of it as I struggle
along.   My husband is mentally sick and I try so hard to have patience
and to lovingly get him well.

"Not until the loom is silent ..   And the shuttles cease to fly . . . will
God unroll the canvas and explain the reason why . . . Dark threads are
just as needful to the Master Weaver's hand . . . As the gold and silver in
the pattern he has planned."

Mrs J. Jones, Llandrindod Wells.
I am easily upset by drugs and medicines.   Can you tell me what I can
do in the food line for High Blood Pressure?   Do you believe in fasting?
Systolic pressure is said to be 230 mm.   I'm desperate.

ED: *A Rice-Fast would appear to be what you need.   Try the following
for the first five days of every month.   Take one cupful of brown rice.
Boil, in three cupfuls of water until it comes out like a porridge.   Take
one teacupful three times daily.   Nothing else should be taken.   And that
goes for tea and coffee.   Yes, it's a spartan fast.   In your case it should
be carried out under strict supervision.*

157

Mr L. I. Kirk, Edmonton, Alberta, Canada.
We are especially interested in what we read about honey in *Grace* magazine. I can only speak for it about what it does for my dogs. They are new animals since I started them on it. I have since found out that it builds firm bone and feeds the red blood corpuscles. Now worms can be caused by an excess of mucus; and that's just what honey clears-up, pronto. I give to bitches in whelp and nursing bitches – one teaspoonful in milk. Good with raw milk for puppies, and I have discovered that water and honey is good for almost any kind of fevers for animals. This is, of course, if the trouble is not too serious. Can be fed about three or four times a day. I know it's good for cats as well – if you an get them to take it!

Fraulein Erika Lang, Mettmann, Germany.
I do not know anything about the battery-system of rearing hens in England but when we tried to lock-up the chickens on our farm they got bored. They just sat about and ate, and ate. We felt all that eating and no scrapping-about did them no good. So we let them out on free-range, which they had been used to, and now they can scratch-about to their heart's content. Result – contented birds, and contented father.

Mrs H. Johnson, London, N12.
We have read in the magazine how Parsley tea is good for female troubles, especially for 'hot sweats' and discomforts of the menopause (change-of-life). Can you tell us how to prepare it?

ED: *Parsley contains trace-elements (or homoeopathic traces) of arsenic, potash and other vital salts. A bloodstream deficient of inorganic salts through malnutrition or other causes, can be exposed to certain complaints. All herbs are rich in potash. Garden Parsley is of special benefit to genito-urinary complaints of men or women. It is not a cure-all, but can often ameliorate cystitis, prostatitis and dispel depression, whether caused by pelvic congestion, or just plain 'out of sorts'.*

Place one handful fresh parsley from the garden into an enamel or stainless steel saucepan and cover with half pint cold water. Bring to boil. Simmer for two minutes. Set the vessel aside to cool. When cold, pour through a strainer, and help yourself to a wineglassful after meals, three times daily. The dose may be increased to one teacupful if desired, as it is quite safe in larger quantities.

A. T. S., Birmingham.
My neighbour tells me that a cup of Lime Flower tea is good for my nerves, and will keep the doctor away. Why stop there? An onion a day will keep everybody away.

Eva I. Scott, Barnes, London, S.W.13.
I know that rhubarb and strawberries are bad for rheumatism, and have proved that the latter certainly are. Some people say that all fruits ending with "berry" are not good for this complaint. I wonder if this is really true? It seems a pity to go without delicious fruits unnecessarily.

ED: *It cannot be generally believed that rhubarb, strawberries, or in fact any fruit ending with "berry" are always bad for rheumatism. Some rheumatics thrive on rhubarb, it savours of the old adage, "What is one man's meat may be another man's poison". However, as a general rule it is wise for most sufferers of rheumatism to avoid "berry" fruits and concentrate on uncooked grated raw vegetables, salad materials and other alkali-forming foods such as celery, carrots, celeriac, chives, cottage cheese, dandelion leaves, dates, figs, grapes, green peas, honey, kale, marrow, molasses, mustard-and-cress, olive oil, parsnips, peaches, pears, potatoes (in skins), runner beans, savoy, tomatoes, turnips, watermelon.*

The following have acid-properties: cranberries, plums and rhubarb, oatmeal and other cereals, breakfast cereals of all kinds, chicken and all game, jams and all preserves, peanuts, all kinds of prepared meats, sugar, confectionery, and walnuts, which should be avoided in rheumatism.

A. B. Kretschmar, West Nyack, U.S.A.
I'd like to pass this on, and when understood, everyone would have it. Here is a homoeopathic remedy worth its weight in gold, and it is Baptisia 3x, which contains three elements, plus the 15 principal minerals as found in the human; which means it contains the power of 15 separate remedies all within this one remedy, but can be taken safely in low potencies as a general tonic and as a preventative of many epidemic diseases. It is good for colds which do not seem to yield to other treatment; in which cases, Baptisia 3x should be taken. It is a great blessing, and I would not be without it. This knowledge comes down to us from the old Aryan Sages of over 3,000 years ago, and is a remedy used by the Science of Tridosha, as revealed by Dr. B. Bhattacharyya, Republic of India. May God's blessing be with all readers!

MY KITCHEN

God bless my little kitchen,
I love its every nook,
And bless me as I do my work,
Wash pans and pots, and cook.

And may the meals that I prepare
Be seasoned from above
With Thy great blessing and Thy grace,
But most of all Thy love.

As we partake of earthly food,
The table before us spread . . .
We'll not forget to thank the Lord
Who gives us daily bread.

So bless my little kitchen God,
And those who enter in . . .
May they find naught but joy and peace
And happiness therein.

(Anonymous)

Miss R. Lupton, Hatfield, Salisbury, Zimbabwe.
Good health, peace and prosperity to all readers of *Grace*. Our rainy season is from October to March but to date we have had only eleven inches which came in one week, and water is desperately needed for our gardens. This is so unlike England, which "enjoys" a rainy season all the year round! Have already lost all my vegetables which seeds I had optimistically planted in October for our growing season . . . but everything depends on the rains.

Both Tuft (my dog) and I have been taking, and feel the benefit of the natural remedy, Lignum Vitae. Tuft is quite mobile now; far different indeed from the poor old chap who couldn't even raise himself from a lying or sitting position due to arthritis in his hindquarters. I would have to lift him up and put him on his feet as he couldn't "make it" under his own steam. But now! To see him chasing butterflies and lizards, etc., or running races with himself when he fails in his efforts to persuade me to play "Touch" with him – he's full of fun and nonsense. As for myself, although still a bit creaky in the joints, I'm more mobile now than I have been for years. So we are both happy we have discovered Lignum Vitae. No more Cortisone for me!

H. Jay Dinshah, Malaga, New Jersey, U.S.A.
Are we worried about protein deficiencies? We are not, if we make use of delicious legumes – green and yellow peas, beans, lentils. An excellent staple dish is brown rice and yellow split peas. Use only 100 per cent whole-wheat flour; you can make delicious pancakes, cakes, muffins, etc. Avoid devitalized white-flour as the plague, and this regardless of whether it has been "enriched", "reconstituted", or "wheat-germ added". Use only raw dark-brown sugar. Make good use of salads with raw grated vegetables and fruits.

Mrs K. Fox, Christchurch, Dorset.
It is all just wonderful . . . how one is looked after . . . if we only trust. I have had a lifetime of hard work in nursing, in this and in other countries. I was one of the first to teach massage to nursing students of Birmingham hospitals before the first world war. I have always been thankful I was born into a home where the Scriptures were read daily. In time of need, I have always been provided for.

On one occasion I was left a few shares, but as the company was having hard times they were worth only a shilling each; the whole lot came to only two or three pounds. However, I held on to them for sentimental reasons.

My father was a Public Prosecuter in India, and when one of his man-servants fell ill with smallpox he looked after him, quite fearless in the

Summer tranquillity and fragrant breezes fill the air in A Sunlit Garden, by Pauline Delacroix-Garnier. A place of rest for the weary mind.
Christie's Images.

face of virulent disease. The eruptions were covered with *Plantain leaves* to exclude the air, and for cooling. As I look back after my 88 years, I can see how God has wonderfully preserved me and ordered it all. This is what He has recently done for me. I wished for a little house of my own, after my ups-and-downs and wanderings. I could not possibly see how this could be. I had a little money, but not near enough. But I thought I would like to help somebody with what little strength was left me nearing the end of life's journey. A marvellous thing happened. There came into my life two people burdened with a great need. I asked that I might be permitted to help them. What do you think happened? It was not long before a letter came through the post offering me a very substantial sum for the shares which unbeknown to me had appreciated to many times their original value due to the firm taking on an unexpected run of success. I was then able to buy my little house. When I come out of nursing home it will make a home for all three of us . . . which only goes to show if you trust enough, some way will open for you. My love to the readers.

James Long, Liverpool.

Reduced by a disorder of the digestive organs to a mental and physical wreck, unable to sleep through one single night for a period of four years without drugs, to which I was fully introduced by a London physician – examined, advised, and treated in nursing homes at enormous cost to both body and pocket, sent to health resorts, and the Alps, and always under the care of a specialist, is it not surprising that I lost confidence in medical skill and readily listened to the 'fairy tales' of rude health restored to others by the abandonment of flesh, fish, and fowl, alcohol, tea and coffee. I commenced the consumption of fresh fruits and salads, vegetable foods, including cereals and pulse, and small quantities of milk, butter, eggs, cheese. The suffering of years with poisoned blood and neurasthenia – the result of both wrong eating to keep up my strength; and of eating too much to increase my weight, which was lost as quickly as it was gained – was almost immediately ended. Health was miraculously restored in almost as many weeks.

Long experience has taught me that orthodox teaching is wrong, that the standard of protein consumption is too high, and that living foods – such as raw ripe fruit and salads – are vital to health and long life. And, further, that the protein, carbohydrate and fatty contents of food are not the sole guide to their energy and vitality value. What has occurred to me, must have occurred to thousands.

The Workshop – Edward Hersey (living artist). Born in Croydon in 1948, Hersey pursued a career in the retail jewellery trade, sketching and painting in his spare time, only recently turning professional. His favourite subjects are rural and farmyard life, reflecting his love of the countryside.
Courtesy of Daryl Davies (British Fine Art)

Should I go Gluten-Free?

By Rita Greer

The Wholefood Cook

TWENTY years ago nobody had heard of gluten-free food. Now everyone knows someone on a gluten-free diet, either because of an allergy or the coeliac condition. But it is not just a fashionable diet. Some people depend on it as a life-saving regime.

So what is so special about a gluten-free diet? Well, it is one of the major 'exclusion' diets. The gluten (protein) in wheat, rye, barley and oats must be left out of the diet completely. This is a problem as without the gluten to bind and strengthen doughs, baking falls into a pile of crumbs. By baking I mean bread, cakes, scones, pastry, buns, muffins, pancakes, batters, biscuits, snack nibbles, batters etc, etc . . . However, it also concerns food which has been thickened like soups, sauces, gravies and a great many manufactured foods such as sweets and confectionery. Some brands will be suitable and others not. The trick is to keep a little book with you to write down brands of foods that *can* be eaten. On a more cheerful note the basic plain foods that are gluten-free are easy to remember – meat and fish/milk and eggs/fruit and vegetables. Appropriate starchy foods to replace the ones not allowed are rice, potatoes and bananas.

You may find some ingredients in the following recipes that you have not bought or used before. These are usually stocked in health stores. Gram (chickpea) flour, potato flour (farina) and ground rice are all useful staples for a gluten-free kitchen.

Bread

Daily Bread, that comforting and age-old staple, is probably the greatest problem for a gluten-free diet. The staff of life is a very important part of a daily diet, special or not. Without wheat flour, bread disintegrates into crumbs so a binder to replace the wheat gluten should be added to any blend of gluten-free flours. This will strengthen the dough for baking and ensure that it can be cut into slices.

Binder

First make the binder. Peel a medium sized cooking apple and put into a small pan with a teacup of water. Bring to the boil, then simmer for about 15 minutes. Strain through a fine wire mesh sieve into a basin, pressing the peelings with the back of a wooden spoon. Discard peelings and put the liquid to one side to cool.

Crusty Gluten-Free Loaf
1 oz (25g) cornflour
1 oz (25g) gram (chickpea) flour
6 oz (170g) potato flour (farina)
3 good pinches salt
1 level teaspoon sugar
¼ oz (7g) instant fast-action yeast
1 tablespoon sunflower oil
2 – 3 tablespoons binder (see above)
4 fluid oz (125ml) lukewarm water

Method
Preheat oven at Gas 4/350ºF/180ºC. Grease a 1lb (500g) small loaf tin. Mix the flours, salt, sugar and yeast in a bowl. Tease out any lumps with the fingers. Add the oil, 2 tablespoons of the binder and the water. Mix/beat to a thick, creamy batter, adding another tablespoon of binder if it feels too thin. Pour/spoon into the prepared tin and put into the oven immediately on the top shelf. Bake for about 1 hour. The loaf should be well risen with a cracked top. As soon as it is baked turn out on to a wire rack to cool. Do not squeeze or handle the loaf as it needs to be left to set. Only cut when cold. Keep wrapped in foodfilm to prevent drying out. Eat on the day of baking and toasted the following day. Any left over can be ground in a coffee grinder to make breadcrumbs.
Note: This is a completely different approach to bread than ordinary wheat bread. This gluten-free loaf is made from a batter which rises, cracks and rises more during baking. It does not need to be left to prove before putting in the oven.

Gluten-Free Crispbreads – makes 6
In their uncooked state, these golden crispbreads are rather fragile and don't like to be moved about. Consequently they are rolled out on the baking sheet. If you do not have a straight-sided tumbler to use for rolling, press out with the fingertips instead.
½ oz (15g) cornflour
1½ oz (45g) ground rice
½ oz (15g) gram (chickpea) flour
2 good pinches salt
3 good pinches caster sugar
¼ oz (20g) soft margarine
1 oz (25g) fresh boiled mashed potato
2 teaspoons cold water.

Method:
Preheat oven at Gas 7/425ºF/220ºC. In a bowl, mix the first 5 ingredients. Rub in the margarine and then the potato. Add the water and mix by hand to a smooth dough, kneading lightly for a few seconds. Divide into 6

equally-sized pieces. Grease a baking sheet. Flatten each piece in situ (see note above) into a thin circle about 4in (10.5cm) in diameter. Prick all over with a fork and bake for 10 minutes on the top shelf until crisp and golden. Leave to cool on the baking sheet. Eat freshly baked instead of bread.

Gluten-Free Carrot Cake – makes 6 slices

½ oz (15g) gram (chickpea) flour
1 oz (25g) cornflour
3½ oz (100g) ground rice
3 pinches cream of tartar
1 good pinch bicarbonate of soda
3 oz (85g) sultanas
2 oz (50g) soft margarine, melted and cooled
3 oz (75g) finely grated (fresh) carrot
2 oz (50g) soft brown sugar
1 generous tablespoon set honey
¼ level teaspoon ground nutmeg
1 level teaspoon ground ginger
1 egg, beaten

Method:
Grease a 6 in (15cm) diameter cake tin and flour with ground rice. Mix the first 5 ingredients in a bowl. In a second bowl, mix the next 7 ingredients. Add the egg and mix again. Turn in the mixture from the first bowl and mix everything together to make a thick cake batter. Spoon into the prepared tin and bake for about 45 minutes on a shelf above centre. (Test with a skewer to see if done). Run a knife all round the edge and turn out to cool on a wire rack. Eat within 2 days or freeze as wrapped slices for later use. Allow to defrost for several hours before eating.

Savoury Nibbles
Parties are always a problem for gluten-free dieters as other than plain crisps most snack nibbles are unsuitable. The answer is to take a bag of your own nibbles and join in with the munching. (If you take extra you'll be able to share them but consult the hostess first).
1 oz (25g) cold, mashed potatoes
½ oz (15g) soft margarine
pinch salt
2 oz (50g) ground rice
1 heaped teaspoon very finely chopped onion

Method:
Preheat oven at Gas7/425ºF/220ºC. Put the potato and margarine into a bowl and beat to a cream. Use a fork to add the salt and ground rice. Put in the onion and mix well to make one ball of dough, adding a little water if it feels too dry. Flour the worktop with ground rice. Press out the

dough by hand to the thickness of pastry. Cut into fingers or small squares with a sharp knife. Use a spatula to put on to a greased baking sheet. Bake for about 8 to 10 minutes and put into a dish to cool. Avoid over-baking or they will be too crisp.

Note: other party nibbles/snacks are little sticks of fresh vegetables such as carrot, celeriac, celery and fennel, tiny tomatoes and radishes.

Gluten-Free Sponge buns – makes 6

Sometimes it is good to be able to knock-up something quickly for a snack or for tea, or a lunchbox. These little buns can be flavoured with a lit-tle ginger or cinnamon, gluten-free cocoa or ½ teaspoon coffee granules dissolved in 1 teaspoon boiling water. Add spices to taste depending on their strength. ½ teaspoon finely chopped rosemary leaves is interesting and aromatic. The finely grated rind of ¼ lemon or ⅓ of an orange will impart a good flavour.

2 oz (50g) ground rice
½ oz (15g) gram (chickpea) flour
1 oz (25g) cornflour
2 oz (50g) caster sugar
1 egg, beaten
2 oz (50g) soft margarine
½ level teaspoon cream of tartar
¼ level teaspoon bicarbonate of soda
1 scant teaspoon vanilla flavouring (omit if using a different flavouring)

Method:
Preheat oven at Gas5/375ºF/190ºC. Put all ingredients into a bowl, includ-ing flavouring of your choice. Mix/beat to a cream. Divide between 6 patty tins lined with cake papers. Bake on the top shelf for about 15 minutes until well risen. Cool on a wire rack. Eat within 2 days. Wrap in food film, individually, after they have grown cold. This will stop them drying out.

Notes: Always check ingredients to see if they are gluten-free. (I have cooked on a daily basis for a gluten-free dieter for 30 years and I can still get caught out). Spices should be marked 'pure'. Cocoa needs to be a gluten-free brand. Margarine should not include wheatgerm oil. Avoid packet mashed potato. Avoid commercially made baking powder. Whenever I peel a cooking apple I wrap the peelings and put them in the freezer to be used at a later date to make the binder. Waste not – want not!

Cooks using a fan oven should lower the centigrade temperature in the recipes by 20% and reduce cooking time by about one third.

There are two ways of looking at a gluten-free diet. One is to despair and become obsessed with what *cannot* be eaten; the other is to take an interest in what *can* be eaten. We are so lucky today when there is a wide variety of food available for the gluten-free dieter. It just needs some pos-itive thinking and a little effort. The reward is quite simple – good health.

"Sunny Sunset", Bathurst, N.S.W.
In place of (or as well as) the highly commercialized "Mother's Day" and "Father's Day", why not institute an "Old Folks Week"? This would assist people who are past looking for gifts of monetary value but would be gladdened by acts of thoughtfulness from the whole community. Many old folk, being unmarried or childless, fail to benefit at all from the present pattern of "gift" days.

Mr L. Williams, Swansea.
Readers might like to hear what Dr. Erasmus Darwin says. He was a poet, naturalist, and grandfather of the great naturalist, Charles Darwin, and a believer in folk-medicines:

"The science of medicine will some time resolve itself into a science of prevention rather than a matter of cure. Man is made to be well, and the best medicine I know of is an active and intelligent interest in the world of nature."

Mrs T. M. Wright, Huddersfield.
Can you give me a good natural remedy for corns?

ED: *The fresh leaves of Houseleek (Sempervivum Tectorum), if broken, exude a sticky excretion. Corns and especially warts have been effectively dealt with by rubbing with the broken leaf. Houseleek was a common sight on low tiled roofs in the country when I was a boy. Today, it is not as plentiful as it used to he. The fresh leaves can be bruised and applied as a poultice in any inflammatory conditions of the skin such as stings, burns or old hard swellings as a result from blows or injuries.*

Mrs Try.
Would it be possible for you to mention a daily "pick-me-up" for nerve tension with head noises'?

ED: *Tension may arise from a number of causes. and if it does not yield to the following simple expedient, you should consult your practitioner. Diet of raw fresh vegetables and fruit, wholemeal bread, milk, and dairy products. Avoid all forms of meat. Cut out salt, sugar, coffee and strong tea. Dry feed – drink only between meals. Do not use aluminium cooking utensils. Take fruit juices or Dandelion coffee, Instant Postum. Potatoes should be baked in their jackets, a large salad should not be accompanied by salad dressing, except for olive oil (or corn oil) and lemon juice mixed into an emulsion: If due to high blood pressure, dried nettles are helpful: one ounce rubbed dried nettles to one pint cold water. Bring to boil. Remove vessel on boiling. Strain when cold. Drink one half teacupful after meals three times daily. Rutin Tea or tablets are also a helpful alternative.*

Miss H. W. Kingsnorth, Weymouth.
Modern times are quite unlike the English way of life at the middle of the last century. Our farm was in marshy country, far from the towns, and

roads poor; the horse and cart being our only transport. Owing to farming depression it was a life of hard work, few comforts and fewer pleasures. All domestic water-supply had to be boiled, lighting was by oil, and we made tallow candles. We made most of our clothing at home. Father had to be vet and doctor, and all. We used to gather the countryside remedies in their 'peak' season and on a rising moon. After drying, they were kept in bags hung in the chimney corner. To us, the Elder tree was indeed the poor-man's-doctor; every single part of it could be used, often with wonderful results. Poppy heads were stewed and the liquor used to bathe painful joints. Hot onion was used to relieve earache; oil of cloves for toothache; marigold flowers to ease cuts and bruises. For boils we had Adam and Eve's own remedy – fig leaves, which were used as poultices.

If anyone was unlucky enough to get lumbago, he got a hot salt-pack. These things were used by my family and the local people from the middle of the last century to my knowledge, and they must go back in time a lot further.

To case the coughing and sickness of whooping cough garlic was put into the children's socks (under the soles); and to take the ache out of a corn or callous it was bound round with ivy leaves.

But perhaps the greatest benefits were received by the animals. The early recovery of a horse with a suppurating foot after being treated with linseed, was a joy to see. Its foot would he inserted into a thick sack filled with hot boiled linseed and strongly bound with twine. To fix this slippery poultice on a restive horse, perhaps on a cold winter's night with only a lantern light with a tallow candle to guide, called for skill and patience. Later, the healed wounds would be rubbed with herbal salves we made ourselves to make the hair grow again.

If a ewe were ill after lambing, and if she could be persuaded to eat ivy leaves, farmers felt quite hopeful of recovery. All these things were done in the usual way, without any fuss, and animals seldom died. Today, when animals as well as humans are getting an overdose of the welfare state, there seems to he more disease than ever.

The herbal knowledge was handed down from father to son, and some was received from travelling gipsies in return for a kindness shown. I cannot help thinking that a lot of valuable knowledge discovered by those working close to the earth, has been lost. One thing is certain, all the yonkers now growing up without a lack will never come within a thousand miles of the satisfaction and happiness of the England we knew.

Mrs J. K. Hammond, Bradford.
I have pleasure in renewing my subscription for *Grace* which I enjoy very much. I wish it was a 'monthly instead of a 'quarterly'. With regards to RAGWORT, mentioned in your last issue. During the war the house next door was taken over for evacuees. One mother had left London in an ill-fitting pair of shoes. After days at a reception centre, she had a very septic heel blister when she arrived here.

I went straight out and gathered some ragwort and made a brew of it, in which she bathed her feet. Before long the heel was clear of pus. Next day there was nothing to be seen but a clean hole which healed rapidly.

Mrs J. Smith, Cornwall, extract:
. . . shares of the famous Eli Lilly pharmaceutical company had had a big rise following a rumour that this company had discovered a remedy for the 'cure' of cancer. But they later had a tumble when a spokesman for the firm said that the new remedy, which was derived from a shrub called Periwinkle, was only for the treatment of patients with Hodgkin's Disease (chorio-carcinoma), which had responded well to clinical studies.

Beaconsfield reader.
. . . two cats were found unconscious by the side of Station Road, Beaconsfield. From a passing lorry a crate of beer had fallen, smashing a number of bottles – it is unfortunate that at that moment the two pussy-foots had exceptionally strong thirsts.

Mrs Sheldon-Flynn, Allston, Mass.
Did you know that one can remove warts by putting one's saliva on the offend-ing growth? I have done this twice – removing warts from two fingers.

Sturdy octogenarian, revealing the secret of his health:
"Now I'll tell you how 'tis. I eats what I like. I drinks what I like. Then I go bed and lets 'em fight it out among themselves."

Mr H. L. M., Brighton, Sussex.
I have a bad time with my eyes in the warmer weather. They get irrita-ble sore, and water easily. What can I do?
ED: *Have you tried garlic capsules? Two taken at night can usually avoid garlic halitosis the following day. Prepare a cold pack by taking a large gentleman's handkerchief immersing in cold water. Wring out. Sprinkle on a little Extract of Witch Hazel. Place over the eyes at odd moments of the day, when resting after lunch – or during the evening. One handkerchief for each eye may be used. Let them stay in position for ten minutes or more. Garlic capsules are also good for Hay Fever.*

E. M., Lanarkshire, Scotland.
Where does superstition end and science begin? After having a bellyful of drugs, radiant heat, diathermy, wax-baths, exercises, steam and water treat-ments over the years, they still couldn't take the pain out of my rheuma-tism. Fed up, I read-up the subject in an old book and was surprised to learn someone was cured from all my symptoms by carrying a potato around in his pocket. Well, I had nothing to lose, so I raided my wife's kitchen for the biggest spud my pocket would hold with comfort. Relief came slowly. You can imagine my amazement when it disappeared altogether.

Miss Emilie Thomson, Edinburgh.
I am Danish born, and 78 years, and God has given me many things. Now He has given me *Grace*, a little book which gives me that wonderful feeling that He is talking to me through every word I read in it. May the great *Grace* Family continue to grow and bring blessing to many lonely hearts. With all good wishes.

C. Giles, Small Heath, Birmingham.
My daughter has painful periods and urinary incontinence which takes much of the pleasure out of her life. She has literally tried "everything" and the "scraping" minor operation has not helped. Are there alternatives?

ED: *Cases are on record showing how Fluid Extract, Helonias (False Unicorn Root) have proved effective. In one case five drops taken three times daily was recommended for the incontinence. In two months both conditions had been overcome.*

Phyllis Goodship, New Southgate, London, N11.
I am sending a thought for the *Grace* Family. It's so well known, and so true, that it can stand repeating. It is, "All things work together for good, to those who love God." He never gives us a burden too heavy, and always gives the strength to bear it. Don't worry, God cares. With kind regards to all the readers.

Mrs M. M. Rainey, Slade, Ilfracombe, Devon.
. . . I find that Castor Oil, used daily, is helping sore and tired feet. I am also taking crude black molasses, once daily, and cider vinegar, and find they are a great help. We had much frost and bitter winds and water frozen in the house last winter . . . all this in Sunny Devon! These things helped me through it.

Mrs Coles, East Molesey.
. . . I certainly know that raw chicory does help a harassed housewife to keep calm, I have tried it over many years.

Miss A. L. S., London, N.W.8.
I keep two pedigree cats and one has had a little trouble with her ears which has kept recurring. As soon as I was told of Calendula (Marigold) Lotion I knew that it would be good for it. And indeed it is I clean her ears with it, once weekly, and they keep perfectly clear now.

Mrs G. Bradley, Ontario, Canada.
Readers might like to know what I use to darken my hair. I take two heaped teaspoonfuls of dried sage and Indian tea and put them into a pint jug. Fill up with boiling water and cover with a saucer. This I heat

gently in an oven for an hour or two. The longer it is stewed the darker the colour. I give it a good stir and keep it in the bathroom where I can rub it into the scalp before going to bed. I add a tablespoon of gin to preserve it. I am told the Indian squaws used this. I have read where beautiful Hindu women use coconut oil on their thick black tresses.

Mrs C. W. Daniels, Kidderminster.
Do you look muddy now your sun-tan is fading? Hasten on the bleaching process with lemon juice. Dab on with tissue and leave for fifteen minutes. Wash with mild soap and water. Rinse. Honey is wonderful for all types of skin. It makes an ideal facial. Smear honey on the face. Tap briskly with finger tips for five minutes. Remove with face cloth wrung out in warm water. You'll be surprised.

Mr J. D. Banham, Liverpool,
At last I have got rid of my cough – with coltsfoot. My doctor is a chummy old boy but I always leave him feeling worse than when I go in!
    One morning I went along and said I had a cough. I coughed. Doctor said, "Why, man, I can do better than that myself!" and gave a terrific cough. I left with the implication that his grievance was worse than mine. Why was I troubling him? I got Mist Tussi Rub. But it was his mighty cough which made me feel sicker than ever.

Mrs M. Ellis, Market Harborough.
I like the way your magazine stands for the open-air and for the home. There's magic in my home. There are the comings and goings of my son and daughter, and their children. There is the milkman always ready for a joke, and the visits of the postman with letters from old friends.
    There's a thrill in making your own bread with the feel of yeast – all alive and growing – on your fingers. There's the unforgettable warm fragrance of hot whole-meal loaves coming out of the oven. How sorry we feel for those who have to eat the pale indiarubber sold in shops!
    There's also the 'feel' of fresh laundry – dried in the garden. We've neighbours who spend months saving for electric driers. But that laundry is soulless, I think. I can smell the fresh-air in my linen. The scientists talk to us about cosmic rays. I'm sure it is better to wear, next to yourself, linen sweetened by wind and sun, and whatever unseen rays that are supposed to be coming down for our good.
    Too much cleaning is drudgery. I sometimes get out my cleaning box just for the pleasure of polishing-up my copper kettle. It fairly glows in the firelight. I try to keep the inside of the house as clean and tidy as my husband keeps the outside. I know there's magic in my house! Love to the family.

D. S. Abbott, Edmonton, Canada.
We have heard how good hazel nuts are for you; being rich in calcium. But my husband cannot eat them as they are. Can they be used in cooking?

ED: *We are glad you have discovered the sustaining power of hazel nuts. Here is a recipe from a very old cook-book, "Gentle Art of Cookery, by Mrs Hilda Leyel and Mrs Hartley, now out of print. Try this for a nerve-builder: "Beat the yolks of two eggs with 3 1/2 ounces demerara sugar for 10 minutes. Add 4 ounces finely ground hazel nuts, two tablespoonfuls dry wholemeal breadcrumbs, a quarter teaspoonful baking powder, and the whites of eggs whipped to a stiff snow.*

"Fill a buttered cake-tin with the mixture and bake for half an hour or a little more, in a slow oven. When cold it can be iced with mocha icing."

Mrs E. Jamieson, Banff, Alberta, Canada.
A friend asked me if I would like to look through your *Grace* Magazines before she sent them away. I have not only looked at them but studied them. You have what the world needs today. I shall do my best to make it known. I and my mountaineering friends have often talked of such a magazine while on our mountain trips. A reporter once asked, "Why do you climb?" I could only reply, "To listen to the silence." We sometimes walk from 12 to 16 miles a day in sheer mountain splendour and serenity. I am sure our Indian friends will also enjoy *Grace*. Regards to all members of the *Grace* Family.

Mrs H. A. Smart, London, S.W.6.
Some time ago I met a woman who boasted she hadn't had a cold for twenty years. She gave me a tip which I am passing on to you. Maybe it can help other members of the *Grace* family.

Take a bus into the country in late September or early October and pluck all the ripe elderberries you can lay your hands on. Make-up into a 'rob' as soon as you can. Do not let them stand about for days before getting round to the job. To every pint of elder juice add one pound brown sugar (or honey), teaspoon powdered ginger, teaspoon of cinnamon and twelve cloves. Boil for half an hour, and bottle when cool. Throughout the winter take two desertspoonfuls in a glass of hot milk (or water), daily. That'll make you sit-up!

L. Thompson, Braunstone Lane, Leicester.
I was interested to read about the home treatment of warts in a back number. Have readers tried 10 grains Epsom Salts twice a day, externally? Simple but effective.

P. W. Wright, Tunbridge Wells.
We love your magazine . . . What safe and easy thing can be used for the hot flushes of the menopause?

ED: *Agnus castus is a simple and speedy means of overcoming them. Obtainable from Health Food Stores.*

171

Miss Hilda Mills, Andover, Hants.
I have tried all kinds of Muesli for breakfast, and think I have hit on a really good one. Followed by wholemeal toast and honey it sustains you through all the day. Readers might like it.

Soak two tablespoons medium oatmeal (or barley kernels) in three table-spoons of milk, and just before eating, grate and mix in a raw apple. Mix well with a little honey (the runny is the best for this purpose) and a dash of Rose-Hip syrup if desired. Add a date or two, chopped up into small nuggets. Any fresh fruit will do, in place of the apple. Soaked raisins, or even grated raw carrot can be mixed in, or prunes, if fresh fruit is not available. I cover the mound with a shower of grated nuts – hazels for preference, as I read these are good for anaemia and tiredness. Since changing my breakfast to this, I am heaps better.

Mrs L. Hammond, Eccleshill, Bradford.
In a Spring issue of *Grace* an article by N. L. Candlin on *The Singing Masons:* referred to honey as a 'help" for chronic eye diseases. My father found it very effective. After two or three applications he found the mistiness in which he lived, clearing. After crossing a road more by sound than sight he can now see a car 200 yards away, and can once more see the buds bursting on the trees. Given good clear print he can now read again and altogether is find-ing life much more enjoyable. Thank you very much for printing the article.

John Tobe, Ontario, Canada.
When I was a youth I drank copious quantities of milk, yet I continued to have caries in spite of the fact that my teachers and the nutritionists and the advertising ballyhoo told me that milk would build strong teeth. But in my later years, when I stopped drinking milk and partook of more raw vegetables, fruits, nuts and grains, I ceased having caries, my teeth improved, and I have had no trouble since.

I've read all sorts of reports trying to tell me that milk builds strong teeth. One day I shall send them by post a big Spanish onion to go with all that tripe they've written.

Mrs W. Fisher, Scarisbrick, Southport.
As a young girl I suffered from dreadful catarrh and was always burdened with lots of handkerchiefs as the catarrh was all nasal. This was a terri-ble affliction and it made me very self-conscious; many were the good-humoured jokes made at my expense.

At that time there was a lot of publicity being given to miracles which were the outcome of pilgrimages to Lourdes. I became quite obsessed with the idea that I, too, could be cured by going to Lourdes, although I was not a Roman Catholic. I did not tell anyone how I felt about this because I knew that it was quite impossible for me to go, yet this long-ing and feeling of a cure persisted.

In those days we had friends in at the weekend and we would all gather around the piano for a singsong. Somebody remarked that I had a very nice singing voice and suggested that I ought to have singing lessons, and eventually I went to see a teacher who, strangely enough, proved to be a Roman Catholic. She accepted me as a pupil and the training comprised a certain length of time each day being spent on breathing exercises on which she was most insistent, and which I was faithful in carrying out. By this time I had youthful romantic visions of becoming a great singer.

It was quite a long time before the fact dawned on me that I had had my miracle. (We take so much for granted.) The catarrh had gone! The cure was complete with no side effects – none but what were good, that is! The lessons gave me good health, great joy and inspiration, and an appreciation of singing that I would not have had otherwise. My cry had been heard and my faith justified.

Miracles do not have to be spectacular; God works in a mysterious way His wonders to perform. Co-operation with natural laws, sound reason, good will and last, but not least, faith in our fellow humans and ourselves – this is itself a miracle, with a regular and increasing bounty.

Mrs A. C. S., Kidderminster.
. . . you remind me of Sundew, a small plant growing on the top of moss in the marshes. Sixty or seventy years ago, Grandpa found masses of it in our home village, but it is now almost extinct. It was given to me for coughs. Mother put two or three of the tiny plants in a little brandy for a few days until all the colour was gone. I always had a bad throat and cough. They gave me two drops when the cough was bad and I never knew it to fail.

Mrs Amy Bostock, Lanarkshire, says.
"I read of the uses of the remedy Coffea, for sleeping, in *Grace*, and have had wonderful benefit. I called at the Homoeopathic Chemist in Glasgow, bought some Coffea 3x. and it has done me a world of good. Among other things. I can sleep better and my health has definitely improved. Many thanks."

Mrs E. M. S., Nottingham.
I hear Parsley Tea is good for general health after forty. How is it made?
ED: *Parsley Tea is a fine help for kidney and menstrual troubles, and is a boon in cystitis. It is very true that it is one of the cheapest and most easily obtainable remedies for 'change of life'. It is also good for hot flushes and, in men, prostatic disturbances.*
Place a handful of freshly gathered parsley from the garden into one pint cold water. Bring to boil. Simmer for one minute. Pour through a strainer as required. Drink half teacupful after meals, three times daily. This harmless help can be taken in larger quantities (teacupful or more) if well tolerated. Commence with half teacupful, or even less, for first day or two, and increase as desired. A wonderful cleanser for the genito-urinary tract.

173

Mrs Ada C. Smith, Ipswich.
My husband snores. What are you going to do about it?
ED: *Yes Mrs Smith, I know your husband has tried everything, including the homoeopathic remedy, Nux Vomica. Snoring is brought to a fine art in some people. But for real nerve-shatterers, give me polypus. There was once an airman with a nasal polypus whose snoring had the velocity of a pneumatic drill. Maybe your husband's is a similar case. If so, you might like to know of the little red drops that restored peace to the troubled dormitory. Blood root (Sanguinaria Canadensis). For insertion – one drop daily.*

Max Samuels, California, USA
Rediscovery of the remedial use of this tree bark for arthritis and rheumatism has brought relief to some people. It was widely used by the old family doctor of 100 years ago but has now been eclipsed by modern drugs.
    I am trying Lignum Vitae compound which I think has taken the cutting-edge off that terrific pain that makes people jump out of twelve-storey windows."

Mrs E. Fairman, New Maldon.
'Years ago my mother made me 'celery tea' for my rheumatism which was a great help in relieving the pains and stiffness in my limbs."

Mrs M. Basson, Essex.
"I want to try herbal treatment because many years ago my mother, who lived to the age of ninety-six, used always to use nettles, watercress and dandelion leaves and (I believe) goosegrass to keep her in good health. As children we gathered nettles for sore throats and I kept her supplied. She was simply wonderful to the last."

Miss I. M. E., Talbot Woods, Bournemouth.
I remember the Croydon typhoid epidemic when I was a girl. Everyone in the street went down with it except one woman, my grandmother. The Medical Officer of Health's Department came round to make enquiries as to how she had missed the plague. On investigation it was found she had hung an onion, cut in half, in the hall. The onion was taken away to the public laboratory and microscopically examined. It was found to be teeming with the typhoid germ.
    ED: *Rue* (Ruta Graveolens) *has the some property but in a lesser degree. Some plants exercise a powerful attraction to bacteria which they localize and deal with in their own way.*

Mrs Payne, Worthing, Sussex.
For some time now my hair has come out badly, and left bald patches now quite noticeable. I have had medical attention (lotion and scalp

massages). I have also tried advertised remedies, but in both cases, no results. Could you recommend something to stop hair falling and to encourage new growth?

ED: *Alopecia areata, the spotty or patchy type.*
To be of any value, treatment has to be for 'the whole person'. Vitamin therapy is necessary, with emphasis on vitamin B. Corticosteroids, should be avoided, as well as other hormonal products.

Have you tried the Biochemic salt, Silica 6x (four after meals three times daily) made by New Era Co. Ltd. Externally, Heath & Heather's Extract of Rosemary is helpful. Weleda Shampoos are also recommended because of their ingredients which include lavender, rosemary and chamomile. These simple names may raise a smile on some faces, but the proof of the pudding is in the eating. Prolonged daily massage with warm olive oil. Uncooked raw fruit and vegetables are a necessity.

Mrs Earl Feick, St. Jacobs, Ontario, Canada.
Last summer, before our trip, we had to have smallpox vaccinations. It was the first I ever had, and about ten days later I did some strenuous work with the result that the area became badly swollen and inflamed. After putting up with it for a few days, I decided to apply a comfrey poultice. Although I expected relief, I was really amazed the following morning, to see that the swelling was reduced by half. That evening I applied a second poultice which drew out almost all of the inflammation. Truly a wonder herb; I'm sure no drug could have acted faster.

Miss M. Marchant, London Road, Leicester.
What I like about your magazine is that it seems to have in it "something for everybody". I like old copper pans and ornaments. At last I have found a way to clean tarnished copper quickly: by mixing lemon and salt, using a little elbow-grease. I know this is not news of any startling cure, but I just had to tell somebody of something I've been searching for for some time.

ED: *Some discovery, Miss Marchant! We wish you joy among your copper pots.*

Marjorie Friend, Attleborough, Norfolk.
Just about everybody appreciates the colour and beauty of a well-kept garden. I am not a gardener myself, and my garden far from orderly. I had a lovely surprise.
I received a free packet of seeds attached to the cover of a magazine and wondered where to put them. Scattering them on the bare border at the bottom of the garden I forgot about them until one day in July when I was confronted by a vast colony of colourful plants.

TRUE STORY

How we got away with it

A. J. LILWALL

FOR TEN YEARS I was a tramp and a drifter, roving my way round the country from the Scottish Border to Cornwall, living in kip-houses and casual wards, or sleeping rough under haystacks and hedges. I begged and scrounged for food and such old rags as I wore. Eventually I got so run down with hardship and semi-starvation that I began to lose my reason and it wasn't long before I was picked up and certified as insane.

I was sent as a hopeless lunatic to one of the biggest and finest mental hospitals in the country. Gradually the good food, rest and kind careful nursing reclaimed me from the land of the lost and, when I became strong enough, I began to work out of doors in the gardens. Eventually my industry and good behaviour earned me parole and I was allowed reasonable freedom to come and go in the village.

In course of time I was given a more responsible job in the hospital and this brought me into contact with some of the female staff. It wasn't long before I found a girl who was kind and understanding and who treated me as normal. That did a lot to restore my morale. We saw as much as we could of one another, grew to like one another more and more and at length really fell in love.

Imagine it: a pauper lunatic and a girl earning her living in the hospital, daring to fall in love! We had to go courting by stealth, hiding our feelings when anybody else was present because, had we been suspected, my girl would have lost her job and I should have forfeited all my privileges.

_But we got away with it. Nobody guessed and she and I saved all we could for the great day We had to go courting in secret and saving what we could for five years. Then I took the plunge. I went for a walk one day and did not come back. I had to hide myself for fourteen days, the legal period of liberty after which a man cannot be taken back to a mental hospital without re-certification. Directly the time was up, I went boldly back to the hospital and all turned out well. I set out to find a job.

I got work almost at once and six months later my girl and I got married. We had no home, just digs, but we were together and ready to face up to anything. For ten years we led a hand-to-mouth existence, moving from place to place as jobs came and went, paying through the nose to grasping landladies, but always together with never a real quarrel in all that time. My wife stuck to me through thick and thin, loyal, loving and understanding.

Then we had a stroke of luck. I won a competition, having a small but useful win. It was just enough to pay the deposit on a little cottage which both of us had seen and liked. Now we are living in our small home. Both of us go out to work. We share everything and are content. We are as much in love now as on the day I asked my grand girl to marry me. But for her I might still be living in darkness. I wouldn't change my partner for the richest heiress in the world.

That is my love story. I am happy to tell it because my wife is a shining example of what a good, honest and great-hearted girl can do towards reclaiming a man, even one who has nearly given up hope and, without help, might easily slip back into the abyss.

Our sincere thanks to the author we have been unable to trace.

Young visitor takes a walk in the sun through the charming village of Stokenham, near Kingsbridge, South Devon. Roy Westlake

Mrs Lucy Leathley, Bridport, Dorset.
Joseph was given "a coat of many colours" by a devoted father. Through a friend, I have acquired a coat with many pockets, and believe me, I appreciate it as much as Joseph must have done his.

It happened like this. An artist friend of mine was sketching in the Isles of Scilly, and for this purpose she designed for herself a gaberdine, sleeveless coat to carry all the usual artist's equipment, plus sandwiches, camera and macintosh. Altogether it had nine pockets, which included two deep front ones, one stretching right across the back, one hermetically sealed for cash, a small inner one for credit cards and sundry others.

Her sister found it useful for rambling in the Lake District. She found she could dispense with the usual "back-pack". With the weight distributed round the body, had her hands free for scrambling.

My difficulty is, that I have to use a stick for walking. Taking the milk in each morning was a bit of a hazard, and I slightly dreaded the walk along to the kitchen, with stick in one hand, bottle of milk in the other, to say nothing of the newspaper, portable phone and specs, tucked under one arm. Finally, there was a crash one day as I dropped the milk, making the kind of mess that only milk can.

177

Now I have one of these "Pollycoats", the problem has disappeared. They are so named because my friend's surname is "Polly" . Can you imagine the free and blissful walk by contrast, as I put the bottle of milk in one of the deep, front pockets, the portable phone in the other one, the newspaper in the rear one, hanky in a small front one, specs in another?

I have a philosophy that there are "no problems, only solutions." Try it out with whatever seems to be the problem!

Grateful Reader:
I am so thankful that you recommended Parsley Piert tea for my wife's dropsy. She has passed a lot of water since.

ED: *Place 1 teasp Parsley Piert herb in teacup and pour on boiling water. Infuse five minutes. Dose: 1 teacup 2/3 times daily.*

Mrs Pearl Taylor, Alba, Missouri, U.S.A.
I'm so happy I've found *Grace*. Wish it was monthly. Can you tell me what I can do for Hay Fever?

ED: *We will try to give you alternatives to mixed grass pollens extracts. In spite of recent advances in the study of grass pollens and seasonal asthma and hay fever, there is still no absolute certainty that any treatment will work in every case. Some sufferers have re-acted violently to prick tests and hyposensitization in the diagnosis of this complaint that we feel we must single out your enquiry.*

Mrs Taylor, have you ever tried honeycomb? Now, it's not sufficient for you to say you already eat plenty of honey. There's a subtle difference. There are cases of honey-eaters who have had hay-fever, but who have lost the distressing itching and streaming of the eyes when they changed over to honey in the comb! When troubled, chew a piece of the comb. Try chewing a small chunk about three times daily in the early spring season.

Mr and Mrs E. Benjamin, London, W.9.
I think you may be interested to know that when reading an old Italian book on the thermal baths of Ischia, I found an advice to "take a course of Lignum Vitae in order to get the full benefit of these wonderful waters". Actually, we have just been for our holiday at Sant Angelo d'Ischia and took a course of baths at the old Roman baths which are almost on the beach. We found them excellent and very enjoyable. We were glad we had (unknowingly) taken the course of Lignum Vitae Bark beforehand, as recommended!

The medicinal waters of Ischia have been famous in Europe since the 16th century, and the book was published by a Neapolitan doctor in 1588.

He writes:
I have observed that all those who take the baths after having first taken sarsaparilla, Lignum Vitae, or China-root . . . have all experienced wonderful effects . . . "
It is an interesting reference to Lignum Vitae for arthritis and other complaints. There are, of course, a number of thermal baths in Ischia, Italy, which are fitted with every modern facility and luxury. We certainly found them attractive and beneficial. By taking a boat from Sant Angelo we reached the beautiful Maronti beach, and the Cava Scura baths are a short distance up a narrow ravine. Special caves have been sculpted out of the cliff, and each cave has a hollow dug out in the rock. This hollow makes a sunken bath into which the hot and cold mineral spring waters are channelled.

J. Smith, Cleveleys, Blackpool.
A shoe shop manager gave me a simple remedy for soft corns. Put a little lemon juice on a corn every day, with a small piece of cotton wool over it to relieve pressure. In two to four weeks the corn comes out after soaking in hot water.

According to a feminine Writer:
Men are like chairs. They vary in shape and size, but all can be sat on. Some men are like mahogany chairs: they lose their polish after a little while. Some are like Chippendale chairs: they need delicate handling. Some are like plush upholstered chairs: one cannot stand them on a hot day. Others are like seats in Parliament: they have to be won. Some married men are like desk chairs: they are always being dragged about and turned this way and that. Some are like rocking chairs: they put you to sleep. And finally, some men are like benches: they are an invitation for more than one woman to sit on – a wife and a mother-in-law.

Irene Railton, Southampton, Hants.
Even though I'm busy packing to emigrate to Australia I felt I must write. I used to suffer from very severe headaches, and sometimes still get them.
I mix equal parts of apple-cider-vinegar with water, in a basin. This I stand in a pan of water and boil until the fumes rise. By inhaling the fumes, it is possible for relief to be felt if persevered with. The headache may not go completely. But it will definitely be eased. I know this works for me. Hope it does for others in need of help. Sincerely

Elizabeth Hildreth, Aughton, Ormskirk.
Yes, I am enjoying the 101st year of my life, with memories of very early age. As I turn back the pages of the record book of memory, I realise it

has taken years to make you realise the beauty and joys of early life and youth. Life today is so complex that the past looms out with greater pleasure and significance.

How spontaneously I have grasped every chance of doing good for whatever cause. Conscience was our guide, mercenary gain not the object. Now in this age of materialism that spirit has deteriorated.

This has been a great generation, and I have seen some wonderful things develop since Edison's talking machine which in my early days was a real wonder.

We have advanced tremendously since then but not always with good results. My only grudge with old age is the loss of our senses, sight, hearing and locomotion. I have had an extremely happy life and hope to continue right to the end looking forward to the next sphere when the time comes. I am very happy in this nice home and treated very kindly by all. Greetings to all the Grace Family.

Mr V. Cartwright, Aylesbury, Bucks.
I used to suffer from cramp and cold feet, being in agony at night. My wife did not know what to give me. That was, until she persuaded me to take vitamin E capsules. We both started taking them about a year ago; now we would not want to be without them. My cramps are gone, and she has lost the pain down her arm. We both have our own teeth and believe this is due to Dolomite tablets (Magnesium and Calcium). We read about this in one of Barbara Cartland's articles in *Grace*.

Joan E, Coudret, Central Otago, South Island, New Zealand.
Hello there . . .! I feel I can call you friends. I am writing this letter to tell readers of my experience when I burnt the back of my hand, having caught it on the grill of the oven. No ointment could clear it.

I was about to see my doctor when I suddenly remembered reading an article in *Grace* about a man who had a miraculous healing from Castor oil. So, I said, "Well, Joan, you can but try." Now, thanks to *Grace* and Castor oil I have only a very tiny scar on my hand. I still use that miracle oil each day. My sincere thanks to all concerned.

Sign on the desk of an executive:
"Make one person happy each day – even if it's yourself."

Sharon Bebbing, Rochford, Essex.
When I first bought Agnus Castus tablets at the Alexandra Palace earlier this year, the gentleman who sold them to me said he brought this plant over. Please thank him for me. I have tried every pain-killer on the market, and every new drug and nothing has ever eased agonising period pains until now. I only wish I could have found them 10 years ago. I now recommend them to everyone. Thank you once again.

Lelord Kordel, New York, USA.
The majority of people are afflicted with the salt habit, consuming an average of 300 grains of salt each day. This is ten times the amount of salt essential to supply body needs. It is agreed by medical men that this excessive consumption of salt is not only futile but actually proves harmful.

G. M. Trevelyan, the historian and walking enthusiast:
"I have two doctors – my left leg and my right.'"

T. Brookes, member of Grace Family.
Fresh beets make a beautiful deep-red juice. A well-tasting combination is two-thirds of orange juice and one-third beet juice to carrot or celery juice, or a combination of the two. Select young beets, wash in cold water, brush skin lightly, cut into convenient size pieces and feed into your electric juicer. Add no vinegar.

ED: *beet juice is rich in iron, the mineral so many people are deficient of today. Assists regeneration of red blood cells. Hungarian research reveals its anti-cancerous properties due to its oxygen-catalizer effect. Other contents: selenium flavonoids and vitamins A, C, E. Half to one cup daily for anaemia and other blood-deficiency disorders.*

Dr John Rudkin.
Instead of messing around with putting nutrients back in the white loaf, the Government should have subsidized the wholemeal loaf ages ago and put a premium price on white bread.

Miss Grace Dainton, Yatton.
A very old friend of the family, living in Australia, and with whom we have had no contact for many years, read my letter under While the Kettle Boils and wrote to me: "If you are the Grace we think you might be, we would love to hear from you".

What a pleasure it was to link up with them! We are delighted that *Grace Magazine* has brought us together again. What a far-flung Family we are!

Dr R. A. Rigg.
Most people eat twice too much. Therefore, they live on one half and the doctor and the undertaker on the other.

L D., Herts.
May I pass on this helpful idea to all who find it difficult to settle down to sleep. Silently, count downwards to give a feeling of relaxation, breathing IN on the odd numbers and OUT on the even numbers.

Gently, start at 49 down to zero; then back to 39 to zero . . . 29 to zero . . . 19 to zero . . . 9 to zero. If still awake, start again at 49 etc.

Sleep well!

Rebecca Killworth (16), Sale, Cheshire.
Why did the rabbit have a shiny nose?
Because its powder puff was at the wrong end.

Anonymous, Y Bala, Gwynedd, North Wales.
While on holiday I bought a bottle of Echinacea tablets, a herbal remedy for skin disorders. I am so pleased with them. They cleared my daughter's acne.

Mrs G. Alexander, Bexhill, Sussex.
I am very pleased with Ginkgo for dizziness, loss of memory and for improvement in the cerebral blood flow and varicose veins. It works for me.

ED: *The Ginkgo tree is remarkable. It is the world's oldest living tree species and which is referred to as "the living fossil". The Maidenhair tree (Ginkgo biloba) has features distinctive from all other trees. It has come down to us from the Ancient World, flourishing before the Flood. Recent scientific investigation has established the presence of medicinal properties in its leaves that are now used for a number of health conditions, especially circulatory disorders.*

The leaves are long-stemmed with two lobes, like a closely-ribbed fan. All parts of the tree are strongly resistant to disease and pests which may account for its value in human medicine. It is exceedingly long-lived, one at Kew having reached 210 years and still flourishing.

Veronica Moretti (age 11), Cheriton, Alresford Hants.
Dear Editor.
I am sending you two poems which I made up myself. I hope you like them. I live on a stud and father breeds horses. Cheriton is a very pretty village, and we have ducks on our village green. My friend Alice who is in one of my poems lives there. Sincerely Veronica.

"Green is relaxing, gentle and calm:
Like a butterfly resting on your palm.

Black is a shadow upon a white wall:
But as dark and scary as nightfall.

Red is spikey. jagged and viscious:
But is also a cherry that tastes delicious.

Silver is the sparkle in Alice's eye:
But alas, is a sad wave to say Goodbye.

Orange is happy, joyful and gay:
Bright and sunny like children at play."

Mrs E. Jarvis, Child Okeford, Blandford, Dorset.
I agree with Ruth Salmon, Surrey, (*Grace*, Spring 1990), except for the
last two lines of the letter.
    Most certainly you must have a cat. A cat's protection league or vet
would gladly supply one which had lost its owner/companion. There is
no need for it to be put-down. Two friends of mine have most successfully taken on "cats in need of love".
    I, also, am a widow with family flown and luckily have the compan-
ionship of Cindy, now 14, and still going strong. She gives me love,
demands food, likes her comfort, and expects me to hug her. She is someone for me to talk to. It is so easy for the elderly lonely to shut up into
a cocoon . . . almost getting to the point of being unable to talk and lose
interest in living. We must find someone who needs someone: and if
there's an "Active over 50's" Keep Fit class nearby, there's a lot to be
said for joining it and having fun! Get a cat! Sincerely.

John C., Gosport.
Last year my wife brought home a coconut for me to bore holes into, and
to suspend with string, like a cup on the clothes line. All through the dark
days of the winter we had the laugh of a lifetime. We had hours of enter-
tainment by the antics of the bluetit acrobats. Within a month, they'd
scoffed the lot. With modern television being what it is . . . the show was
worth a guinea a minute. Never a dull day!
    ED: *We, too, enjoy the same programme from inside our kitchen win-
dow. It's the early bird that gets the coconut!*

Member of Grace Family, Brackley, Northants.
It is necessary for transplant patients to take special drugs to avoid rejec-
tion, but they are known to have unpleasant side-effects. Are there any
natural alternatives?
    ED: *In reality, there are no natural alternatives, as replacement or dis-
continuation of prescribed medicines could place the patient at risk. It has*

been discovered that drinking grapefruit juice has a beneficial and modest anti-rejection effect. The juice can increase concentrations of cyclosporin (anti-rejection drug) according to researchers at the University of Florida.

Jeanette Harper, Calderwood, West Coast of Scotland.
I noticed in the last issue of *Grace* that someone was asking for help for catarrh.

After suffering sinusitis and catarrh for many years, I discovered Cider Vinegar as sold in the Health Stores. Consistently for a year I have taken a tablespoon in either water or diet lemonade every morning. I am pleased to say I have had no pain in my sinuses for over a year. Cider Vinegar is a cleansing agent and it has proved successful in my case.

Cider Vinegar can sometimes be helpful for arthritis, but it needs to be taken persistently as it is the build-up in the body that brings the benefit.

Catarrh and sinus troubles are something many of us have to suffer, living in the West of Scotland. Yours sincerely.

Ian Robins.
Laugh and the world laughs with you . . . snore and you sleep alone.

Phyllis Rabbitts, Dorset.
I would like to tell you of my wonderful recovery by the aid of Lobelia. I was so unwell that my doctor sent me to the hospital for X-rays and found I had a very nasty patch on each lung. This upset me very much as I had not long lost my dear husband.

When reading letters from members of Grace Family under *While the Kettle Boils*, I learnt about Lobelia tablets and took them for five weeks. On my last visit to the hospital I was told that both lungs had really cleared. I did not have to attend any more. The specialist could not get over how it happened. I just told him I took Lobelia tablets after reading about them in *Grace Magazine*. Thanking you once more. Yours sincerely.

Mr H. C. Allsopp, Lincoln
It is 64 years since I was married. I can remember the day well. My young brother was as impecunious as all other schoolboys and had no money to buy a present. He presented my wife and I with a number of apple pips which, after the ceremony, he proceeded to plant in the garden of the house we were to occupy.

Only one of the pips "Struck". It grew up into a fine Cox's pippin tree that produced buckets and buckets of lovely sweet apples in autumn and clouds of pink blossom in spring. I cannot tell you all the pleasure it has given me over the years – and all from a small boy's kindness.

Cockington Court, South Devon.   *Roy Westlake.*

IT is the same beautiful old country
always new . . . and the love of it rises
in our hearts as constantly as the coming of the leaves.

Richard Jefferies.

Mrs Shirley Ellis, Emsworth, Hants.
I have been using Comfrey Ointment for a long time.   A few months ago
I bruised my leg and applied the ointment.   After a couple of days, not
only had the bruise gone but my varicose veins were a lot better.   I then
applied the ointment to all my varicose veins on my leg – some were very
black.   To my amazement they started to clear.   So now I apply Comfrey
every day after my shower.   My leg now looks and feels much better.

Yvonne Smithson, Leicester.
Slice bananas into a sundae dish.   Add raspberries, strawberries or some
blackcurrants and spoon over a little clear honey. Top with cream and add
a teaspoonful of chopped nuts.   Real yummy!

185

From the Editor.
A member of *Grace* Family stopped me in the Street to tell me of an impressive result from the use of cider vinegar and honey. She had a melanoma on the side of her face for two years which nothing would eliminate. Her lady doctor was most sympathetic and told her nothing would do anything: when it was 'ready' she would burn it off in the surgery.

A life-long convert to natural methods of healing, the member wiped it two or three times daily with Cider Vinegar. After a fortnight she anointed it with fresh honey. Half an hour later the scab came away in her hand. All that is left is a discoloured area of skin and no discomfort.

She was so pleased she simply had to stop me in the street to tell me. I am glad she did. It enables me to pass on the information to other members of *Grace* Family. Some may have the condition, and who may wish to discuss the matter with their GP or specialist.

Mr L. Bailey, Dover.
I read my first copy of *Grace* Magazine in 1963, and still enjoy it. I have learnt a lot in that time.

When I was forty-two I had angina and cured myself (within a year) with nettles. At eighty-one, I have been clear of it for forty odd years – thanks to nettles.

On a sunny day, gather nettles anytime from March to September; cut off the top five inches. Dry, rub through a colander, and store in glass jars. Place one heaped teaspoon in one pint boiling water and cover to prevent escape of the precious steam. Drink a glassful for three days. On the third day make up a fresh supply. Continue to take daily until the condition has improved.

D. Parsons.
Grow you own herbs. You don't need a garden. Chives or parsley, two of the most useful herbs of all, can be grown in a large flower-pot or windowbox.

Robert Addison (14), Cumbria.
Why did the golfer wear two pairs of trousers?
In case he got a hole in one.

M. Ellis, Altrincham, Cheshire.
Incontinence is my trouble. I noticed a slight leakage after my second child and it has persisted for over two years and nothing seems to arrest it.

ED: *More than half of all women under fifty suffer from incontinence at some time. It may come on after lifting, running, coughing, laughing or sneezing. It can get worse over the years if nothing is done to improve it.*

186

Herbal urinary astringents help tighten-up a sphincter muscle which has lost tone. One of the most effective is American Cranesbill, available in form of tablets, liquid extracts, tinctures or powders.

Try to stop urinating midstream – stopping and starting – which should contract muscles of the pelvic floor. Pull up your pelvic muscles as if to arrest the flow of urine. Regard it as an exercise five or more times daily. Those muscles must need to be strengthened and the condition could improve within two months.

Ken Gaskell, Amersham, Bucks.
Some years ago, following a long period of stomach trouble for which I had been consuming numerous proprietary alkaline medicines, I consulted the late Dr C. H. Sharma the noted Homoeopathic practitioner.

He prescribed that I should each morning, on rising from my bed, swallow one black peppercorn and wash it down with a tumblerful of water to which had been added two teaspoons of cider vinegar.

He explained that the use of alkaline medicines had neutralised the hydrochloric acid which was secreted by the stomach to enable food I ate to be digested. As a consequence, my food was not digested but was retained in the stomach until it fermented, creating gas, flatulence and inflammation.

The black peppercorn, he explained, would cause a slight irritation sufficient to precipitate the release of mucus which would bathe the lining of the stomach so as to heal the inflammation. The cider apple vinegar, being very close to the properties of hydrochloric acid, would restore the stomach's ability to digest food, as it was intended to do.

I followed his prescription and in a few days I was well again. This is a remedy I have on many occasions recommended to stomach sufferers who have, like me, been restored to well-being in a comparatively short time.

Perhaps readers might wish to know of this wonderful remedy.

Prayer for today.
O God, who has prepared for those who love Thee such good things as pass man's understanding: pour into our hearts such love towards Thee, that we, loving Thee above all things, may obtain Thy promises, which exceed all things that we can desire; through Jesus Christ our Lord.

(Collect for sixth Sunday after Trinity)

Member of Grace Family.
More and more people are looking for alternatives to caffeine drinks (coffee, tea, Cola) and this is where a South American herb can offer a refreshing as well as an anti-arthritis drink – Maté tea. Maté is similar to China tea in aroma and flavour. Very refreshing when tired, especially during hot weather.

Mrs Winifred Spray, Oxford OXI 5QZ.
This is my Dunkirk memory – a sequel to Syd Metcalfe's article: "Why I believe in Fairies" (*Grace*, Summer, 1990).

I happened to be the first nurse the assistant matron met as she entered the ward on which I was working. "Come with me, nurse, quickly!" a sense of urgency in her voice told me I must leave unfinished the task in hand. Several other nurses waited in the corridor, similarly taken from other wards. We were led to a hitherto unused hutted ward in the grounds of a provincial hospital. 'Work as fast as you can. Prepare all the beds as if for operation beds, (this was a special method used to enable minimum disturbance of bedding for covering and uncovering a patient without the usual delay of normal bed making) there is a contingent of wounded soldiers on the way, we don't know what their injuries are," she informed us as she rolled up her sleeves and busied herself with the rest of us . . . an aspect of assistant matrons rarely seen!

How privileged I was to be in at the deep end when those men rescued from the beaches of Dunkirk, arrived. Though exhausted, dirty and injured, they were the most cheerful patients I ever nursed. Many slept for a full twenty four hours and more. But the silence was shattered as seen as they began to recover. It became great fun,despite some of the terrible injuries, to help in their recovery. They never talked of their ordeal. Backchat, laughter and teasing of the nurses were the overriding attitudes of those men. Rigid hopsital discipline of that era 'went out of the window'. They softened the heart of a most 'straightlaced' sister. They never got 'out of hand' with our spoiling. We owed them so much.

Jessie Heaps, Halifax, W Yorks.
Perhaps this simple remedy may help someone else. I had a nasty cracked lip which wouldn't heal (even after using my favourite castor oil!). Two days after applying Calendula Cream it was back to normal.

Since then, I've turned to Mother Nature for other things. After major surgery I was troubled with cystitis for months. Lots of antibiotics were prescribed before it cleared. Then a few months ago I suffered bowel trouble, having great discomfort and pain . . . Thanks to *Grace* I learned many readers had found help for this condition from Calamus root. I finished my first bottle of the tablets and find them of great help.

Also, when I suspect a hint of cystitis I drink Parsley tea right away, so as to avoid more antibiotics. What a great help it is to share natural remedies with other readers through *Grace* – a magazine with varied interests, outstanding in wisdom, love and caring – surely in a class of its own. Long may it continue, always with God's blessing. Yours sincerely.

Mrs F. L., Boreham Wood
To keep rose bushes free from greenfly, put garlic around the roots.

Mrs Oliver, Bournemouth
I had a diabetic callous on my foot for which you advised Tinctures Myrrh and Goldenseal. I thought readers of the Family, similarly troubled, may wish to have knowledge of this effective cure. It worked very well, indeed.

Anonymous
Having read in *Grace* Magazine so much about the goodness of vitamin B6 for crippling rheumatism, carpal tunnel syndrome, and pre-menstrual tension, I wonder if readers unfortunate enough to have to undergo radiotherapy treatments, are aware that this versatile vitamin can prevent radiation sickness (2mg thrice daily was mentioned in the British Medical Journal).

According to Dr Kaorn Hara, Japanese physician, vitamin B1 improves hearing defects caused by excessive noise. May be tried for tinnitus.

A wife at TV set to her husband:
"Shall we watch the six o'clock news and get indigestion, or wait for the 10 o'clock and have insomnia?"

Mrs C. McDonald, Clacton-on-Sea, Essex
With regard to a request for advice on macular degeneration by Ms B. Bailey on page 64 of the Summer 1987 issue, I have found that the only help is keeping strong light from the eyes – sun, TV, etc. Particularly helpful, when I remember to do it, is attention to circulation of the neck by gentle head rotation, neck stretching, etc. Also, notice if any dietary habits are related. I am a coeliac and believe that eating wheat (and wheaten products) ruined my eyes. I think perhaps 'difficult to digest' food attracts circulation from the upper parts of the body, including the eyes, to the stomach. It makes them worse. This approach I find more beneficial than bathing, though cold-tea applications do help. Yours sincerely.

Anonymous
A perfect wife is one who doesn't expect a perfect husband.

Mr J. Thomas, Edinburgh, Scotland
My wife has taken drugs for chronic anxiety which came on after an unfortunate incident within the family. She becomes more agoraphobic over the years and we seldom go out together.

ED: *Anxiety may be caused by a number of conditions. It is usual to discover the cause and deal with the underlying trouble which may be due to endocrine disturbance: hyperthyroidism, pre-menstrual tension, etc. Fatigue, exhaustion, stress and depression may be related. It is good to remember that prolonged consumption of strong tea, coffee and other*

*caffeine drinks may lead to a deficiency of vitamin B1 which manifests as
general anxiety, even agoraphobia!
A cup of German Chamomile tea may prove helpful. Other teas which
relate are: Oatstraw, Lime blossom, Hyssop and Scullcap. For anxiety
before menstruation – Evening Primrose oil capsules. With heart symptoms: Hawthorn, Valerian tablets have been known to be beneficial.*

Jessie Hicks, Derbyshire
I make comfrey tea from the leaves, and drink it as I have been doing for
the past 20 years. Comfrey grows in profusion everywhere around here.
I collect it and dry sufficient to last me through the winter. Some years
ago it cured my frozen shoulder which the doctor said I would have to
learn to live with.

Did you know?
A woman of true charm is one who can make a youth feel mature, an old
man youthful, and a middle-aged man completely sure of himself. (Bob
Talbert)

Mrs M Hughes, Cornwall
When on holiday in Lymington, Hampshire, I visited a health shop in an
effort to find some relief from menopausal problems, especially 'hot
flushes'. The Manageress recommended Agnus Castus tablets. They
were an instant success. Within a week, I felt better than I had been for
two years.

Mrs E. M. Ellis, St Ives, Cambridgeshire.
Thank you very much for the help your leaflet "Some of My Favourite
Remedies" has been to my family. I am sure it has helped in a
number of ailments and prevented serious illnesses developing.
My sister was much helped by Calamus when the hospital could find
no reason for her jaundice and sickness, except some inflammation of the
intestines. My daughter has been helped with menstruation and urinary
troubles by Cranesbill. My husband finds Hawthorn very good. It is
also good for my blood pressure and angina . . . also Motherwort. At
present, I am finding much relief from stomach pain and severe indigestion with Wild Yam and Papaya.

Daphne Lawes, Dorset BH21 7HE
This is a letter of gratitude that should have been written before. It was
in the Winter issue of *Grace* 1986 that I saw a paragraph that has meant
so much to me. (p.39). It reads:
"I always advise anyone who is taking antibiotics from the doctor, to
take at the same time large amounts of vitamin B which will prevent side-
effects. (Dame Barbara Cartland).

I had such deep depression after taking antibiotics that I did not think I could face taking them again. But all is well now as I am having brewer's yeast as well. I wish that every doctor's surgery in the country would display that good news on their notice hoards. Thank you, Dame Barbara Cartland and Mr Bartram. Yours sincerely.

Mrs A. H. Somerset
One day when my five-year-old nephew was helping me in the garden, there were several bees buzzing around the raspberry canes. "Did you know, Auntie, that the bees are our friends?" he remarked. "In the summer, they take pollen from the flowers back to their hives and make it into honey." Then, after a short pause for thought, he added "And in the winter they stay at home and put it into little pots for us to buy from the shops!"

Cigarettes Anonymous
When you feel like smoking, you dial a number and hear a lot of coughing.

Helen Hayes, WA 98221, U.S.A.
I have never written to the Editor of any magazine before, but because I have been a subscriber since 1964 I want to tell you how very special your magazine is. It has a personal touch so unusual these days. It is timeless. Your excellent information on nutrition, health and herbs are outstanding. Your magazine accentuates the positive, a refreshing change from news magazines and TV. Your stories are well-chosen and interesting. I enjoy all sections of your excellent magazine, especially your personal remarks at the beginning and end of the issue. I wish you continued success.

Barbara Charles, Wareham, Dorset.
I have lived alone for nearly thirty years and I never fail to say *Grace* before a meal. I always use my own words, just thanking God for the food I have and asking him to help those who have none or very little. Now, I have a great choice in your little book: *Grace at Table*. Thank you so very much. Yours sincerely.

    ED: *Readers of this book are invited to send for their free copy (Editor's Grace gift) – "Grace at Table" – a selection of Graces spoken before a meal. Send stamped addressed envelope (name and address in capitals) to Grace Publishers Mulberry Court, Stour Road, Christchurch, Dorset BH23 1PS*

Oggi Illustrator
One of Italy's greatest lawyers, Francesco Carnelutti, was asked on television the secret of his success. "My wife", he replied.

Noticing the interviewer's surprise, he added: "She never studied law, does not meddle in my work, never asks for or gives me advice. But she fills my life with her presence. She anticipates my wishes, guesses my moods, listens to my outbursts, always finds the right word.

"In the evening, while I am consulting my papers, she sits by me knitting, without saying a word. The noise of the needles is the best tranquilliser I know. It breaks the tension and gives me an infinite sense of security. Without her I would be at a loss. With her I feel I can do anything."

Prayer for today
Lord, teach me the art of patience while I am well, and give me the use of it when I am sick. In that day either lighten my burden or strengthen my back.

"Our heavenly Father, who has so ordered our days that we have to dwell together in families, help us, that others may find us pleasant to live with.

Teach us to be patient with those we cannot understand, to be considerate with those who serve us, and to be loving to those who depend upon us. May we remember the burden of weakness and anxiety that other people are carrying, and never add to that burden by our thoughtlessness or lack of sympathy . . . Amen."

Mrs Anne Cumming, Highgate, London N6
I feel I must write and thank you. After losing my husband four years ago I visited a Harley Street doctor, also my GP, who both gave me tranquillisers and sleeping tablets. I began to feel dependent. After taking Valerian tablets for the past three weeks, 4 a day, I feel a different woman. I am now able to drive my car, something I have not been able to do for four years. I have also recovered my appetite for food and living my life once again. I am a very thankful lady. Sincerely.

SERENITY

DROP thy still dews of quietness
  Till all our strivings cease;
Take from our souls the strain and stress,
  And let our ordered lives confess
The beauty of thy peace.

John Greenleaf Whittier

ARNICA. One of the most important remedies of homoeopathy is Arnica Montana. Homoeopathy is a medical doctrine teaching that drugs capable of producing disease symptoms in a healthy person can, in infinitesimal doses, cure the same group of symptoms met in a particular disease. "Similia Similibus Curentur" (Let likes be treated with likes)

The Irish Digest
"No intelligent person believes in anything that can't be explained by his reason", said the scientist.

"Well," asked an old farmer, "why is it that, though they all feed from the same field, hair comes up on the cow, wool on the sheep and feathers on the chicken?"

Mrs M. W. Williams, Mid Glamorgan
My sister is finding that the Essence of Feverfew is having a good effect on her tinnitus. She finds the noises more bearable.

Bill Kennedy
When novelist Robert Carson had an ulcer his doctor told him, "The only thing I'm going to prescribe for you is exercise – a little skipping. Like skip smoking, skip drinking, skip rich foods."

Miss O. Campbell, Midlothian
I have found Dolomite tablets so helpful for my spinal injury.

A male OAP who always has to wait
A Dutch barber in Zaandam put traffic lights outside his shop. They showed red when the place was very busy, yellow when customers had a good chance to get a haircut, and green when they could get one straight-away.

Exerpted.
A friend entering church one rainy morning noticed that the verger was ringing the bells more vigorously than usual and asked the reason. Replied the verger, "If they're not coming to church, they're not sleeping either."

Miss Evelyn Haig, Bangor, C. Down.
A short time ago I started to have poor sight in one of my eyes, so went to the optician who told me it was a cataract. I had just read of a man curing his horse's eye of that condition with a few drops of honey. So I put a few drops in my eye, out of a jar of honey, and that cleared it. I have had no trouble since I thought this might be useful for other members of *Grace* Family. The Lord bless you in His service. Yours sincerely.

Prayer for today.
O God, help us to understand the power of prayer. We know that no cry sent up to You is ever in vain. Whether the answer is seen at once or held over until our life is ended, grant that we may take advantage of this

The Sheep Drover, By Octavious Clark (1850-1921). The Bridgeman Art Library.

great force according to Your will. Give us a portion of your Son's own belief in the miraculous power and overwhelming strength of prayer. So help our faith in Your way, giving us patience and a happy outcome of present experience.

Miss D. A. Roth, Benoni, South Africa.
A friend of mine is going through a rather traumatic time. She developed muscular dystrophy after devoting her life to working with handicapped children. These are the verses she sent. I wonder if other members of *Grace* Family know them.

"God has not promised skies always blue . . . Flower-strewn pathways, all our lives through . . . God has not promised sun without rain . . . Joy without sorrow, peace without pain.

But God has promised strength for the day . . . Rest for the labour, light for the way . . . *Grace* for the trials, help from above . . . Unfailing sympathy, undying love."

Daphne A. J. Lincoln, Southampton.
The magazine which you edit so magnificently, has become, for me, a source of endless pleasure and refreshment. I can recognise in its pages many of my own thoughts and feelings about God and the Universe and my fellow creatures, both great and small.

Miss E. L. Millar, Camberwell, London, SE5
I would like to share with readers a benefit I have found. After surgery my hair came out by the brush-fulls, so I was advised to use a Nettle remedy and take the Biochemic remedy, Silicea. The last item was unobtainable but I found and used a Nettle shampoo. To my amazement, the loss stopped immediately. It has not occurred again. I continued with the Silicea tablets for some weeks. Recently my friends have remarked on the improvement in my hair. I continue to use the shampoo – obtainable from the Health Food Store.

Mrs I. Jacobs, Warminster.
For two years I was troubled with night sweats and hot sweats by day for which the usual run-of-the-mill tablets didn't do a thing. Then, someone said she found an answer to her problem in Evening Primrose capsules and bee pollen. I took both. The result was totally unexpected relief, night and day. What a blessing!

Simon and Helen de Yong, St. Paul's Bay, Malta.
Greetings from Malta. We wish you and all readers of *Grace Magazine* a joyful and peaceful 1985. In your Winter 1984 issue, on page 64 of "While the Kettle Boils" we read a letter from a reader who, when she gets angry with the world, bakes bread.

Open-air market in the centre of Norwich, Norfolk.   *Roy Westlake.*

A Fine City

ONE of the fascinating features of Norfolk is the open-air market in the centre of Norwich.

Famous sons and daughters of this city of character include Lord Nelson, Elizabeth Fry, John Crome and J. J. Colman.

Julian of Norwich, the 14th century anchoress and seer, lived in a tiny cell in St Julian's Church, King Street. Her book, *The Revelations of Divine Love*, is regarded by scholars as one of the most beautiful expositions of God's love in the English language.

She writes, " When aggression builds up I know it's time to make bread. There's nothing like baking bread for getting exasperation out of the system. Take a lump of defenceless dough and go at it proper. An indifferent shop assistant? Thump, biff, thump. Etc. Etc.

Humbly, we suggest the very last thing you should do when baking bread is to be in an angry frame of mind. You should never allow people with bad thoughts anywhere near the preparation of food. Cleanliness of mind and spirit are as important as hygiene. We feel any kind of emotion and personal vibration is conveyed to the bread. We believe anyone eating it could be affected by your anger.

Try to bake your bread lovingly. This will help you see the world differently. Food preparation is very special. It is best left to those who are calm and at peace. In this way we think you will get the maximum nourishment from it.

Thank you for your wonderful production, *Grace*. It always gives us so much pleasure. We have been able to pass it on to friends here, whom we have taught to make bread. Peace to you all. Sincerely.

ED: *Thank you, Simon and Helen. I am sure you are absolutely right. Your letter is an object lesson to us all. Greetings from Grace Family.*

Mrs M. Johnson, Combe.
I have been very pleased with results from slippery elm tablets for my hiatus hernia.

Shepherd of the hills.
Whatever happened to that fragrant herbal smoking mixture we had as an alternative to tobacco?

ED: *Coltsfoot is the chief ingredient of most smoking mixtures. It can be used alone, or in combination: 2 parts coltsfoot; 1 part eyebright; 1 part wood betony; ½ part rosemary, ½ part chamomile flowers; ½ part thyme. Good to hear from you. Hope the sheep enjoy the flavour.*

A Reader of Grace.
Help! My husband, in his late twenties, is 1.85m tall and weighs only 10st 3lb. No matter how much or what he eats, he has the unfortunate tendency to lose weight, and only rarely gains any. Would you have any ideas that might help him put on weight in a healthy way? Many thanks.

ED: *It sounds that your husband must be a very active man. In which case, his carbohydrate intake may be quickly converted into energy. This is something for which you may be thankful. Added protein intake is advised but it need not take the form of meat and dairy products. Rather let it be vegetable protein. Soya bean products are very high in protein and, curiously enough, if taken regularly, put on weight. This I have proved myself. Use daily in the kitchen.*

Vitamin B complex, including vitamin B12, would appear to be indicated for the metabolism of extra carbohydrate and protein. Foods favouring weight increase are: eggs, cheese, milk, porridge, potatoes, butter, baked brown rice, etc. Much depends upon the individual.

Coffee and all caffeine drinks should be avoided as they increase the metabolic rate, thereby spending those precious calories. Nicotine and alcohol should also be avoided as they too increase the metabolic rate and peel off those coveted pounds.

Care should be taken to see that consistent weight loss is not associated with any wasting condition, cachexia, etc. A check-up with your doctor or other qualified practitioner should dispel fears. Does his thyroid function normally? An over-active thyroid is a common cause of weight loss.

I would advise Agnus castus tablets; calcium supplements and kelp tablets. Fenugreek seeds usually put on weight, and where not included in the diet may be infused in a teapot by pouring boiling water on a teaspoonful of the seeds. The liquor may be drunk warm, or cold, once or twice daily.

Your husband is not very old, and doubtless may put on more weight as he gets older. Is he a late-to-bedder? If he lives at a pace which speeds up his normal biological clock the body has little time in which to lay down substantial reserves.

Mrs L. Smith, Bolton.
I thought your readers would like to know how I cured a whitlow on my finger. I read in one of my old herb books that an old Chinese doctor once wrote: "I always cure felons (whitlows) with lemon." I snipped off the end of a lemon with a knife and stuck my finger into the lemon and bandaged it so it would stay on all night. In the morning some pus came away. I did this for five nights and was then able to rub away the hard flesh.

Odd verse.
Mary had a little lamb, its fleece broke out in spots. She brewed a pint of Clivers tea, and now it's goldilocks. (Gercher!)

Miss B. Rew, Exmouth.
Having a swelling in one nostril that hindered breathing, I went to a doctor. He told me it was a polypus, and removed it by cutting.

In six weeks' time it was growing again. Feeling that cutting it out was useless, I used a preparation of garlic. This was taken internally, and put up the nostril on cotton wool. After a few weeks of doing this the polypus disappeared and has not returned.

Mrs A. Hewlett, Middleton-on-Sea.
I still receive help by taking Essence of Feverfew for rheumatism. I very seldom have back pain now, and less pain in my right shoulder, arm and left hand. It is indeed wonderful relief.

Extract from a book by Sir Henry Jones, one-time professor at Glasgow University.
I cannot but marvel at the skill that secured its comfort for us all. A happier household, I believe, there never was. Though my father, I should say, never made a pound a week, we never lacked anything . . .

We were all partners in one family enterprise, and all ran smoothly in their course . . . But we helped. I think I may say we inspired each other. We were very happy.

J. T. Brining, Leeds.
I had a patient with chronic inflammation of the great toe of 12 months' duration. There was passive pain, decreased upon depression of toe. I tried various remedies without satisfactory results.

Lastly, I used hot fomentations of pressed potato juice applied every hour for several hours, at night, the man being in business during the day, and a thick saturated compress at bedtime. This was continued for ten days, when the pain had entirely gone and there was no return after six months.

An American magazine.
L. B. Mayer, head of M.G.M. studios, believed that what you sow, so you reap. He writes:
" Once I came home after school with a black eye, and, while my mother bathed it, I told her it was the other boy's fault.

"But she said it took two to make a fight; led me to the back porch, and told me to call out some insulting phrase as loud as I could. So I yelled at the top of my voice, and the hills sent back the echo.

"Then she told me to call out: 'God bless you,' and this time the echo returned: 'God bless you.' I've never forgotten that lesson."

C. H. P., Glasgow, Scotland.
All the usual medicines having failed, a psychologist knowing that Angus was unduly "careful" about his finances, resorted to a strategem. He prescribed a new inexpensive medicine which drew from the patient an enquiry as to its contents. "Chiefly ambergris," said the doctor.
"But isn't that the expensive stuff they use in perfumes?"
"Yes," said the doctor. "Each dose costs £21." The hiccoughs stopped immediately.

From a reader.
Twinkle, twinkle, little star! . . . How I wonder if you are . . . the shining heart of garden sage . . . comforter of my old age.

Cyril Scott
Parsley seems to bring some kind of relief where rheumatism is concerned. So crippled with rheumatism was an elderly man that he could only hob-

ble about with the aid of sticks. Starting to take parsley tea (1 oz to 1 pint boiling water, and simmered for 2 minutes) on the advice of a friend, he was able to discard his sticks within one week.

Without making too extravagant claims for this homely pot-herb, it is obvious that it must contain some very valuable properties beneficial to humans.

Anonymous.
I thought you would like to read the following brief note discovered by a bereaved wife after the event. Her husband was very much the strong silent type; but for this brief note might never have known he loved her.

To Margaret. "You brought me the sun . . . when you entered my life . . . and did me the honour . . . of being my wife . . . You doubled my pleasures . . . halved every sorrow . . . and gave me such faith . . . in a brighter tomorrow."

June White, Leighton Buzzard, Beds.
A little love, a little trust . . . a soft impulse, a sudden dream . . . and life as dry as desert dust . . . is fresher than a mountain stream.

Mrs Marjorie Gray, East Dean, E. Sussex.
The little booklet you so kindly sent is a fascinating collection of *Graces* for all occasions. It reminded me of an incident during those days of the Dr Billy Graham Crusade at Harringay. Thank you very much.

Living with us at the time was a delightful Russian schoolgirl whom I had taken to London for the day, to go on to Harringay. We went to the *Salad Bowl* at the Corner House (Lyons) at Marble Arch, and sat at a table with three chairs. A uniformed American Army officer asked if he might join us.

My friend and I chose our salads and returned to the table, and, as I always did, I gave thanks audibly for our lunch. On looking up I saw the officer had tears and was obviously deeply moved, saying:

"O, Ma'am, thank you for reminding me of my dear mother who always gave thanks before eating a meal. (To Him be the Glory). Yours sincerely.

ED: *Readers of Grace Magazine are invited to send for their free copy of "Grace at Table" (Editor's Grace gift). Send stamped addressed envelope (name and address in capitals) to Grace Publishers.*

Dolly Sewell, Stapleford, Nottingham.
It is nice to be important . . . but it is more important to be nice.

Mrs Ida Lunt, Lancashire
I thank you for putting my plea for help in the Spring issue of the Magazine. You have created a wonderful family loyalty in *Grace* Family.

I received ten wonderful letters with help from people who had experienced a Colles fracture – from England, Ireland, Scotland and Wales.

(continued on page 201)

Success is a Way of Life

WHAT KIND of a person are you to live with? When you close the door behind you in the mornings, do you leave behind an agreeable atmosphere? When you return from the shop or office, do you bring home laughter or a touch of honey?

Many natural laws govern our personal lives. One of the least remembered is, *like attracts like*. A frown provokes a frown. A crinkle at the corners begets latent good humour. Blessed are they who are pleasant to live with. If we give in good measure, well pressed down and flowing over, others will gradually do the same for us.

Are you faced with change? It may be a change of job, a change of house, a change of responsibility. Let us remember the old and familiar were once new. Look forward in confidence, not apprehension, to an expression of your dormant powers and abilities.

Have you learnt to welcome new circumstances as they occur? Maybe there is an area of your consciousness as yet undiscovered. When a new door opens how we need to keep our attitudes positive!

We will expect to be well. Nothing helps as much as saturating the mind with positive thoughts. Your life may be quite different a few weeks from now!

Look your best. Feel your best. Cheerful people resist disease better than gloomy ones, a medical survey reports. In other words, it's the surly bird that gets the germ.

Gracie Fields, when undergoing an operation in hospital
"You lie in bed saying nowt about nowt while a collection of red-hot needles are sticking into you. Folk send flowers, but sometimes you think the next lot will be lilies. Then the surgeons get busy again, and one day you wake up feeling better – things are more rosy and not so lilyish. You begin to sit up and take notice. Suddenly you begin to realise you're getting better and better. You come to think that it's almost worth being ill because of the pleasure it gives you when you feel you don't need the lilies!"

Local wildlife await choice morsels from the sailing fraternity seeking anchorage for the night at Salhouse Broad, Norfolk.   *Roy Westlake.*

They all gave hope and reassurance that my wrist and hand would get better. At that time I was losing hope and near to despair.

Now, after 6½ months of physiotherapy, Comfrey and Lignum Vitae tablets, and massage with peanut oil twice a day, my wrist, hand and frozen shoulder are almost better. I can once more do all my housework, and look forward to doing my garden again.

May I thank you all for your help for over 25 years from *Grace* Magazine. As I get older I realise what a wonderful thing you have created in *Grace* family. I send you love and peace. Sincerely.

Anonymous
My father, at 21, was blind for six weeks in one eye . . . with cataract. He used to tell us how, after trying one professional man after another . . . a gipsy told him to use Elder flowers. He did so. Following her instructions, the thing cleared up completely. He was nearly 61 years when he died and never had it again all those years.

ED: *We never cease to marvel at the gentle healing influences of the Elder tree. Every part of it has value. A tea made from the dried*

201

flowers deal swiftly with a cold or influenza. Rich in vitamin C the ripe black berries are helpful for laryngitis and sore throats generally. A decoction of the bark may be used as a lotion or 'wash 'for chronic skin disorders. A tea made from the dried leaves (I teasp to cup boiling water; infused for 15 minutes: dose, one wineglassful thrice daily) can take some of the smart and sting out of cystitis.

Take John Constable's picture, "The Hay Wain" in the National Gallery. Have you seen the Elder tree growing at the entrance of Willy Lott's cottage? That was a common sight up to the 18th century. It was the only medicine chest known to the humble country folk of those days when doctors were scarce and whose services were beyond the reach of the destitute.

Author unknown
A gossipy tongue is a dangerous thing . . . If its owner is thoughtless at heart . . . She can give when she chooses full many a sting . . . That will painfully linger and smart . . . But each gossipy tongue would be baulked in its plan . . . For causing distress, hurt and tears . . . If it weren't helped out by the misguided one . . . Who possesses two gossipy ears.

Signs of the Times
A young daughter, after a visit to her dentist, placed her extracted tooth under her pillow on going to bed. "Do you still believe in fairies?" asked her mother.

"No," she replied. "But I still believe in Daddy."

Mrs G. E., Liverpool
Every week I visit one or two house-bound friends. Sometimes, owing to bad weather I cannot get round to them – yet they will expect to hear from me. One thing never fails – their enthusiasm for my tape-recordings!

I take tapes of special events in the family, such as my son's wedding service, the visit of a schoolfriend, the Christmas family union. I once took it to the zoo where I persuaded an elephant to blow into the cassette recorder as I described a walk through the park.

These are much enjoyed and friends say they look forward to hearing them. This might be a good idea for keeping in touch with relations overseas.

Miss B. T., Middleton, Manchester
Vitex Agnus Castus was recommended to me as a hormone regulator and has proved most effective.

Harry G. Barnes, Washington D.C, U.S.A.
Anonymous asks about cancer treatment by Dr Anthony Sattilare by use of the brown-rice diet. He wanted to know how to cook it. We put a

cup of rice and a cup of water in a pan and place it in a moderate oven until the rice has absorbed all the water. Each grain will stand apart. It will then be ready for eating. Sincerely.

Mr F. J. Warnes, E. Sussex
Early last year my wife died. I had nursed her for 10 years. I wept bitterly for weeks and felt cut in half and numb. Here I was, out of work (I had sacrificed my career to look after my wife) and a victim of the computer age because I was a Linotype operator and, during my absence, all this had become computerised.

But as time passed I came to terms with my situation. Instead of sitting around and weeping and looking back (my wife would not have wanted me to do this) I decided, at the age of 61 to start a new life and look forward.

I invited a lady friend out. She had lost her husband 18 months previously. As we got to know each other we found we had a lot in common. I proposed to her in October last year and we married in September and spent our honeymoon in Tenerife.

Having each other has opened up a new outlook on life for both of us. We are not jealous of each other's former mates and we freely talk about the lovely times we had with them, because we loved them dearly. But we can't bring them back.

Far better a thing to comfort each other and to begin to live again, because romance in your senior years is just as happy and exciting as it is in your twenties. In fact, it can enrich one's later years because one is older and wiser. Best of all, it can prolong one's life on this lovely earth and give it greater depth and meaning.

Seen in the window of a shop in Blackheath:
"Mature, dependable, caring nanny wanted for professional couple. Regular employment caring for twins aged three, spaniel, cat, tortoise, goldfish, gerbil and canary. Must have a sense of humour."

Mrs D. Mansfield, Redman's Road, London
Nine months ago I was suffering from very bad arthritis in the feet. I could wear only the softest of sandals. To walk only a few yards caused me to suffer great pain. A friend suggested I try Devil's Claw tablets. I have been grateful ever since. After the first month the pain began to ease and has lessened every day. I can now wear shoes and do my own shopping. I shall continue to take these tablets but reduce the dosage for as long as I feel necessary.

Sign, on a fruit stall near the beach at Eastbourne:
"Soft ripe peaches – no teeth required."

Anonymous
I read that women who smoke are more likely to be infertile, suffer an early menopause, and have hair growing on parts of the body such as face and abdomen . . . compared with women non-smokers. It is unlikely the condition can be reversed. However, what herbs would you think suitable?

ED: *Excessive growth of female hair (hirsutism) is a sign of abnormal androgen metabolism associated with the ovaries and adrenals; glands most at risk from stress.*

Two remedies with specific reference to the condition are: Vitex Agnus castus and Red Clover, which are available as teas, powders, tablets, tinctures, etc. The thought of going hairy might be a sufficient deterrent to giving up the habit of smoking.

Child's letter to God.
Dear God. "I think it is terrific the way they got the astronauts to go up and go around the world. Please don't let it fall on our house." Your friend, Norman.

Child's letter to God
Last week it rained three days. We thought it would be like it was in the days of Noah's ark. But it wasn't, I'm glad, because – do you remember – you could only take two of things? And we have three cats. Goodbye now . . . Donna.

Mrs B. Mildenhall, Isle of Wight
I would like to congratulate you on the high standard of your magazine which has never wavered in its style and sincerity. I have been an avid reader or should I say disciple for the last seventeen years or more (the first at 2s 0d a copy).

To those readers who suffer the torment of sinusitis with its terrible pain and blocked nasal passages, I would strongly recommend the herbs: Burdock, Buchu and Scullcap. I cured myself by drinking at least one pint of this medicine per day. The method I used was simply using a tablespoon of each herb to a pint of boiling water, allowing to cool and then drinking. I do hope this will help others. Yours sincerely.

Mrs K. R., Birmingham
Most people judge others by appearance, but I go by gardens. The front of a house is a façade; it shows what we'd like others to think we are, and round the back of the house we reveal our true selves.

If a back garden is kept in trim, I think the owners must be clean and tidy; likewise a profusion of plants and flowers stands for generosity and warmth. A wilderness indicates illness or loneliness; empty spaces, meanness; lots of ornaments, a dreamer. Trees tell of roots and love of home and family.

Josephine Mason, Bovey Tracey, Devon
Health problems following withdrawal from drugs combined with a removal to a new district causing depression, it was suggested by a friendly neighbour that she visited her doctor. This she did. Her letter continues: "The doctor looked at my records, and said, "How come you have not seen a doctor for 30 years?" Keeping a straight face she replied: "I eat an awful lot of apples." Then she added in her letter: "Somehow, I think he didn't like it."

From the front page of Horticulture Weekly:
"Today sees the biggest shake-up in the compost industry for 21 years. See special spread inside . . ."

Nicola Peterson, Moseley, Birmingham.
More people are discovering the herb Feverfew for overcoming distressing headaches (migraine and others), rheumatism and painful joints. Some ask how it should be taken.

The herb Feverfew may be taken as tablets, essence, freeze-dried capsules, or as fresh leaves. I would recommend the fresh leaves as the best form. The plant is easily available at herb nurseries – the botanical name is Tanacetum Parthenium. Buy four plants, so you will have some to use immediately and some to seed themselves for future supplies. The foliage starts to grow in March or April.

The best dose is the equivalent of two large leaves daily. Put these in a sandwich if you find the taste bitter. If you take the tablets you will need 100-125 mg daily. Do not drink alcohol while taking Feverfew as this reduces its effectiveness. Anti-rheumatic drugs may do the same.

Feverfew has proved to be very useful in rheumatic problems. It may take a good few months using Feverfew daily before you feel its benefits. So be patient.

ED: *Mrs Nicola Peterson is a Member of the National Institute of Medical Herbalists in practice.*

Miss B. Rew, N. Devon.
After having a polypus removed from my nose by a surgeon, it soon again returned. I was told of a local plant remedy "Passo" supplied by a Mr O. Earp. After taking it internally and applying it externally for about a month the growth disappeared. It has never returned. That was eighteen years ago. I discovered "Passo" is another name for Garlic – a great antiseptic.

Mrs E. Reeves, Warminster.
My sister at Hastings is delighted. Since taking Valerian tablets she has been able to give up Mogadon.

Ruth Walsh.
I wouldn't say he was cantankerous . . . And I don't his character question
. . . But I'm sure whatever's eating him . . . Is suffering from indigestion!

Miss Ann Bentley, New Maldon.
I am writing to you about a cure. Maybe some unfortunate animal may be helped from the intolerable itch and eczema.

"Kem was a big dog, stripped of fur from chin to tail, underparts and part of the thighs and lower back. After various treatments the Vet advised that Kem should be put to sleep. However, I persuaded the owners to wash the dog with a brew of Chickweed (stellaria media). They did so. In two weeks there was no sign of the trouble.

I also told another owner "near Champions, the Timber Merchants". He had spent pounds on vets. It also cleaned up this dog of the same trouble in good time.

"I am a lover of herbs, and of animals, and feel that these experiences may prove helpful to some of your readers."

Weather and Blood Clots

CHANGE of weather apparently tends to cause clotting in deep veins of the leg. A doctor correlated weather records with 66 cases of thrombosis observed in the year and found that blood clots in the veins developed most frequently the day after passage of a meteorological front and usually coincided with a rise in barometric pressure and a fall in temperature and in relative humidity, sometimes occurring after rain.

Grace readers wishing to do all in their power to prevent clotting in the veins should make a practice of drinking an infusion of Nettles, once daily. Fresh plants are best, and contain a higher percentage of chlorophyll and mineral ash. They can be gathered with a glove, the square stalks being snapped off at the base of the plant. Cut with scissors into an enamel (not aluminium) saucepan. Just cover with water; bring to boil; remove vessel on reaching boiling point. Allow to cool. Drink a teacupful once daily. For thrombosis and cardiovascular disorders generally, take morning and evening.

Vitamin "E" therapy is also indicated, but never take so-called chlorophyl tablets in preference to the natural substance as contained in nettles. So many chlorophyl tablets on the market are just a vehicle for the crude minerals iron phosphate and calcium phosphate—not to mention the sugar, of course.

Clots formed more often in spring and autumn than in summer and winter, when meteorologic fronts are less apt to occur. Climate may affect emotion and thus help to produce constriction of blood vessels.

ED: *Many thanks for bringing to our notice this useful information. Chickweed has a long traditional reputation for relief of skin diseases. We would like to make the following recommendation for internal treatment also; One Echinacea tablet, morning and evening, until relief is felt.*

Mrs J. B., Cheam.
Husbands, like peaches, will not keep unless preserved. First, select him carefully, not too green or over-ripe. Husbands grown in the tropics of pleasure look very fine, but are usually insipid. The home grown ones are best.

Select your husband, if possible, from a family tree growing on the sunny side of life. You will be sure then that he is sound at heart. Having selected your husband, make a cheery fire of love. Your preserving pan (the home) must be clean and spotless.

Give him plenty of sweetness. Vinegar is never used. Do not keep stirring him up. Should you keep poking him to see if he is done, it will spoil his looks. Follow this recipe and he will be well preserved.

Mr M. Smith, Garforth, Leeds.
A couple of years ago I could hardly move from a chair and walked with difficulty. I took a course of Prickly Ash tablets. A friend gave me my first hundred. They worked wonders for me. Since then I have recommended them to several friends, and in turn have given them their first hundred. They have told their doctors about them and are quite amazed at the results.

Author unknown.
Three monkeys sat on a coconut tree . . . discussing things as they're said to be . . . Said one to the other "Now listen you two . . . There's a certain rumour that can't be true . . . that man descended from our noble race . . . the very idea is a shocking disgrace . . . No monkey ever deserted his wife . . . starved her babies from domestic strife . . . or pass them on to one another . . . till scarcely they know who is their mother.

And another thing you'll never see . . . a monkey build a fence round a coconut tree . . . and let the coconuts go to waste . . . forbidding all other monkeys to taste . . . Why! If I put a fence around a tree . . . starvation will force you to steal from me . . . Here's another thing a monkey won't do . . . go out at night, and get in a stew . . . or use a gun, or club or knife . . . to take some other monkey's life . . . Yes, man descended the degenerate cuss . . . But, brother, he didn't descend from us.

A. R. B., Durham.
My father was suffering from an incurable ulcer of the leg. After 14 years' orthodox treatment he despaired of it ever getting well. We had tried the Specialists' and hospital treatment to no effect. We followed the advice

of a Naturopath who put him on a diet, but it simply would not heal. One day I was talking to a friend who happened to mention that her mother's leg had been cured by a herbalist who gave her comfrey leaves.

You can imagine how excited we were after we tried the comfrey leaves for about one month. It began to slowly heal. True, it was a painful process, but we boiled the leaves in linen, wrung them out, and put them on the gaping sore. This went on for some months, a lot of foul matter coming away. Now, after nine months it is nearly closed and looks healthier than it has been for years.

ED: *Many thanks for putting pen to paper for the benefit of others. It is our opinion that the nub of the matter is that the comfrey first facilitates expulsion of morbid exudate before the healing process really begins. It is a question of healthy elimination of purulant matter which must proceed before permanent healing takes place. You did well to allow the process to continue until blood and lymph had been wholly cleansed and normalized.*

Jack Green, Paignton, Devon.
I am writing about an article in an issue of a well-known Sunday newspaper about cancer prevention. I think it might confuse and worry a lot of people because, in addition to many other things, it says that honey, herb tea and toast, are suspect.

Surely honey and herbal teas are good for you and could not cause that disease?

ED: *To the best of our knowledge and belief no evidence is available to substantiate the article by a journalist. On the contrary, honey and herbal teas have much to offer sufferers of that dread disease. Honey is unquestionably one of the most remarkable natural substances known to man.*

Honey has bactericidal power and was used by surgeon Michael Bulman, Norfolk & Norwich Hospital, with good results for festering wounds with necrotic surfaces. He said: "This very simple substance is non-irritating, nontoxic, bacterial, nutritive, cheap, easily applied and above all effective. "

Dr D. C. Jarvis, Vermont, sums it up: The taking of honey each day is advised in order to keep the lymph flowing at its normal tempo and thus avoid degenerative disease which shortens life. The real value of honey is to maintain a normal flow of the tissue fluid called lymph. When this rate slows down, then calcium and iron are precipitated as sediment: When the lymph flow is stagnant, then harmful micro-organisms invade the body and sickness appears.

Dr Robert Blomfield, Chelsea, London, says: "I have been using pure natural honey in the Accident and Emergency Departments where I work: I have found that it promotes the healing of ulcers and burns better than anything else."

If honey has such a salutary effect upon the survival of body tissue, is it likely to be carcinogenic in character? We suggest the journalese was

208

just one more attempt to discredit the use of natural substances, health foods, and herbs in favour of drugs.

A. Waerland.
Doing away with hot food and drinks was the last step taken towards the complete recovery of my voice. I could now speak in halls of any size for almost any length of time and be clearly heard by everybody. As a speaker I am now considered tireless.

I had cured myself of "chronic" throat catarrh in my own way, in spite of the doctors. For whenever I mentioned hot drinks and hot foods as one cause of my troubles and as never intended by Nature for human throats and stomachs, I was only met with a smile and a laugh.

Your prayers are requested:
For all who are sick. For all who tonight will weep. For those forgotten by family, that reconciliation may bring a joyous tomorrow. For peoples of East and West, that all may live in harmony. For all who look to us for succour, that we may not be slow to recognise human need, and do what we know to be right.

For all members of *Grace* Family that each may feel he or she has a purpose in the world. That they may sense the beauty of the world of Nature. That a new understanding may illumine their minds of the mystery of Christ. That to all may be given the spirit of a sound mind. That they may discover that Love alone is the ultimate reality.

We ask that all who handle this magazine may feel a benefit in body, mind and spirit. We ask that, from within its pages, they may find an answer to their personal problems.

Josephine Brown, Kent.
Here is a quotation which you might like. It was written for me years ago by a schoolmistress in my autograph book:
"You will never do anything great, unless you can think a little deeper, work a little harder, and aspire a little higher than the crowd. The crowd dreads solitude, it dreads silence; you must dread neither."

V. Roberts, Cumbria.
Why do so-called experts insist on telling us that the things we believed in for generations are all wrong?

Witch Hazel has been magic for the complexion over countless generations. Camphorated oil soon breaks up a tough phlegm and stops the wheezing of the chest in next to no time. Wintergreen takes the pain out of an arthritic joint when other lotions fail. Yet not one of these are easily obtainable.

Will the world be much happier for all the experts have compounded drugs, which appear to create as much disease as they cure? Why can't they leave things alone?

Extract from an old magazine.
People who attain the ripe old age of 90 years have certain characteristics in common. They are usually of slender build and do not look their age, are in possession of their faculties and rarely suffer from want of hair. Their only ailment is rheumatism.

Of the 100 nonagenarians interviewed, none had had an operation, or even placed under an anaesthetic. None among them was a first-born child or an only child. All like to write letters, are early risers and scorn lying in bed. They are strong-willed, self-sufficient and of a positive nature; adapt themselves readily to circumstances and are industrious. They do not worry and are not inclined to be sociable. None plays cards; none of the men smoke.

With such temperaments and habits, these 100 have succeeded in resisting the blight of old age. To emulate them we need to live simply, regularly and keep active. A calm or turbulent youth, or the nature of one's occupation, has no bearing on reaching advanced age.

Higher education.
How clever we are. Even the birds get wiser. Last week a pigeon flew into a maternity ward of a London hospital and laid an egg.

Mrs E. B., Newport, Gwent.
You have helped by brother-in-law very much with the Pulsatilla. There is now no need for him to have an operation for the prostate gland. This is wonderful. Thank you very very much.

Anonymous
It is surprising how many people need ginseng and don't know it. Last week I had an appointment with someone from the Ministry of Energy, but he didn't turn up. Why not? Because he was too tired.

Miss A. S., Sheffield.
I am delighted to inform you that after taking Vitex Agnus Castus tablets my inter-menstrual bleeding has disappeared and that my last period was normal, after eighteen months of misery and inconvenience. Incidentally, not only has my pre-menstrual tension lessened considerably, but I also found that my emotions seem to be more balanced. I do not now depend so much upon tranquillisers.

Many thanks for your help and understanding. I hope many more women will try, and benefit from, the marvellous remedy which in my opinion is safe, effective; a very preferable alternative to interfering with Nature by using "The Pill" and other synthetic hormone drugs. Thank you, once again. Yours sincerely.

Barbara Cartland, (the well-known novelist). Dame of Grace of the Order of St John of Jerusalem.

My idea of Hell is to be fed meat from beef cattle which have been given tranquillisers so they have fattened quicker; fish which are full of pesticides and the toxic waste from factories and sewers carried by the rivers into the sea; chickens which have been caponised with the female hormone stilboestrol so they have fattened like the eunuchs they are; eggs from hens which have been imprisoned like a chain-gang in batteries; vegetables and fruit which have been sprayed with poisons.

I am also (in Hell) served with artificially sweetened, gaily packaged, persistently advertised other foods containing 2,000 chemicals, many of which, if taken in any quantity, are lethal. While I eat and drink water doctored with sodium fluoride, I write urgent letters which I know, despite the high price I pay for the stamps, will never be delivered, and I listen to the eternal stentorian speeches of politicians who browbeat me into believing that tomorrow, next month, next year, everything will be better.

And in Hell I know they lie, but go on hoping – like now.

Jimmy Robinson.

My tortoise, since coming out of hibernation, will not eat anything. He hasn't opened his eyes. He seems lifeless and has a thick discharge from his nose. Is he sick, or is it old age?

ED: *You should see your vet about your pet. The trouble is more likely to be sickness than old age, but he would confirm. For the catarrhal discharge and to enliven him the vet may have something special. I wonder if you know that powdered Valerian root is a favourite with tortoises? Try mixing a little in his food.*

Miss C. C., Gloucester.

I must tell you that since taking Iceland Moss tablets my friend, who suffers from emphysema, has found great relief. Especially with bronchitis last winter. He was very ill when I sent him Iceland Moss tablets; now we both firmly believe they are working wonders.

Mrs P. P., York YOS 8JA.

As I do a considerable amount of Welfare work among ailing people of all ages, I should like to say that – Cranesbill tablets for incontinence are wonderful – and so versatile! They can help instead of a prolapse operation. A child of eleven who is away at Boarding School, with a tendency to bed-wetting – and my dear old Boxer bitch who sometimes "leaks" – are only a few! Yours sincerely.

211

Member of Grace Family, Rustington, Sussex.
I find it difficult to chew apples and lettuce. I'm fond of both. Some of your readers may like to know my method. I peel and core two eating apples, put them in my Kenwood liquidiser, add half pint milk, and liquidize for nearly a minute. This completely mashes the raw apples and makes a lovely apple-flavoured milk drink.

I do the same with my lettuce. Clean and prepare the leaves. I use up to six large Cos-lettuce leaves to half pint of milk, and it liquidises the leaves to nothing. It makes a very pleasant drink and an easy way to take either apples or lettuce. All best wishes, Sincerely.

Girl of eleven.
God made the bees . . . The bees make the honey . . . We do the work . . . And teacher gets the money.

Mrs Jeanette Tempest, Essex.
For ten years I suffered with deep depressions and fears of everything. I had two breakdowns and was under a psychiatrist. Drugs of various kinds kept me numb and sleepy but did not cure me. As I had two small children and a husband to look after they did not enable me to stay alert.

After a really bad week about two years ago, I decided only nature and my own efforts would make me better. So I searched.

I took meditation classes to learn to relax; I had never relaxed in my life before. It took six months before I even began to feel the benefit; but I persevered every morning. I used to set the alarm to "go off" half an hour before anyone else got up. This was the only way I could achieve quiet. I still keep this up. At the same time, I discovered a new spiritual direction and joined a prayer group for once a week.

A friend gave me a bottle of Dr Bach's Rescue Remedy, one of the "flower" remedies. I also followed *Grace* Magazine. Gradually I improved. I learnt that vitamin B Complex was good for nervous people. I also read in an article that zinc tablets were helpful for them, and took them. Well, it took eighteen months to get me where I am today – which is happy, peaceful and contented. *But I did it.* "Nerves" can be terrible to live with. You have your own personal hell; anyone who has not had the experience could not possibly understand.

I am now able to help friends who get "low" and feel I am a much better person. What I have gone through may help others with similar trouble. Yours sincerely.

Ruby Hughes, Leicester.
May I take this opportunity of telling you how very much Rose Hip capsules have helped me. Until three years ago (when I started taking them) I used to have bronchitis every winter, with several colds, but since I have been taking them I have had neither colds nor bronchitis. I am so grateful. Thank you, also, for a lovely magazine – *Grace.* Yours sincerely.

Dr E. Linnell.
Reports the cure of a sick headache of two years' standing (invariably induced by eating anything sweet) by Blue Flag root.

Mrs Beryl Prutty, Thames Coast, New Zealand.
Thank you so much for your lovely magazine, *Grace* received today. Yes, miracles do happen!

For many years I suffered agonies with migraine but, praise the Lord in all His mercies, this year has seen a dramatic change. First of all, I had an "anointing"; and also, I eat three feverfew leaves daily; the healing took place suddenly.

(continued on page 216)

Herbs for your kitchen

THERE are signs of a revival in culinary herbs. We find they all have one great thing in common—benefit to the digestive system. Bay, thyme, dill, basil and chamomile come creeping back into the kitchen. Did you know that they exert a specific influence upon certain organs of the body? The flavour of fresh herbs is more piquant than dried ones. Why not start a Culinary Shelf by placing dried herbs in tins and carefully labelling?

The tiniest pinch of marjoram can add another flavour to summer salads. Angelica leaves help out lettuce when in short supply. Why not have a bay tree in the garden? Its freshly plucked leaves put new life into the pot; staying power to the soup.

Now, take a sniff of fennel. That's a slimmer for you. Pliny listed over twenty of its medicinal uses. Some spend all their hard-gotten fortunes in trying to shed fat. Perhaps the cheapest means is by drinks and salads of fennel. Place a spray in a vase in the house and enjoy its clean aromatic scent.

Mint, which is really spearmint, is the perfect accompaniment to new potatoes. Some people prefer their potatoes and cooked carrots tossed in chopped parsley and melted butter. They say we ought not to overlook easiest to grow—chives. Chopped-up with cheese dishes and nut savouries, omelettes or salads, they keep the stomach as fresh and sweet as a daisy._That's what most herbs do when we gather them straight from the garden._There are some things we would never be without. Not only are they a pleasure to the palate, but to be able to walk across the lawn and smell them after the soft summer rain . . . that's real living!

Juniper.

213

Time and Tide

DO WE take all these things for granted? There is a great danger in taking little things like the sparrow's chirp and the fresh air, or the letter of a loved friend for granted. Freedom to walk through the park or down a local country lane might sound so cheap when we have it. We may not even notice it. Freedom is a precious possession. Only when it is taken away from us will we see its true worth.

Today, we are free to do these things. Sometimes we need to make an effort to enjoy part of this glorious heritage which is ours. Prize it. It has been built up painfully over the centuries of effort, war and peace, death and life.

This England . . . as we know it . . . etch it upon your mind in blazing colours. Relish its simple pleasures. When you come upon a tree newly bursting into bloom, pause to take it in . . . and give thanks.

This is our freedom. True freedom has its roots deep within the human spirit. He who understands the secret of the celandines cannot be corrupted or broken. Somewhere out there, away over the hills, there is a place where he regains a consciousness of real freedom—the quality of life swiftly being withdrawn from the world.

Before our woods are lost to faceless government departments, we need a renewal and a deep desire to preserve the good earth—at all costs. She has so much to give in return. For us, she weaves her timeless pattern of beauty and goodness out of a living soil to nourish man's body and soul. She is the inspiration of his most wholesome pleasures and a true revelation of that mighty Heart beating at the back of it all.

What is it we need in life? Do we pursue phantoms of pleasure, position, property . . . all gained at the expense of our nerves, year-in and year-out. Position can be lost, friends can be lost, health can be lost . . . and everything can be lost, except a sense of harmony with the One who swings the stars in their spheres and sustains the good earth.

Let us live with a steady hand on the controls, not afraid of failure, sickness or misfortune. We will accept with good grace the evil as well as the good. The bitter years come to an end . . . and the sweet make it all so well-worthwhile.

It has been good, for an hour or so, to forget the scarlet-fever of these days, and catch a breath of that everlasting comfort of the woods and fields. I know you can't afford the time—that you cannot be spared—but why not seize the opportunity for a brief hour, while you may—away from it all?

214

Epping Forest, England. All is peace at the River's edge. With the swan goes strength and silence. You too can have peace.   *Dennis Mansell*

River Walk

WHAT more pleasing summer spectacle than the easy grace of the spotless-white mute swan as she glides across the mirror of the river? First introduced into England by Richard Coeur de Lion when he returned from the Crusade, she is a real 'Queen-bird' with a flight attaining speeds up to 40 miles and hour and mating once for life. The largest swannery in England is at Abbotsbury near Weymouth where sometimes over 1,000 nesting birds were cared for by the famous Dorset naturalist, Fred Lexter.

(from page 213)

Also, my husband is a living miracle, surviving a coronary and heart block. The last clot dissipated down the arm instead of passing to the brain. He is now fully recovered. We follow the health rules given in the Bible and trust God daily with our lives.

We live in a beautiful part of the North Island and enjoy sunshine for nine months of the year. I grow over 40 different kinds of herbs in my garden, using them daily. With over 50 fruit trees and all kinds of vegetables we are almost self-sufficient. May you have continued success.

Florence Swann, Taunton, Somerset.
In your Spring issue of *Grace* (1978) you featured an article on sweet violet (viola odorata) which I have used ever since. I had been a martyr to sinus trouble for years but soon felt relief. However, my nasal and internal catarrh have also been much better. I was unable to take any of the doctor's painkillers for the arthritis without getting side-effects, and this is where I have been considerably helped by Calcium Pantothenate tablets. I am now much better able to get about the house and have nothing like as much pain.

Then there are Vitamin E capsules which have been a great help to my daughter's circulation. Her fingers used to go quite white and 'dead' in cold weather or when she bathed in the sea. Since taking the vitamin E this has quite disappeared.

I have been a subscriber to *Grace* Magazine since its first issue, I can't remember how many years it has been since I first received so much help. I enjoy every bit of each copy. Thank you for everything. With all good wishes. Your sincerely.

Anonymous.
What would you recommend for bad breath?
ED: *I would like to let Adelle Davis, the well-known nutritionist, answer this in her own words, from her book: "Let's Get Well" (George Allen & Unwin):*

"Diseased gums or tonsils can cause halitosis (bad breath) but, more often putrefactive bacteria, living on undigested food, form foul – smelling gases which are thrown off in exhaled air."

"Any deficiency that impairs digestion is a contributing factor. Volunteers lacking vitamin B6 developed foul breath, which disappeared

after the vitamin was given to them. When there is an odour to the stools, halitosis invariably occurs simultaneously . The condition is rectified by improving the digestion and destroying the putrefactive bacteria by taking yoghurt or a preparation of Lactobacillus acidophilus . . ."

Mrs D. Burton, Staffordshire.
We have a friend who lives in a little country terrace house, who is active in her Women's Fellowship, and yet finds time to make her own bread. She makes jam from fruits and preserves from vegetables grown by her husband in their large garden at the back. She even cleans out the chickens.

She's an excellent knitter and grows her own herbs. Her rooms are filled with the scent of lavender. Does this sound like some dear old lady with a trug and trowel? No. She's a "settler" from Bradford, in her twenties with two children to look after. Who says family home-makers are scarce, these days?

Mrs A. Oates, Bradford, West Yorkshire.
After trying for months to cure athlete's foot with ointments, etc., from doctors and chiropodists, and having no lasting success, I finally decided to try bathing in salt and water for ten minutes each day.

To my great surprise and satisfaction, gradually over a few weeks they improved and finally healed completely. If occasionally the trouble reappears in a small area I repeat the bathing. It soon clears.

Vera Chapman, Bournemouth.
In the Spring issue of *Grace* we were given alternatives to white sugar and other foods to be avoided. Can you enlarge?

ED: *While we haven't space to deal with this subject as fully as we would wish, here are more examples: Consider: Carob and carob products in place of chocolate and cocoa. In place of jam and preserves – honey and raw sugar preserves. In place of white rice – brown rice and other grains. For table salt, iodized salt – use sea salt, sesame salt or powdered kelp in your salt-cellar. For breakfast cereals – muesli with an oatmeal base to which is added grated nuts, raisins, sliced fresh fruit, dried fruits, yoghurt, and cracked grains – rye, barley. In place of sweets and confectionery such as chocolate eclairs – dried fruits, dates, nut bars, nuts and raisins, honey, sesame bars, carob snacks and anything from the wide range of natural sweetmeats at your Health Food Store.*

Anonymous.
Do you talk to your plants? Yes, so do I. At one time, I would lose a plant or two during the summer holiday through thirst. Besides, leafy friends feel neglected when you are away for two or three weeks.

I spread over the bottom of the bath several thicknesses of newspaper, and turn the tap on. When they are thoroughly saturated, I run off the water and place my pots on the newspaper. The paper may still be damp when you come home.

This is my plan for survival. I think my plants must appreciate it, and can be quite perky and upstanding on my return.

Mrs F. G. Annert, Bath, Avon.
I feel I must write to you on what has been the joyful cause of a minor miracle. I read of the uses of Palma Christi (castor oil). I was determined to do something about a big toe nail which for three years after a fall, had been black and dead and so ugly that I dare no longer wear open-toed sandals in summer.

The result is that that nail has not only turned a healthy white/pink again, but has started to grow. At least three-quarters of the nail was dead, now three-quarters is clean and new. I am absolutely thrilled and know that if I had not read about this in your magazine I would never have had such wonderful results.

I hope my use of castor oil will help someone else with the same problem.

A Member of Grace Family.
Now that summer is here and the garden may need watering, would it not be sensible for everyone to install a water butt or tank in which to collect rain as it comes from the roof?

It makes a wholesome alternative to the chemical-ridden tap water with its chlorine and other noxious additives. Rain water can be used for cooking, drinking, and a hundred-and-one other uses in the home – even flushing down the lavatory!

Who knows! We may have yet another drought! Our own natural water supply can help out the 'mains' should there be shortages.

Anonymous.
My trouble is angina (pain down the arm) and intermittent claudication when walking uphill. I am sceptical, but am willing to try what you call a 'natural remedy'.

ED: *For heart and arterial pains, on exertion, and which are caused by cramp of the heart muscle you may find helpful "Cramp Bark" which may be used with success in some cases. Not every case. But it is worth a trial where there is a temptation to take more drugs for an attack.*

The modern consulting herbalist uses "Cramp Bark" for palpitation and clutching pains in the region of the heart. Some say it can relieve the pains of cramp (muscle spasm) in various muscle groups (shoulders, etc) and it is known to be helpful for painful periods (menses).

Our own experience of "Cramp Bark" (viburnum opulus) extends over the past thirty years, and it can prove to be a very useful mild analgesic

218

when other treatments lose their efficacy. Its other names are: High Cranberry, Red Elder, Snowball tree. It works well with Hawthorn Berry (Crataegus oxyacanthoides) for angina.

S. H. C., Devon.
Have you ever thought what it is like to be just a few weeks off eighty and still possessed of that magical gift . . . imagination!

Living in a small compact bungalow in Devonshire, with all your remaining possessions around you – things that remind you of the happy days with one who shared everything with you – pleasures, poverty, sickness, prosperity, your garden, your home – you sometimes find yourself in a reflective mood.

Sitting quietly, one evening, you pick up *Grace* and you read a touching story of two lonely people brought together by their former nanny. Yes, the ending is obvious. Both suffered a lack of parental love when young. Meeting for the first time by the bedside of their old Nanny, they find something common to each other – the need to be loved.

Those of us who have known love cannot possibly understand what life would be without it. Suddenly, out of the blue, two people meet and find they need each other. What a lovely story!

What does an old chap of eighty feel when he reads Ann Lovell's simple romance? It brought a lump to his throat. Yes, we all need love. It is a hard thing when a happy partnership is severed. At first it is a blow. But we must never allow ourselves to be "counted out". We *have* to live on. The world about us has its own troubles – let us not add our own.

The pity is we cannot still the passing of time. But there are times when the sun sinks and we sit alone; we pick up a magazine and read such a story that Ann writes, and it all comes back.

Perhaps, even now, someone may come along to share our love – a little child or someone interested in our simple pleasures. Thank you, Ann, for that sweet story. Who said the fairy world belongs to childhood?

Mrs Jesse Heaps, Halifax, W. Yorks.
Like Mrs G. Morrell of London wrote in the Spring issue of *Grace*, she many times had meant to write and thank you for benefit she gets from your magazine, and at last had got around to it, I'm doing just that.

Thank you for the joy *Grace* has brought me for a few years now. The first copy I ever saw was given to me, after that I have had it regularly and look forward to it so much. I can only liken the delight of receiving it as to the joy as a child, when I got my weekly children's magazine – the anticipation!

Grace is a "Pandora's Box" of so many things that I have never come across in any other magazine. Many times I've read various remedies of a healing nature which I felt, "Yes, I'll second that," and never got round to it. After reading the Spring issue I must put pen to paper and endorse one or two things I've read.

(Continued on page 222)

On Our Side

THIS is the time of the year when the book of nature is opened wide. It is when thoughts return to the simple life. When we open our minds, beauty and joy wait upon our coming and going. Next to beauty is the power of appreciating it. At such a time who can fail to be in love with the good earth and its people?

It is good to take our ease; to be quietly contemplative. But life is made of sterner stuff and the challenge of tomorrow keeps us up and going. In the meantime we reflect that a lazy day such as this comes only now and then, fresh with new discoveries.

Nature is so good to us. Even the best qualified physicians would be lost without her. She is on our side. She is ever on her toes to bless, sustain and protect us from the hazards of this world and from our own follies. But, you know, health is a two-way affair. We cannot leave everything to this unseen spirit of conservation. It is when we respond to her loving care with all the passion of a grateful beneficiary that she turns to smile on us.

When sickness sets us aside, she joins battle from her inner citadel. She rises to resist invasion by bacteria, safeguards the heart and vital organs, ever-renewing, ever-rebuilding. It is over a vast powerhouse of healing she presides.

And what is her price for this overshadowing vigilance? All she asks is discipline of our body habits, fresh air and exercise, regular sensible meals, and adequate rest. It is worth ten-thousand times the cost. But not one of us learns the secret until it is too late.

The soil is generous. The law of nature is to give. Today is your day, and mine. It is a day in which we play our part in the great whole. Our time is now. We know that as long as we contribute to the pleasure and comfort of another human being we shall be of importance in the world.

A garden can be a gladsome place for re-orientating our thinking after opting out of the struggle for a brief hour. Ultra-violet rays from the sun warm to life an inanimate circulation and build firm bones in young and old. May we be a magnet not drawing to us the unhealthy, disagreeable and the destructive, but attracting all things bright, healthy and joyous.

If winter has visited some unfruitful area of your life the sweetest thing to remember is that summer comes again. There never was an ideal world. I believe there one day will be. Every now and then, in poignant moments among green growing things, or from the depths of a great book, there flashes upon the inward eye an understanding of the nature of Grace—unmerited favours lavished upon us by a beneficent Creator in so many ways.

Nothing can erase the lovely things in your life and mine: the loyalty of friends, summer days with the family in the country, or the cleaving triumph of an unselfish job well done.

So, take heart, reader and friend. Count every blessing. Be not afraid. Lift up your head. If it is ever so small a part you play, the world has need of you.

The Herb Garden, Sissinghurst.   *Harry Smith*

What's more pleasant than a walk in the sun? We hope you are all making the most of the sunshine by getting out into the open-air as there is no better way of "topping-up" our vitamin D reserves.

Of course, nobody has ever seen a vitamin. They were not even heard of until a few years ago. But they are important factors without which we cannot stay healthy. The essential vitamins are A, B, C, D and E. Vitamin A helps protect us against colds and infections. Vitamins of the B group are good for nerves and appetite. C is the anti-scurvy vitamin, and E is associated with arterial health and perfect function of the reproductive system.

Perhaps the most important of all is vitamin D. Its two richest sources are (a) sunshine and (b) cod-liver oil. Anyone with half an eye can see that if we are no good at drinking oil from cods' livers, the best thing we can do is to take every opportunity of sunning ourselves. If your sunbathing days are over, then a leisurely hour or two in the park is what you need. Thus shall we build up our resistance against the hazards of winter. I have a notion that sunshine is not only good for rickets but for most kinds of bone troubles. Did you know that bad teeth can follow a lack of this vitamin? Make sure, this summer, you will not go short of it. Work-up a real tan. What is not generally known, vitamin D helps us to sleep.

Talking about sleep . . . Isn't it hot? This park seat may be somewhat "hard" to the "sit-upon" but you don't notice it as the drowsy scents of summer flowers exert their soporific effect. Pssssss . . . Who's that lazy-bones over there who can't keep his eyes open? Who's that a-noddin' in the noon-day sun?

Fondest regards to you all.

221

(from page 219)

Firstly, good old Castor Oil! I've had one or two flat warts on my face. Dabs of castor oil each day have almost diminished them. Going back over the years (I am 61), I've had eczema since babyhood. During teenage it was very severe, but my face was cleared by a castor-oil-based ointment. The result was a bonus of beautiful eyelashes!

Still on the subject of eczema and related allergies – I got 'em all – and learned over the years to cope and live with them. I agree with the piece written by Dr Arthur J. Snider about the misconception that children will outgrow their allergies.

I had infantile eczema and after having treatment to clear up a very bad flare-up in my teens developed asthma, then hay fever. Woe betide me, if ever a Doc. gave me ephedrine, or, any de-congestant later on in years. Within 24 hours, I wouldn't be fit to be seen – ears, lips, eyes, etc swollen out of all proportion resulting in a terrible weeping later.

The allergy test I had years ago didn't show, with me, anything positive from dairy foods. The positive reaction for me was tremendous, it being all known irritants: i.e. animal hair, household dust, etc.

Now, that good old healer Comfrey. This I have taken for a few years now, ever since I started getting twinging hot shooting pains in the nodules I've developed in the first joint of my fingers. I did not know the name of the nodules. (ED: *Heberden's nodes*).

Since taking Comfrey I've had no pain whatsoever. It is a long time since I've had an attack of asthma. It does me good I'm sure.

Also, I've had spasms from spraining my ankles badly. Poultices of Comfrey work wonders. Never shall my husband and I throw it out of the garden. Thank you for a wonderful publication and trust it will never cease.

Film struck.
My wife and I went to the Theatre last night to see a Tennessee Williams play. On coming out she said: "Well . . . if I wanted to be depressed, I could have stayed at home and done the ironing."

Mr Arnold Edwards, Halifax, West Yorkshire.
I read an article nearly two years ago in *"Grace"* by Barbara Cartland. She prescribed a remedy for any who found difficulty in getting a good night's sleep. Prior to reading it I had been on sleeping tablets for some 15 or 16 years.

I resolved to try the remedy she prescribed, namely: honey, cider vinegar and dolomite tablets. I had some initial problems but, in a very short time, I found I could dispense with sleeping tablets prescribed by my doctor and which I had taken for the past 15 or 16 years. I found I could get a good night's rest and sleep with the honey, cider vinegar, Dolomite tablets.

Anonymous.
I have just read "While the Kettle Boils", Summer, 1982, in which reference is made to Chartwell, Westerham, home for many years of Sir Winston Churchill .
. . . but, Dear Editor, please . . . Sir Winston *and* Lady Churchill. Lady Churchill did so much to make the home at Chartwell.
ED: *Our unseen friend is asked to accept our sincere apologies for such an unpardonable omission. You see how easy it is for us to overlook our better half! We have the greatest admiration for Lady Churchill who was a most accomplished lady. She did many things for which I am sure the country will be grateful. We are so glad she had the courage to destroy that ghastly Sutherland portrait of her husband which portrayed him as a gormless nincompoop, which of course he wasn't.*

Mrs P. A. R., Walsall, West Midlands.
Slippery Elm tablets have proved successful for the chronic flatulence from which I was suffering.

Howard Bygrave, Cheshire.
An intricate dental operation lasting an hour left me with one side of my face hugely swollen. I live in the country and comfrey plants grow in abundance in the lanes. People living nearby use the leaves to reduce the swelling when horses have injured their legs. Would it work for me?
I picked some leaves, stewed them in water, then used the leaves and the water to make a poultice. I slapped it on my face and inside an hour the swelling had gone down dramatically. A few more applications and it had almost vanished.
They know a thing or two in the country, don't they?

L. S. C., Glasgow, Scotland.
My family tell me I can smooth away headaches with the palms of my hands. Do you think this means I have the gift of healing, and if so, what ought I to do about it?
ED: *It is no exaggeration to say that healing by the sense of touch is today more prevalent over the world than scientific medicine. When a friend is in need what could be more helpful than augmenting the work of your doctor or surgeon by giving the patient the benefit of your own vital force?*
Who knows! You may discover yourself to be a competent healer! Whether it has a bearing on faith healing, or is a straight transmission of vital personal energy, what does it matter how it is done as long as the distressed person derives benefit? One thing most faith healers can do very well – and that is the temporary (sometimes permanent) relief of pain: a far more desirable alternative to aspirin or chemical analgesics.

*We all enter this world with some specific gift: it may be music, paint-
ing or craft. Why should yours not be the gift of healing? We often stum-
ble upon our gifts by accident. Undoubtedly you have a desire to relieve
pain and a latent gift only needs encouraging. Your husband should help
you to develop your ability by supporting you in all your efforts. Try
radiating love and compassion when applying your hands in this way;
they are powerful healing influences in themselves. Do you remember
how Fanny Craddock had cancer and her doctor described her case in a
secret letter as "hopeless". But she was determined not to give in.
Someone laid their hands upon her, in prayer, and she got better.*

Mrs Day, Faringdon.
I am very pleased to be able to tell you that the "Vitex Agnus Castus"
was an excellent help to my usual painful period. I didn't experience
anything like the pain of previous months.

John Tobe.
You want to know what to do with your garden mint? I'll tell you. There
are many uses for it. Try it in pea soup – sprinkle a little on salads – on
cooked peas and potatoes. And, how about a cold refreshing summer
drink of mint tea? You will of course be aware of the digestive properties of this priceless plant for colic and collywobbles. All this we owe
to the Romans who brought it to Britain.

Arthur Russell, Bradford, West Yorkshire.
Judging by the sour looks I get from so many people in the bus queue or
in the shops, one would think cheerfulness was hard to come by.
There was a time when I thought I smiled because I was happy. But
that's nonsense because I've found out that I get happy when I smile.
You can do it. Anyone can do it. When newspaper headlines send your
spirits down to zero, just walk around with a smile – however difficult –
and within a few minutes you'll feel like a million dollars.

Winifred Spray, Kennington, Oxford.
I expect most readers of *Grace* find, as I do, that there is always something to which they can relate. I had a bonanza in the Spring, 1990 issue
. . . at least two being in Mr Bartram's 'Beloved Reader', referring to
Lady Mendl's remark, "I never think of myself as being old" as I suppose
all of us are when our three score years and ten are reached.
I find I frequently refer to 'old Mrs X, Y or Z only to learn that they
are scarcely older than I am, even younger! So often, once that 'allotted

*Harvest Time on the South Coast, Littlehampton, Sussex. By Henry H.
Parker (1853-1930).*
        Fine Art Photographic Library Ltd/Burlington Fine Paintings.

span' is attained, I see a tendency in some of my contemporaries to shed activity thus losing muscle tone and mental alertness. How often I've heard, "At my time of life I don't want the responsibility of garden, pets, a large house . . . They leave the home they have cherished and stagnate in strange surroundings until they become beyond coping.

The Editor goes on to stress the importance of love in our lives and the high mortality of institutionalised infants in a bygone era as described in Dr Ashley's book. This took me back to my time as a sick children's nurse and later ward sister in 1935-45. Those children were deprived of their mothers except for the weekly one hour allotted on visiting days but, though I have since wondered at the possible harm inflicted on the toddler age group, the bottle-fed babies and those on weaning diets who were taken onto our laps and cuddled and loved at feeding times, responded to our love . . . and how we loved them! I saw more than one miracle cure in those pre-antibiotic days. We worked long hours, were always 'run off our feet', we never gave a thought to our pittance of pay, but we had the satisfaction in the love and faith reciprocated by our little patients. In the rare event of inevitable death, silent tears overflowed in a quiet corner of the sluice.

Elsa Pike, Mayfield, Sussex.
I recommended Lobelia Compound tablets to a friend who suffered from severe bronchial problems for most of her life. She was so impressed with the improvement in her health that she asked me to obtain more for her.

This is the first time my friend has had any relief from her awful chesty condition. Perhaps you can imagine how delighted she is from a course of Lobelia which until now, she had known only as a pretty blue flower used in hanging baskets.

Yvonne J., (10).
What do hippopotamuses have that no other animals have? Little hippopotamuses.

Cyril Turner, Sheffield.
I had a cholesterol problem for years and there were times when my doctor was really worried. I was very surprised to find I was a lot better taking Garlic capsules: now my cholesterol level is satisfactory – for me – and my doctor is pleased. I buy it from our health store.

ED: *Many thanks for writing to tell us of a personal experience which we know will surely help other members of Grace Family. The UK is at the top of the league for heart disease, but more people are finding garlic is of value for accompanying high blood pressure. We believe Garlic will be the food and medicine of the future.*

The Harbour Window. By Stanhope Forbes RA 1857-1947.
Copyright: The Royal Academy of Arts, London.

By the way, I've been intrigued by the names of some of the new health stores up and down the country; Goodness Gracious. Country Kitchen, Eggstasy, the Nitty Gritty Grain Store. What Comes Naturally, Nut 'n Mag, Funny Foods. Bonkers. Well, if ever – I'll eat my hat!

Anthony Baird, Director, Institute of Complementary Medicine, London W1.
Government research scientists want £200,000 for research into the use of Willow as a medicine (Report, March 6). Might they not save themselves and the taxpayer both trouble and money if they looked under "Willow" in any herbal book of reference?

White and purple willow bark have been used for centuries as an anti-rheumatic, anti-fever, anti-'flu and as an antiseptic. No need for research. Just apply the remedy.

Mary Johnson, Solihull, Warwickshire.
In the last issue you gave us some alternatives to caffeine teas and I found them a refreshing change. Can we have more?

ED: *Here are some more. You'll find their whole range in your local health food shop. Chamomile, Peppermint, Mixed Fruit, Rosehip, Fennel (enlivens sluggish appetites). Maté (Brazilian reviver), Lemon Verbena (indigestion), Orange Grove, Lemon Grove, Apple & Cinnamon, Wild Strawberry. Wild Raspberry. To re-cap from the past: Morning Time (energising morning drink) and Night Time (Soothing blend for promoting restful sleep); as grateful and as comforting as nectar. Just what the doctor ordered!*

Anonymous, Bournemouth, Dorset.
Having prostate trouble I called at my nearest health store over a year ago and received some excellent advice, since which I have been more comfortable and trouble-free. When I last attended the Specialist I heard the good news that he no longer thought an operation necessary.

The knowledgeable lady had advised Pulsatilla tablets and Pumpkin seeds – both old traditional remedies – which are well-known by herbalists to be helpful for the condition.

From the Gardening Section of the Fenland Citizen.
"Don't kill yourself in the garden. Let me do it for you."

Anonymous.
My husband (after 41 years of happy marriage) died in 1986, and my whole world seemed to collapse. Then a friend sent me a copy of *Grace* and immediately I started on your Daily Affirmations. They seemed to have been written specially for me, and I have found this true with every new copy of the magazine. It is just like magic. Now, after working through three years of mourning I have come out of my eclipse and find life is very much worth living again.

I cannot thank you enough but I would also like to compliment the photographers who produce such lovely illustrations. Yours very gratefully.

Member of Grace Family.
I have had stiff joints for a very long time. The year before last, I was at a loss to know what to do next. I tried so many things. Then my wife remembered how her mother had taken cod liver oil to ease the pains of arthritis. Well. I had nothing to lose, so I went on cod liver oil. Within two months my joints were easier and I improved. I have never gone back. I still take a bottle occasionally, which keeps me 'in the clear'.

ED: *Many thanks for an account of relief without the aid of drugs. We are reminded of a fascinating book entitled "Arthritis and Common Sense" by Dale Alexander, in which he records the use of cod liver oil for eczema, psoriasis and rheumatic disorders. He reckons it is one of the most reliable protectors of the skin and the joints. Alexander believes we need some form of "lubrication" of the joints as we get older. He may be right. Some people swear by it. Others are not so sure. Some like it in the form of capsules, but there's nothing like the real thing – if you can tolerate it. A good reliable brand may have something to offer.*

Mrs G. Winnett, Southampton.
One evening last summer a baby owl fell out of a large cedar tree near our house. We were wondering what to do when it started to climb very slowly back up the tree. We rushed off to get a camera before it disappeared – and in that moment a cat appeared from nowhere and started to go after it.

We couldn't reach the cat and waited in horror for the next few moments until, believe it or not, a huge owl (mother/father?) suddenly appeared, ignored us, and with one great sweep of its wings knocked the cat for six to the ground! With that it flew silently back to another tree and the baby got home safely. The parent owl had evidently been watching the whole time and took action as soon as it was necessary. The cat was not injured but beat a very hasty retreat.

Mrs N. P.
Passing a café recently I was drawn to a sign which read: "Don't he bored – come in and get fed-up!"

Stella Bryant, Suffolk.
Every year for several years past I have sent a year's subscription for *Grace Magazine* to my aunt who lives in Florida. She loves it, as we all do, and appreciates its message of good healthy living.

She has been an advocate of "live" food, healthy living and spiritual standards all her life long. When I tell you that in January she reached her 100th birthday I am sure you would agree that she is a good advertisement for these things. She still lives in her own home, with a devoted daughter to care for her. When I telephoned her on her birthday, she told me she was aiming to chalk up a much higher score. Truly an indomitable lady.

J. W.
After supper with friends, our host insisted that he and my husband would do the washing-up and let us girls relax. Looking helpless and unenthusiastic, my husband replied feebly, "I always feel so lost in another man's kitchen."

R. A.
A woman who bought some brightly striped sheets reports: "I suppose they're right, but they make me feel as if I've been gift-wrapped."

Member of Grace Family.
Recently one side of my face has twitched uncontrollably and whatever I do does not seem to prevent it. I lead an ordered life but have had some stress with my daughter's family. The spasms come and go. Can it be psychological?

ED: *Irritation of the facial nerve may arise from a number of causes, chief of which is tension and anxiety. Get your husband to observe any distortion of your face when you are asleep. If it happens when you are asleep, its cause could not be psychological.*

It would be wise to consult your practitioner to ensure that it is not a premonitory symptom of Bell's Palsy, a temporary paralysis of the facial nerve which usually clears in a few days without incident.

For a mild twitch, Valerian tablets offer a natural nerve-relaxant and are usually successful. Some people have found an answer in the popular Biochemic combination: Kali Phos, Mag Phos and Calc Phos. Others have used zinc tablets.

Label on a jar of honey:
"Honeybees have gathered nectar from approximately 4,500,000 clusters of clover and travelled about 150,000 miles, or equal to six times round the world, to deliver this honey to you.

Ray Barnes, Golden Beach, Golden Dam, Texas, USA.
I have always been bothered with constipation. At last I have found a remedy: one rounded teaspoon flax seeds (linseed) and one rounded teaspoon psyllium husks. I mix the two on my cereal and take it once daily with my evening meal. Results the next morning are entirely satisfactory.

Thank you so much for *Grace* Magazine – the one magazine we don't throw away. The title is so appropriate – *Grace*.

Our apricot, plum and pear trees were in full bloom much too early and were unfortunately nipped by the frost. We had an early spring – our January and February weather being much too mild, causing the fruit trees to bloom too early. Our best wishes, sincerely.

Mrs I. Hayhurst, Levenshulme, Manchester.
I was very interested in the letter from Mrs Ruth Salmon, Surrey. I can understand how much she misses her pets. I am 76 and alone except for my little dog. I just pray I can continue to look after him while he is with me. I have no one else who needs me.

I wonder if Mrs Salmon has considered giving a home to an older cat or dog? I am sure it would be very rewarding. They are frequently passed over for young animals. I am sure they would be grateful for a kind and loving home in which to spend their last days in peace. Yours sincerely.

Member of Grace Family.
For years I have had cracked lips that are more of a nuisance than painful. They are worse during the cold weather. What do you think might be the cause?

ED: *So many cases are due to a deficiency of vitamins A, B and C. Alcohol is sometimes implicated but not always. Why not make sure of your vitamin A intake by eating oily fish once or twice a week, or by taking a fish-oil such as cod liver oil?*

The vitamin B-complex is well represented on the health market and a good combination would be obtainable from your local health store. And vitamin C? It goes without saying that the best sources are citrus fruits, acerola, rosehips or other reputable preparations.

Have you tried smoothing them with a little vitamin E cream, evening primrose oil or chickweed ointment?

Mrs Helen Guest.
My sister was put down for an operation for hysterectomy and was a little unhappy about the prospects. Imagine our surprise when somebody tried to raise her spirits by saying: "There is no need to worry, my dear . . . George had the same operation and says he's never felt better in his life!"

Prayer for today.
I said a prayer for you today, and know God must have heard . . . I felt the answer in my heart, though He spoke no word . . . I didn't ask for wealth or fame, (I know you wouldn't mind!) . . . I asked Him to send treasures of a far more lasting kind.

I asked that He'd be near you at the start of each new day . . . To grant you health and blessings, and friends to share your way . . . I asked for happiness for you and all things great and small . . . But it was for His loving care I prayed the most of all. *(Author unknown)*

A Sense of Wonder

SO MUCH beauty is lost to the world because of a lack of wonder. How precious is a sense of wonder? Whether it has for its object the rising and setting of the sun, the scent of pine trees after rain, the soft or brilliant gleam of gems and sea-shells, a song and dance of burning coals, it is one of those faculties you can acquire. In some lucky people it is an inherited gift like music or natural good taste. Books and pictures and all the wonders of this world belong to them who love and understand them. It is a light in the eyes, demanding neither good breeding nor expensive education. A sense of wonder does much to quieten our fever and pain.

One of the delusions of this world is the idea that money makes a man happy. No man is rich except he who is solvent in the Hereafter. An appreciation of the goodness in the world of men and women is the only investment which yields real dividends. When you are in want, it is good to have money in your pocket. But it is also good to make sure you haven't lost the things that money can't buy.

It is possible to possess a whole string of degrees, be a respected member of learned societies, yet lack a sense of wonder. You know, there is such a thing as seeing life, and not seeing it whole. A few are driven by an insatiable restless curiosity in the pursuit of knowledge at the expense of tenderness and beauty. These people spend a lot of time out of the sun. A sense of wonder keeps life sweet and the heart at peace.

It is to be preferred to much so-called intellectual achievement. It is an impulsive appreciation of the astonishing beauty still to be seen in common things. It can be enjoyed when other pleasures pall.

Do you try to be fair with yourself? Never think indulging your sense of wonder is unimportant and a waste of time. If so, you will be wrong. Nobody criticizes exuberant children for the innocent rapture and excitement they feel. This sense is just as vital to grown-ups. It is a healthy outlet for our untapped energy and creative impulses.

❧

Join the whole of creation of animate things in a deep, heartfelt joy that you are alive; that you see the sun, that you are on this glorious earth which nature has made so beautiful and which is yours to conquer and enjoy.

SIR WILLIAM OSLER

Grindelwald, Switzerland.   *Photo: Verlag Gyger, Adelboden.*

ON THE ROOF OF THE WORLD

Our sincere thanks to the photographer we have been unable to contact.

Ian B. Jordan, Bury.
I have been using Essence of Feverfew for several years now and, since I started taking it, the incidence of migraine attacks has reduced from about once in every six to eight weeks to one or two milder attacks per year.

Anonymous.
As a diabetic I have to attend the hospital on a regular basis and the last time I was there I spotted a poster showing the delivery of a new baby headed, "Did you know the first two minutes of your life are the most dangerous?"

Under that someone had written: "The last two are pretty dodgy as well!"

J. V. M.
The other day a friend of mine coped masterfully with a situation which has baffled many a woman driver. She was driving through heavy traffic when a man squeezed his car in too close and promptly blamed her – profanely and at length. My friend listened quietly until he ran down, then leaned out of her window and said:

"Relax . . . take a deep breath and say 'Ah.' "

I am now 91 years, live very simply, and have no aches and pains. Again, this is remarkable because in 1916 I had an emergency operation for appendicitis and peritonitis, and later an emergency operation for perforation. With TB abscess of the lung I was given three months to live. Some years later, I had a duodenal ulcer which I cured by diet.

Altogether, I've had a great deal of illness but now, thanks to vitamin E, honey and careful dieting I can enjoy life. *Grace* has been a great help to me. I usually keep one at my bedside. So thank you for a lovely magazine which I have made known to a good many friends over the years, for whom I buy a subscription as a Christmas present. Greetings to all members of *Grace* Family. Yours very sincerely,

Ruth Salmon, Surrey.
First, let me say how much I enjoy *Grace*. I have bought it for many years but this year my daughter surprised me with a postal subscription – she knows that now I am retired pennies are a little scarce.

I would like to comment on the letter from Mrs H. G., East Midlands. I, too, used to feel like her when we were a family of five, plus two dogs and a cat. I was holding-down a full-time job too. I used to long for a couple of days in solitary confinement.

Now that I have been on my own for nearly twenty years, my husband dead and the children married and all living some distance away, I look back on those hectic days with nostalgia. Even my beloved dogs and cat are no more. At sixty-nine I hesitate to take on any more who might outlive me. Yes, they are our happiest days – when we are needed.

Mr Ted S., Guildford, Surrey.
Your magazine is supposed to tell us how to deal with trouble.
Trouble! You don't know what trouble is! My wife lost her purse. I
have prostate trouble. I have just come back from visiting my sick mother-
in-law. My daughter has had twins, and the dog chewed up a library book.
And, that's not all. Two days ago I landed up miles from my destina-
tion. I'd got on the wrong train!

Mrs A. J. Fox, Natal, SA.
Having suffered for many years from a bad skin and delicate digestive
system, I find that after giving up sugar, white flour and avoiding preser-
vatives and food colouring I am at last enjoying better health and can
cope with my complaint. I have also learnt what herbs, herbal teas and
health coffee can do for me and wish that I had taken the trouble to try
all these wonderful things long ago. I am now also a firm believer in
honey and apple cider vinegar, taken especially on retiring to ensure a
restful sleep.

Mrs J. Watts, London SW4
My grandson has a glue-ear. We have tried everything to no avail.
   ED: *Squeeze the contents of one or two Garlic oil capsules into the ear
at night, with cotton wool ear plugs.*
   *More glue ears are caused by the questionable confectionary, loaded
with additives and consumed by today's children, than this world dreams
of!*

Mrs B. K. Birmingham.
Our Puss was missing five days and we were so worried. Enquiries with
neighbours didn't help. Once before, she had gone off on her own, so we
didn't worry .
   Imagine our surprise when a parishioner of the church brought us a
cardboard box and invited us to peep inside. There were three of the
cutest little newly-born kittens you have ever seen. When they brought
in Puss from the car she was so ravenous that she lapped up two whole
saucerfuls of milk before claiming her family.
   What happened? We learnt our Puss had slunk into the church during
a wedding and got locked in. Unable to escape, she settled down to prepare for her confinement in a cosy corner off the pulpit where they found
her in a bed of fur scratched from her own body. Goodness knows how
she survived. My husband said she must have existed on the proverbial
church mouse.

Mrs Lucy Long, Sheffield, Yorks.
Fourteen years ago, when I shared a flat with a girl friend, I turned the
scales at just over 13 stones. I thought: 'Time you did something about
this, my girl." So I joined a weekend club for long walks. We had wonderful times. It was not long before I lost my rubber tyre and the puffi-
ness receded from my face.

I must have looked "good" because a fellow wanderer always seemed
to keep up with me, and we found ourselves walking together – off the
track of the main party. Soon the Dales really got into our blood, and we
further pursued the cult of fitness by footing-it mid-week, as far as we
could get in the evening.

Though we walked pretty hard, stoppages to admire the scenery became
more and more frequent. One weekend, after an uncommonly long pause,
we decided to get wed. By that time I had walked off one and a half
stones and was slimmer than I had been for years. There was a little dieting thrown in.

After marriage, for one reason or another, the walking ceased. Neither
of us had had a home of our own, and for the first time in our lives, we
could relax in peace. Since then my ballast has increased to tip the scales
at 13½ stones. Do you think I can get my old-time rover to hit the road
again? Not a bit of it. He who once walked his way into my life now
slumps contentedly behind a steering-wheel, grinning at my efforts to contain my ever-widening horizons.

Does anyone know of an energetic bunch of weekend vagrants looking
for a recruit?

Winifred Spray, Oxford OX1 5QZ.
The warning suggested in "Beloved Reader" winter issue 1989. "Credit
cards are injurious to wealth" transported me back down the years to the
timely advice of my beloved grandfather, born in 1866. I had succumbed
to the temptation to buy twopenny bars of chocolate "on tic" from a fellow pupil at school whose parents kept a sweet shop. Undetected by the
school authorities, we used to gather round her in a corner of the play-
ground at break and select from her satchel of goodies, mounting up debts
far beyond my sixpence a week pocket money. I resorted to "borrow-
ing" pennies from my mother's purse . . . fortunately nipped in the bud.
On a subsequent visit to my grandfather he handed to me the customary
few pence for extra spending money with words I have never forgotten.
"For every sixpence you have if you spend some and save some you will
he happy but if you spend more than you have in your purse you will
have increasing worry and unhappiness." He didn't mention my "stealing" but I knew he knew. I had learnt a hard lesson! The temptress was
later expelled for stealing. She had taken the chocolate without her parents' knowledge. Is this how today's drug addicts often start on the
downward slippery slope?

PS. My son, who lives in Los Angeles, tells me that only people living on credit are considered reputable . . . in other words it is an asset to be creditworthy! What an upside-down world we live in!

A. S. Stokes.
Some years ago when my wife was expecting a baby she mentioned to a very old woman in the village where she lived that she badly wanted a boy for her first child.

The old woman said: 'Never sit down when you can stand up – and you will be sure to have a boy."

For the next nine months my wife followed the advice rigorously. I now have four children – all girls. And a wife with flat feet.

Margaret Blakesby, Derby.
My son is on benzodiazepines and we would like to get him off them. He is not the same person as he once was. The problem is anxiety.

ED: *Benzodiazepines are a group of minor tranquillizers much in use in present-day medicine. One third of those taking tranquillizers become addicted. One of the problems of psychological dependency is the discomfort of withdrawal symptoms that may include tremors, restlessness, nausea and sleep disturbance. The greater the potency of the drug the higher the rebound anxiety.*

It would not be wise to introduce any new remedy without the knowledge of your doctor. He should be informed of any new medicaments you may be taking. Doctors' drugs that have been used over a long period should not be summarily discontinued.

Today, when more doctors are cooperative towards herbal medicine, the chances are he would agree to supplementation of this treatment with, say, Valerian tablets. Also, a cup of German Chamomile tea, or Scullcap tea, can offer safe support.

Avoid high blood sugar levels by rejecting alcohol, white flour products, chocolate, sugar and high cholesterol foods. Vitamin B6. Mineral: zinc. Stop smoking.

Mrs Nellie Jackson.
I have been looking through some of my old *Grace* Magazines which I have bought regularly since 1962.

It was from these magazines that I obtained knowledge of vitamin E and which I've taken regularly for some years. Because of this, maybe readers might be interested in my experience with that vitamin.

Originally, I took 200 mg daily with my doctor's knowledge but not approval, until two years ago when he started prescriptions for 600 units per day in addition to my Digoxin.

Four years ago I had (a second) minor stroke and practically lost the sight of my left eye (a thrombosed vein). At that time I took 200 mg vitamin E. Two years ago my doctor put me on 600 units. I saw the eye consultant at that time and the eye had improved so that I could read the two top letters of the chart. Two years later, all the "blackness" I saw had disappeared and I'm back to my usual short-sighted but clear vision and have returned to the Social Services office the table-lamp I'd been lent.

My eye consultant is now retired and I thought he would be interested, so I wrote to tell him. He said that throughout his whole experience he had only two patients who *partially* improved from that eye condition. My case was remarkable as he'd never heard of this eye condition being cured. He made no comment on the vitamin E.

For myself, I'm convinced that vitamin E was the cause of my wonderful recovery. I'm grateful for having read about it in *Grace*. I continue with the vitamin E, but also take 500 mg vitamin C as I'm on a very restricted diet. I also buy natural wheat germ, bran and honey.

Mrs H. Ball, Ollerton, Derbyshire.
This is the time of the year when I have in my garden rosemary, silver-tinted thyme, sweet cicely, sorrel, lemon-scented balm, and eau-de-cologne mint. Ward nurses in hospitals often wonder what on earth to do with all the flowers left by solicitous visitors. Last week when visiting a friend in hospital, I handed her a bunch of my sweet-scented herbs, freshly gathered, with dew still on them. She said they were the most fragrant things she received – a pleasure to others around her, and a joy at night. A bowl of these in ward or room on a hot day is really refreshing. Do not forget to add a sprig of lavender.

Mrs A. B. Robertson, Chiswick, London.
You urge us and inspire us take up new interests, implying that people with hobbies are not likely to go crazy. Does this apply to the people they live with?

Mr Arne Notland, Morrin, Alberta, Canada.
I have read the issue of *Grace* for Summer 1972 and find it most interesting. The write-up on honey really 'rings a bell' with me as I had an interesting experience many years ago. Through a sad mistake I had a considerable part of my abdomen scalded with hot water and steam. A very painful experience indeed. It dazed me and I did not know what to do. Away out on the Alberta Prairies on my own – no one to turn to. Somehow, a thought hit me. I had a can of pure honey. I dissolved some of it with hot water, slopped plenty of it over the scalded parts, twice covered it with a cloth wet with cold water. In less time than I write this, the pain was gone and I went to sleep. After that I dressed the parts once a day with honey with a few drops of lemon juice added.

I carried on with my regular farm work every day without any discomfort whatever. The wound healed and left no scar.

Miss A. Donald, Hayes, Middlesex.
Can anything be done for lack of alertness and ability to cope. I have
had check-ups which show my blood and organs are O.K., and the specialist says "Nothing is wrong with you". Yet there are days when I can't
get further than my front door. I feel so scared. I am normally a sensible person, capable of looking-after myself, but something comes over
me, I don't want to see anybody. I feel flushed, and I panic I don't want
to be written off in my forties.

ED: *Your trouble might be diagnosed as agoraphobia, and for which
we would not be able to offer detailed advice.*

*Doubtless you have overhauled your diet in favour of fresh raw veg-
etables and fruit, wholewheat bread, honey, and especially Brewer's Yeast
rich in the Vitamin B group. Look to calcium intake by having a course
of tablets: one after meals three times daily.*

*This is one of the few complaints for which it is not necessary to find
the original cause. If you went through the long drill of exhausting clinical and pathological tests, knowledge of past mental trauma is not going
to help very much. The original cause could well have been replaced
months ago by a stress reaction. A flash of panic can set the heart rac-
ing while the sympathetic nervous system may be highly sensitized.*

*In place of heavy tranquillizers, a simple herb like Scullcap (scutellaria
laterifolia), may sustain the nervous system and make it easier to bear.
One source declares the condition to be due to a deficiency of vitamin C.
In any case, a reduced tea and coffee intake should prove rewarding: caffeine (in coffee) and theophylline (in tea) and theobromine (in cocoa) containing xanthine which can over-stimulate the nervous system, especially
the higher cortical centres.*

*Try to go easy on these three beverages for a number of reasons. All
raise the blood-sugar level which, if hoisted too high through immoder-
ate drinking and lots of sugars, can lead to restlessness, tinnitus (ringing
in the ears) excitement and hallucinations. All this makes for anxiety.
Cut down fats, especially cheese, fat of meat, and milk, as a raised cholesterol level can react on the hypothalamus – which regulates body temperature.*

*Output of adrenalin is likely to be increased when in this state of anx-
iety-stress. Anything which inhibits hyperactivity of the adrenal cortex
would be welcome. Cutting out the adrenal stimulators coffee, tea and
cocoa may mean you are already half-way to recovery. What to take in
their place? Fruit juices, carrot and other vegetable juices, herb teas:
lime flowers, lemon-balm tea, rose-hip and hibiscus tea.*

*Try not to be demoralized by your intense reaction to stress. In spite
of fears, go out to meet other people, buy yourself a new dress, realise*

your limitations and learn to live cheerfully with them. Hoping it will not be long before all is well.

F. Foley, New Barnet, Herts.
Our little girl is irritable, sleeps badly, and has a head full of tiny lice in spite of very clean habits. When I was a boy I believe my mother got rid of them with sulphur ointment, but I cannot believe this is the best thing to use.

ED: *The killing of these parasites with strong chemical creams (especially sulphur ointments) may remove the unwanted guests, but can do incalculable harm to the host. Space does not permit to enlarge upon the startling account that these have come from within the body of the host herself. True, they can be 'caught' from others. These are psoric taints which Nature is trying to eliminate.*

A lady, belonging to a refined family, suffered from chronic headaches and nervous twitchings for years. As a school girl she was troubled with head vermin and her mother treated them with sulphur ointment. Internal uncleanliness favours the development of these parasites acting as Nature's scavengers in purifying the system of scrofulous and psoric poisons. Chemical ointments arrest this form of elimination via the skin and, through absorption, can be the cause of trouble elsewhere in the body. Natural treatments culminated in an out-cropping of head-lice later in life, when she was wisely advised not to interfere with anything stronger than cold water and a comb. The visitors stayed-around for two weeks before disappearing altogether. 'Catching' was absolutely out of the question, for she did not mix with society or see people at close quarters.

You don't have to believe that from the time of departure of those 'nasty things' she never again had chronic headaches or twitching of the limbs.

This is no isolated case, Mr Foley, The moral is: cut out the suppressive ointments and be patient. Wash the scalp night and morning with a strong infusion of quassia chips, prepared in cold water. Never steep the virtue out of quassia with hot water. Its volatile properties just vanish into thin air and it is worse than useless.

Where do these creatures come from? We do not know. But one thing we do know: that body miasmas related to internal poisons attract bacteria and parasites as surely as carrion attracts vultures.

Anonymous
One small pleasure of life can be to learn the marvellous virtues of herbs. Tell us about Chamomile flowers!

ED: *This is one of our oldest favourites among garden herbs and its reputation goes back to Egyptian days. The flower-heads are used. Two to five flower-heads may be placed in a teacup filled with boiling water; infuse for five minutes, and drink when necessary when nerves are 'on edge'. A natural tranquillizer. Good for getting you off to sleep when other things have failed. Menopause without tears.* What else? *Of definite value for over-acidity, troublesome wind, and indigestion generally. It used to be called an 'antispasmodic' because it can relieve pain in certain conditions. Of course, it has no deep-acting action like Benzodiazepine or Librium, but for anxious patients where tears are not far away Chamomile may act like a charm. It will even quieten excitable cats or dogs and make them more manageable. Fancy that!*

Anonymous
We have been married four years with no family, and have heard that vitamin 'E' has solved the problem. Is it true?

ED: *Yes, we confirm that cases of inability to conceive have been assisted by this vitamin. Two capsules (800 international units) may be taken daily. You should consult a specialist who may be able to help you further.*

Mrs Jenny Turton, Franklin, Tasmania.
I've read dozens of ways of getting off to sleep in different magazines and papers. Nothing did me any good until one night someone told me to try to keep my eyes open in the dark. The more you try to keep them open the tireder they get, until you have to let them have their way. I now have no difficulty.

Dulcie Hills, Worksop, Notts.
My husband belongs to the brotherhood of the perpetual stoop. He has Parkinson's. I know you can do little for this complaint. Could vitamins help?

ED: *We are sorry indeed to learn of your husband's condition and though it is usually regarded as irreversible, express the hope that some improvement may come about as regards the tremor, balance, and possibly a loosening-up of the unyielding rigidity. Do not expect too much: do not overlook some regular daily intake of vitamin B6.*

Remember, its shortage can stoke-up nerve tension generally. Also, see that he has other B vitamin supplements. Do not run-down his protein defences too low. Wasting muscles are not helped by stringent diets. Walnuts. Scullcap herb.

Mrs Nora Adamson, Kingston Road, London.
I *must* endorse what many readers say about the healing properties of Honey, for in January I had the most alarming outbreak of skin trouble (from which I have suffered since 1938) – and had a deep sore on the side of my right calf. Amazing, I did not feel afraid, as is the usual reaction, but calmly studied what was best to do – spread it with honey, and laid a gauze cooler over it – and soothing and healing was nothing less than

miraculous. I have achieved much composure since studying and prac-tising Yoga, becoming vegetarian/raw food eater, and reading *Grace* and so on. Wish I'd time to write more. Send loving thoughts to all read-ers and staff. Sincerely.

T. Powell, Melton Mowbray, Leicestershire.
Thanks for advice given in a past copy of your Magazine on Wood Betony herb tea for nervous tension and headache. It has done my wife good, and though she wouldn't admit it – I say her dyspepsia has improved. I know she must be better, because she used to find her few friends irritat-ing and was a bit too free with a critical tongue. She says the herbs have not done any good . . . but thinks other people are now behaving a lot better.
ED: *You don't say!*

Mrs Katherine Blanchard, Calgary, Alberta, Canada.
On page 65 of the Autumn 1982 issue, a reader thanks Miss Barbara Cartland for her prescribing honey, cider vinegar and Dolomite tablets for insomnia. This reminded me of what I read in "Prevention" about research into insomnia which revealed that the level of calcium in the blood determined our actually going to sleep. The Dolomite tablets con-tain both Calcium and Magnesium. Magnesium is necessary to utilize Calcium, so Dolomite certainly aids sleep and promotes the necessary bal-ance. With every good wish.
ED: *It was in her article in Grace, Summer 1981, that Barbara Cartland described her method of getting off to sleep. I quote part of it again for readers who missed the original: Barbara Cartland wrote: "Before I turn out the light I take what is the most effective and to my mind, the most wonderful sleep-evoker in the world. It consists of one spoonful of honey – it does not matter whether thick or thin – one tablespoon of Cider Vinegar in a tumbler of water and two Dolomite tablets.*

Mrs Perry, Lower Dunton, Nr Brentwood.
Thanks to Hawthorn tablets, my hearing is a lot better and I have not had any noises in my ears.

Just Jumble.
A woman who placed a bundle of jumble-sale items for collection from the doorstep of her home in Kettering, Northamptonshire, had a shock exactly a week later when she received them back from the local laundry, all neatly washed and ironed. With them came a bill for £6.50.

Mrs R. B., Leeds.
I dialled the speaking clock on the telephone and allowed my four-year-old daughter to listen.

She looked awestruck and when I had replaced the receiver, whispered: "Have I been listening to the Queen?"

Mr J. L. B. Gill, Portsmouth.
I have taken Pulsatilla tablets for prostate trouble and found them very effective and can thoroughly recommend them to poor old chaps like myself (89 years). Yours sincerely.

Mr George Walker, Sheffield, Yorks.
We are great pip-planters in our family. As well as my garden, I have a row of home-grown saplings on the kitchen window, each from four to eight inches tall. I set an apple-seed in a flower pot and it grew to about eight inches. Then, for some unaccountable reason, it stopped growing.

Thinking it was dying, I tipped it onto the compost heap and left it. Some time later it was salvaged by the children who planted it in their patch at the bottom of the garden. You can imagine our surprise when, some weeks later, it sprouted green shoots and started growing again. It is now doing well. We simply can't wait for the apples!

Anonymous.
Do we sometimes view the medical profession with too much misgiving? When I visited my doctor he looked very efficient and very formidable sitting there waiting for my report on the month's treatment.

I looked at the white shirt, well-groomed appearance and severe expression. I thought to myself I shall never be able to admit I had not taken his pills, but had accepted the services of an acupuncturist. And here I was   back-ache now gone – and feeling better than I had for months!

How wrong I was! On closer acquaintance he turned out to be a most understanding, willing practitioner. "No, I don't mind a bit what therapy cures you – as long as you get cured. It's your back, and it's up to you to do the best for yourself. Only, next time . . . let me first know where you are going."

I think some of us view the doctors with too much misgiving. I really believe some of them have come round to our way of thinking.

Mrs M. W. G., N. Yorks.
I thought you would like to know that I have boiled feverfew leaves until the colour comes out – boil just for a minute or two. My neighbour, who is 92, was crippled with arthritis – and also my neighbour on the other side with arthritis of the hip – have taken a wineglassful every day. After ten days' improvement they continued to take the decoction and now both are cured.

Moment of history

I WANT to tell you about an act of sheer grace which saved many lives.

On 5th August, 1620, the Mayflower, a vessel of 180 tons, sailed from Southampton, carrying 41 men and their families, 102 persons in all. It had been decided to make the passage with the Speedwell but the captain of the latter lost courage, with the result that the Mayflower made the voyage alone. They were bound for the banks of the Hudson; but after a long and stormy voyage they landed, 21st December, on the bleak shores of Cape Cod.

How they survived that first terrible winter will never be known. Some died of fever. Malnutrition from chronic vitamin deficiency from weeks of restricted sea-diet had left them in feeble health. Shortage of fats exposed their bodies to the paralysing effects of severe cold.

Then came a sickening distemper bringing the added discomforts of gangrene with revolting abscesses. If some felt their prayers were unanswered, it was only because the limits of human endurance had been reached.

When all seemed lost, it happened. The sky cleared. A breathless hush fell over the winter landscape. They were not alone. Animals, also had been lashed by hunger and the elements. With their teeth, deer were seen stripping off bark from a tree. Fear of man had strangely deserted them in their hour of desolation.

The message was clear. Strongest of the settlers limped over a snow-silted slope to prize-off slivers of bark with the aid of a boathook. It was quickly placed in the colony cauldron to simmer. Providence had not forsaken them. They found strength in the thick demulcent gruel. Eyes began to see again. New hope lit tired hearts.

Soothing the thick gruel on their eroding ulcers they were soon to give thanks for another unfolding miracle. Skins cleared. Sores healed. Colic disappeared. The virtues of Slippery Elm had been discovered.

Today, finely powdered slippery elm bark of the Ulmus Fulva tree is added to a base of pre-cooked wheaten flour (in some cases from the wholemeal), and barley-malt. The finished base is in the form of a very fine powder which mixes readily with water, or milk, without forming lumps. On its own the powdered bark of this tree is difficult to mix. An important feature of this new method of preparation is that the mixture contains active enzymes of malted barley which have the power of converting cereal starches into soluble, hence more digestible, carbohydrates – dextrins and maltose.

What is its other abilities? It aids the digestion of milk by separation of the casein particles. This can be of benefit to children, invalids, and to those with a touchy digestion. This is done without the aid of pancreatin or other similar unnatural digestives.

Today, Slippery Elm is on sale in every Health Store in this country, Canada and America. It has been a sheet-anchor to the unregistered practitioner for many years for gastric and duodenal ulceration.

It has diuretic and pectoral properties, and can be used to buffer mucous membranes against irritation and inflammation. It can prove a boon to chronic ulcerative colitis. Its healing-touch was first felt by the Apache Indians whose trails made detours to bring them within easy reach of the 'Gohooska tree', which they regarded as both food and medicine. It softened and protected faces exposed for days to harsh weather.

"It was in the following spring," wrote Bruce Catton, "that those early fathers went to church in Plymouth town to thank God for His goodness. For they had known hunger, pain and want; gone thinly clad through iron winter; thrown the gauntlet down to Death himself, and let him take his toll. And now they had won through. And so they prayed their word of thanks, and stood up unafraid, and faced the future with undaunted soul."

It was at Cape Cod that they drew-up their famous pact which became the political bulwark of that brave little colony of Puritans. The covenant agreed to constitute "just and equal laws that shall be thought most meet for the general good of the colony." From it emerged a great nation. Its keynote is still freedom: It is a tree which blossoms in the soil of the New World, but it had its roots in Britain.

This goes to prove that with sufficient trust and the stickability to hold on long enough help is always at hand. The age of miracles is not past.

Mr G. D., Swansea.
My wife continues with Vitex Agnus Castus. She is experiencing about 75% relief from her "hot flushes", which is fantastic. Neither does she suffer from mastitis now.

Anonymous.
My hair is coming out in handfuls. I've never had anything like it before; I don't want to be bald. My father is pretty thin on top. I've tried all sorts of lotions and shampoos.

ED: *Are you sure you are not washing the hair too frequently in hot water? This, as well as some commercial shampoos on the market can have the effect of removing the natural oils from the hair, causing the scalp to become too dry. The hair should only be washed once a fortnight using warm water and a bland vegetable soap or shampoo (rosemary, etc.).*

While it is natural for any of us to lose about a hundred hairs a day, they are usually replaced by new ones. The scalp, however, has "resting" periods which may last for a few months when new growth is minimal. Severe stress can change the hair cycle resulting in hair loss. This may occur in severe illness, shock, or having babies. Such loss may indicate a deficiency of iron or the thyroid hormone.

You are probably run down and in need of a diet rich in minerals. Take at least one mixed salad daily, with as wide a range of green and root vegetables as possible. If not already taking them, call at your nearest Health Food Store for a supply of B vitamins, kelp (iodine), prunes (iron), and dates (a rich source of minerals) .

Are you quite sure it is not due to anaemia, thyroid trouble, or exhaustion of the adrenal glands? Stress, anxiety, over-work, irregular meals and prolonged emotional tension all play their part. Make room for early nights, rest and a well-balanced diet including wholegrains (oats, corn and barley) and olive oil.

The element Silica (present in horsetail herb), or as it appears in the Tissue Salt (Silicea), stimulates the growth of hair if it is capable of recovery. Trace elements zinc and selenium have also had favourable reports and are worth trying if other remedies fail.

Hair-care, at the present moment, centres around jojoba oil, extracted from the seeds of a desert shrub which flourishes in Southern Carolina, Arizona and Mexico. It is claimed to be a match for dandruff and hair loss.

The funny thing about hair is that it always evens up the effort you have to make. If you have less hair to comb, you have more face to wash. I am told the most delightful advantage of being bald, is that one can hear the snowflakes.

Mr Guy Ragland Phillips, Holt, Norfolk.
I have discovered the virtue of comfrey ointment. After a stroke, my left leg became liable to gout (without alcohol). Comfrey immediately and

completely dispels the pain of gout, reduces swelling and inflammation, and the benefit is lasting. If the gout recurs, it yields at once to the comfrey ointment. Yours sincerely.

Mr H. Short, Beeston, Nottingham.
Saccharine is the stuff that keeps your torso from getting more so, but it might also cause your bladder to get badder.

Mrs V. C., Manchester.
We hear it all around that you are too old at forty. For me, everything happened when well over fifty, when my children were married and left home.

For the first time in my married life I had time to spare. After my youngest daughter went to the altar I did not know what to do with myself. I mooned around the house, and read a lot of books. That was good for me, for my eyes were opened to the advantages of wholesome foods and vitamins. I have taken garlic ever since, and it has done me a lot of good. A whole new world has opened up. By collecting recipes, I now take more time cooking my husband's meals, with appreciative results.

We bought a new car, re-furnished the lounge, and now have time to visit friends. I actually learned to drive! Five years ago I would never have dreamed my husband and I would take up ballroom dancing. What fun we have!

It simply is not true that you start to wane at forty. I'm past 55, and reckon I've only just started living!

Your prayers are requested for:
All members of Grace Family who are in hospital or undergoing medical or surgical treatment, that they may soon be restored to their homes whole and healed.

For everybody who handles *Grace Magazine*, that they may derive some blessing; physically, mentally and spiritually. That they may feel a kinship, one with another, and be conscious of the welfare of all.

For those concerned with the production of the magazine, that it may go from strength to strength.

For the sick, lonely and homeless, everywhere, that it may not be long before the tyrannies of the world yield to the coming of the Kingdom of Heaven upon earth.

D. E. Howard, Colden Common, Winchester.
I would like you to know that my blood pressure returned to normal after I had taken Rutin tablets for a few days. I had taken the doctor's tablets for blood pressure for three weeks to no effect. So you can imagine I am very pleased that Rutin has done the trick.

Ralph Lewis, (Union Street), Brighton BNJ.
Look upwards. Think outwards, stretch to help other people. Eat little and well, choosing simple pure food that God has provided so abundantly. Fishes and loaves, wild herbs and honey, home-made cream cheese and produce from orchard and vegetable garden. Avoid worry, which has never solved a single problem. Before sleep, ask for forgiveness, for a peaceful mind – after a day of hard work and harmony.

Hell is having nothing to do, and heaven is having sufficient each day. Live one day at a time, feeling the joy of being alive, of being loved and blessed.

Debora . . . (Philadelphia, U.S.A.).
Little Kristina's kiss will remain with me as a poignant memory of my summer as a recreation aide. Teaching arts and crafts to pre-school children, I found, was enjoyable, sometimes difficult and most of all rewarding. Kristina was one of my many small friends who helped make it so.

Large tears, I remember, would silently well-up in her eyes during her first few classes with us and her pathetic expression moved me to make her my own special pupil. Each day I sat with her, colouring, talking and trying to draw her out of her wide-eyed silence.

One day, before going to meet her mother, Kristina beckoned to me and I bent down to be rewarded with a kiss. By the end of the arts and crafts programme Kristina was a talkative, active five-year-old, no longer fearful and shy.

Miss M. Harrison, Hove, Sussex.
I would like to tell you about pure fresh carrot juice. I took it for a month. It does improve eyesight. I am now able to read and write without glasses, which I have not been able to do for ten years.

Most people know that carrot juice is good for the eyes, but cooked carrots are no good; neither is the small amount the average person takes on a salad. What is needed is a small cupful of raw fresh carrot juice.

Jerome Frank Slezak, Lakewood, Ohio, 44107, U.S.A.
I have read, re-read and retained in my library, *Grace Magazine* for over 15 years!

I work as an inspector in an aluminium die casting foundry. One day hot aluminium metal spit from a machine into the air and a piece, the size of a quarter, landed on my shoulder between my neck and my right shoulder.

I began to worry as a red spot 3" by 3" did not disappear for over four months from that burn. Reading about vitamin E in *Grace* several times, I took two vitamin E capsules, broke them, and rubbed them all around the red area.

WHILE THE KETTLE BOILS

Nothing happened after a week and my thoughts were not on the spot. Then! during the second week it lightened up and disappeared! My peace of mind returned with my deep thanks for *Grace Magazine*!

ED: *Thank you, Frank, for a fascinating account of your natural healing without the aid of drugs. You see . . . it can be done! Harmless alternatives can be found all around us, and we are delighted to know you have fully recovered.*

We never cease to be amazed at miracles arising from the use of natural substances. Of all vitamins, vitamin E (d'alpha tocopherol) is the one which throws up most controversy. The trouble is: it is so versatile.

It is capable of producing positive results in such diverse conditions as burns, heart disease, cramp, menstrual pain and gangrene. With the terrific pressures of modern life on our heart and arterial system, it would appear that everybody needs this strength and stay. Varicose veins, arthritis, fragility of blood vessels . . . we could go on for ever! When will conventional medicine catch up with all the evidence piling up in its favour?

C. T.
A rheumatic subject from birth, with a grim medical history during childhood and youth, including two years on my back, I can now walk with a pack fifteen miles – considerably more without one. I have been completely vegetarian for eleven years and was almost vegetarian for five years before that. *Breakfast*: Dried fruits and nuts or porridge, then wholemeal bread, honey and butter. *Midday*: Conservatively cooked vegetables and a savoury of pulse foods, cheese or nuts; fruit in season. *Evening*: A large salad. There is an enormous variety of salads – but get away from tired lettuce, withered tomato and flabby boiled beetroot soaked in vinegar. I heartily recommend Dr Bircher-Benner's books on food science.

Mrs Bridie Barrett, Coventry.
Congratulations on the beautiful magazine, *Grace*. A friend passed a copy on to me and I must say I have never read a book that has helped me so much. I have read many and various books on practically all topics – as I read Classics at University – but *Grace* is the most unique I've ever come across. I did want to put my feelings on record. Ad multos annos! Yours sincerely.

Miss M. Felgare, Basingstoke, Hants.
Not long ago I was sitting in the local restaurant, which was crowded, and while waiting for the young lady to come and take my order, I overheard someone at a nearby table giving her order for lunch. When asked what vegetable she would like, she said: "No, not swede, thank you, it's a bit blow-you-uppish, if you know what I mean."

Miss M. I. Bateman, Bath, Avon.
I must tell you of wonderful results of Lobelia tablets. After 'flu. I was in despair with quinsy-like obstruction deep down in the throat . . . the larynx . . . for several days. I thought it would never clear . . . with the choking and the cough. Lobelia came to the rescue. Many thanks, Yours sincerely.

Lis Kurtz, Los Angeles, California.
My cat suffered from a condition known as military eczema. He lost most of his hair around the base of his tail and along his back, and he was going bald on his haunches. There were red sores on the bald places.

The vet prescribed shots and pills, which didn't provide any permanent relief. So I began my own treatment plan. Each day I gave my cat a flea bath, one teaspoon of brewer's yeast in his food and a dose of vitamin E oil rubbed into his sores. After four days of this regimen his sores were gone! I have a feeling that his hair will start growing back, too.

Sunshine Magazine, Litchfield, Illinois, USA.
Muscular back pain is often suffered by people on long flights. To help prevent this discomfort, it's recommended that the seat be tilted back about 20 degrees and one small pillow placed against the lower back and another at the base of the neck. Also, every 20 minutes or so, bend forward from your waist to your knees, arch your back, do wrist and ankle rotations and neck rolls.

Mrs J. N., Cambridgeshire.
We were having an at-home holiday and on one typically cool and cloudy English summer's day we stayed in the car to eat our picnic lunch, pulling up by a tall hedge bordering some fields. To our delight, a tiny wren decided to build her nest at just the right height for us to watch. As she flitted in and out of the hedge we marvelled at the speed, skill and tenacity of such a little creature.

This marvellous lesson in patience and fortitude has remained one of my most treasured holiday memories.

Dorothy Knopp, Wroughton, Swindon, Wilts.
A young lad of ten years had suffered from eczema since the age of two years, particularly around the body and ears, which were red and scaly. He had had all sorts of medicine to no avail.

I suggested (apart from a diet) that he bathed the areas with Cider Vinegar, which he did for three weeks. The redness, scaling and soreness all subsided. Application had to be daily otherwise the condition again flared up. At present he is much better and along with diet and chiropractic treatment the eczema is slowly going. Other members of the family have found Cider Vinegar effective for arthritis and weight loss. All good wishes.

Uncle "Willie", Stoke on Trent.
Man comes into this world without his consent and leaves it against his will. On earth he is misjudged and misunderstood. In infancy he is an angel; in boyhood he is a devil; in manhood he is a fool.

If he has a wife and family he is a chump; if he is a bachelor he is inhuman. If he enters a public house he is a drunkard; if he stops out he is a miser. If he is a poor man he has no brains; if he is rich he has had all the luck in the world. If he has brains he is considered smart but dishonest. If he goes to church he is a hypocrite; if he stays away he is a sinful man. If he gives to charity it is for advertisement; if he does not he is stingy and mean.

When he comes into the world everybody wants to kiss him; before he goes out everybody wants to kick him.

If he dies young there was a great future for him; if he lives to a ripe old age everybody hopes he has made a will.

Advertisement by a Health Farm
Tubby, or not tubby . . . fat is the question.

Miss Irene Everton, Liverpool, Merseyside.
As I was going through some of my mother's papers I found this recipe for whooping cough and wondered if it would be of interest to you. I remember her telling me when I was a little girl (I'm now a pensioner) that I had terrible whooping cough which none of the doctor's medicine seemed to help. She cured me herself with the following:

"Take 1oz Mouse Ear herb and ½oz Slippery Elm bark. Boil in 2 pints of water down to one pint. Dose: a wineglassful frequently. This will be sufficient in most cases. It may be found advisable to administer an emetic in order that accumulation of mucus may be removed. Care should be taken to ensure that the bowels are in a healthy condition . A wholesome but light diet is recommended."

Mrs Edith Harvey, Limuru, Kenya.
Once again I am most grateful to *Grace Magazine*. Here is another tip for other members of The Family.

Hiccups. I find if I press my fingers onto the openings of my ears hard, and hold my breath, my hiccups stop. I think it must be an acupuncture point. It works with me everytime!

Newspaper weather forecast.
Low temperatures tomorrow night. Mild with periods of sin possible on Monday or Tuesday.

249

Contributed.
Parkinson's Second Law, like the first, is a matter of everyday experience, manifest as soon as it is stated, as obvious as it is simple.

When the individual has a raise in salary, he and his wife are prone to decide how the additional income is to be spent; so much on an insurance policy, so much to the savings bank, so much in a trust fund for the children.

They might just as well save themselves the trouble, for no surplus ever comes into view. The extra salary is silently absorbed, leaving the family barely in credit and often, in fact, with a deficit which has actually increased. Individual expenditure not only rises to meet income but tends to surpass it, and probably always will.

Mrs Angus McIndoe, Ontario, Canada.
Your unique *Grace* arrived last Friday. I was so pleased to receive it. It is a lovely and inspiring magazine. Last summer I visited my beloved homeland for one month. We were met at Gatwick by a younger cousin. From picturesque Hampshire we travelled to the Isle of Wight – next place to heaven on earth – then on to beautiful Cornwall. I also visited my birthplace, Birchington, Kent. Truly England is still a marvellous country with flowers, tasty food, with so many charming places to visit, and not to forget all the friendly people. I wonder if many of the natives appreciate it? Thank you again. With best wishes, most sincerely.

From the Editor.
Top 'O the morning to Jo Hilton. Thank you, Jo, for your Valentine card. What a lovely thought! It fairly made my day . . . and many laughs. We like the words: Happy Valentine day . . . Today, Tomorrow, and Always.

Anonymous
I read with interest your column on Alzheimer's disease. It now seems that aluminium salts from cooking vessels, antacids and certain foodstuffs, are implicated. Can anything be done by alternative medicine once the disease is estimated?

ED: *Once aluminium has been laid down in plaque form in the brain it is difficult to understand how it can be resolved. Such elderly patients are most likely to suffer from deficiency of calcium; this puts them at risk by laying down more aluminium. While the first consideration is to avoid the source of contamination, the new technique of chelation appears to be indicated. To facilitate elimination of aluminium salts, a 48 hour fluid-only fast each month for six months, should assist. Improvement has been reported by large doses vitamin B complex.*

Indicated herb teas: Alfalfa, Chaparral, Ginseng, Gotu kola, Horsetail, Hawthorn, Mistletoe. 1 teasp to cup boiling water; infuse 15 minutes. ½-1 cup 3 times daily.

R. R. Davey, Devon.
We have two friends who are taking Echinacea tablets for their leg ulcers which are closing. They are no longer kept awake at night with pain.

Contributed.
People who tell you not to let little things bother you should try sleeping in a room with a mosquito.

H. Maxwell.
Anyone overtaken by years who starts getting disillusioned or embittered, turning inward away from people, is fast becoming old, crotchety, unloved. Keep up the friendly side of your nature and be good friends to those who have proved that to you.

Whenever you can, make friends with younger people, too. A true, active friend, a real friendly person, never has time to worry about whether he or she is growing old, for life is too full and rewarding.

Mr V. Lucas, Grantham.
Did you hear about the chap who went on a diet, eating only powdered foods? One day he got caught in the rain and gained 22lbs.

Mrs H. Hitchings, Carlisle, Cumbria.
I have been taking Motherwort tablets for hypertension which I have found very effective for migraine headaches from which I have suffered severely.

ED: *Tincture of Motherwort is an alternative to tablets.*

Contributed.
A pessimist is a person who spends a lifetime in a dark room – developing only negatives.

From "The Best Medicine", by Graeme Gorden.
A patient suffering from insomnia was told by her doctor to be sure that she never went to bed on an empty stomach.

"But you once told me never to eat before going to bed," the puzzled woman replied.

"That was last year," the doctor said. "Medicine has made enormous advances since then."

Weekly News, Wellington, Somerset.
A report on a meeting of the Appleby Cross Women's Institute stated:

"The speaker for the evening was Mrs Oates, whose talk, 'We are what we eat," provided a great deal of interest and discussion.

Anonymous.
For diverticulitis I have taken Propolis capsules and Goldenseal tablets
for a few years now. They keep me fine.

Beatrice Ball, Gosport.
Anyone having painful breathing on account of dry nasal passages may
get immediate relief by applying a thin smear of honey outside. It's wonderful what honey will do – inside and out! Wishing members of the
Family every joy and blessing.

Sign on the bumper of a car:
"Keep Tooting" – It's your ulcer not mine."

Miss D. Hutchings, Holland-on-Sea, Essex.
My sister is almost 90. Just over a year ago she developed a septic cyst
on the top bone of her spine. The doctor's treatment cleared the septic
tissue but it didn't heal. As it was just where the collar of her dresses
rubbed, it was very painful. I decided to try natural vitamin E.

I pierced a capsule with a sterilized needle and squeezed it on the wound
and covered it with gauze. This I did night and morning. In 48 hours it
was healed. It has been no trouble ever since.

Also, I have discovered that vitamin E conditioning cream is wonderful for taking out aches and pains caused by gardening, etc. Just a little
rubbed-in takes away a lot of stiffness.

I can't remember how long we have been reading *Grace*. We wouldn't
be without it for anything.

From Brownie Notes in the Harefield parish magazine:
"We are very sorry to lose our Tawny Owl (Miss Crowe)".

Marian Pitt, Mont a l'Abbe, Jersey, Channel Islands.
Tinnitus.

Summer sun, the sound of toddlers playing at a bucket filled with water
on the grass . . . A blackbird's song of lusty serenading, and the hum of
busy insects flying past . . . While here, inside my ear drum's twisting
passage of bone and flesh and blood and skin . . . A shrieking hiss, a thun-
dering tumult. Peace without but a cacophony within.

Yet by some developing act of concentration I can filter out this bedlam.

Once again the choice is mine . . . And in night's 'silence' when nothing in the place moves, only me . . . I can listen to my private wild Niagara
or clasp my thoughts and focus them on He who said "I'll never leave
you nor forsake you . . . The choice is mine, unwanted sound allowed to
overwhelm me, with it's insistent discord and it's din . . . Or concentrate
on life's sweet soothing music, and hear 'The still small voice of God
speak soft within'.

Miss M. Mair, Vancouver B.C., Canada.
I must report a complete and lasting cure of a leg ulcer. I tried eating tapioca daily as mentioned in this magazine under *While the Kettle Boils* submitted by another reader in Vancouver (strangely enough!) in the issue of Autumn 1986. What a blessing it is now to be free of that tiresome trouble!

I've read *Grace* for many years but have never come across any reference to *Aloe vera gel* in which I have great faith. It performs wonders on skin problems, burns, etc., and can also be taken internally. I feel certain it should be available in the UK. Thank you for the valuable information given in *Grace Magazine*. Sincerely.

ED: *Many thanks for writing to report a cure of leg ulcer without the aid of drugs. It is a pleasure to hear from you. Aloe vera is, of course, a remedy with a great future. It is exceedingly versatile not only for external, but for internal ulceration. It has a bacteriocidal action against staphylococcus aureus and five strains of streptococcus mutans – a cause of dental plaque. Contains 18 amino acids and vitamins, and is a precursor of vitamin B12 which so many people need these days.*

It is claimed that its future use will be concerned with radiation burns. A segment of the fresh leaf (it may be growing in your garden!) rubbed on the skin has been a centuries-old sun-screen by desert arabs against sunburn. They regarded the plant as a natural medicine chest. There is so much we could say about it, but space does not permit. It is rich in Germanium (an up-and-coming supplement to support the immune system) and helps eliminate toxic materials from the body. It is believed that one day it will be used as a weapon against cancer. Aloe vera is on sale in your nearest health food store.

Anonymous.
A doctor asked a patient who had come to see him with two badly-burned ears. "What has happened to you?"

He replied, "My wife was doing the ironing while we were watching television. She had the iron near the phone and when it rang I answered the iron."

"But what happened to the other ear?"

"Just as I hung up the phone rang again."

What Every Heart Patient should know

MAKE it a general rule to have your meals: 75 per cent vegetables and salads: 25 per cent starches and proteins; and very little fat. Meals should be taken at leisure. Masticate your food well. Do not use aluminium cooking vessels. Dry feed. Drink only between meals. Nowadays one danger of eating raw vegetable is that they have been chemically sprayed. Care should be taken to wash them thoroughly. Consult your dentist at regular intervals. Try to remember that correct food combinations are proteins and fats, and starches and fats. Do not read with your meals.

SODIUM-FREE DIET. Little salt should be taken at table, or in the cooking. Foods containing a low salt content should be used. Salt increases the volume of the blood and therefore raises the blood pressure. Table salt is not the only thing containing sodium. Avoid bicarbonate of soda (baking soda) where possible, and headache powders. Remember all those Egyptian mummies embalmed in salt.

EXERCISE. Keep in gentle motion as much as possible – walking or "pottering' about the house and garden. However, take long periods of rest after meals, with the feet up. Do not sit up late at night. The heart, like any other limb, must have its exercise, otherwise it will lose its "tone". Lack of exercise tends towards degenerative disease. When listening to television don't dance – unless you have to.

SMOKING. Smoking raises the blood pressure, constricts the vessels, and is detrimental in your case. There now exists definite evidence that smoking can have a damaging effect upon the muscular wall of the heart. Try not to incur this risk.

HONEY. Friend and sustainer of weak hearts, and equaliser of the circulation in cases of high blood pressure. Eat as much as desired, it is a great strengthener of the heart and allays the onset of arterio-sclerosis (premature hardening of the arteries). I have never known a person who regularly eats honey who has had any kind of kidney trouble. They all have clear complexions, good eyesight, and seldom succumb to rheumatism. It also promotes activity of the bowels. Before going to bed take a glass of hot water with honey and lemon juice. Repeat later, if in distress during the night.

GARLIC. Two garlic perles should be taken at bedtime. Garlic is effective for reducing high blood pressure and for favourably influencing cardiac rhythm and contraction. All's well that smells well.

VITAMIN "E". Recommended because of its anti-blood-clotting property. It is the natural anti-thrombin in the human bloodstream. Prevents the occurrence of anoxia (lack of oxygen) which is the trigger that sets off anginal or heart pain. Helps to prevent hardening of the arteries. Wheat Germ Oil or Olive oil may be added very sparingly to salads. Foods rich in this vitamin are: all green vegetables, beans, butter, green peas, turnip greens, wheat germ oil, and peanut oil.

POTASSIUM-RICH FOODS. Foods rich in potassium prolong the diastole in "flutter" or tachycardia. We shall endeavour to prolong the resting (filling) period of the heart and promote a better coronary blood flow by including in the dict a number of potassium-rich foods as follows: bananas, washed soaked raisins, figs, dates, cherries, dried peaches, walnuts, almonds, parsley, blackcurrants or blackcurrant syrup. Asparagus is fine for kidney elimination.

POTASSIUM SUPPLEMENTATION is necessary in heart conditions and high blood pressure. Pure fruit juices contain most potassium and little sodium. Only buy bottled

juices when unable to extract from fresh fruit at home. High on the list of bought preparations are pineapple, apricot nectar and orange juice. Pure lemon juice is lowest and Schweppes tomato highest of all.

THINGS TO AVOID. Cut out white flour and all products made from it. Cut down consumption of meat, bread, puddings, pies and cakes – these and all stodgy foods place an extra burden on the heart. Eliminate all artificial sugar from the diet, taking honey or cane sugar in its place. Avoid sweets, pastries, soft drinks and sugar in tea. Do not eat anything from the pig – bacon, ham or pork. Avoid preserved or smoked meats, corned beef and sausages. These are loaded with salt and chemical preservative. No greasy or fried foods. No food which has gone through a factory, such as processed cheese, canned meats, fish or vegetables, potato chips. Avoid margarine which may contain too many synthetics. Coffee induces rapid heart action and should be avoided. I guess that's enough to be going on with.

ON RISING. Glass of dilute fruit juice, lemon, or cup of tea.

BREAKFAST. A selection from the following:

Stewed apples, half grapefruits, raw apples, oranges, grapes, prunes, baked apples. Fresh or soaked fruit with Wheat-Germ, or grated nuts. Wholemeal bread and butter. Honey, Cup of tea or Dandelion Coffee.

11am Cup of Dandelion Coffee, or tea, Instant Postum, milk, or glass of any kind of juice – lemon, carrot, blackcurrant, pineapple, prune, grape fruit or orange juice.

LUNCH.

Soup: Celery or any vegetable soup made at home.

Salad: Comprising grated beetroot, celery, lettuce, chopped apple, mustard and cress, grated carrot, dandelion leaves if desired. Cheese, baked potato and butter. Make your own salad dressing with lemon and olive oil.

Any one of the many nutmeat luncheon preparations as sold in Health Food Stores may be used; luncheon rolls, spread, or savouries.

Dessert: Grapes, prunes, stewed apples or pears, tinned peaches, baked apple and raisins, baked apples stuffed with dates, grated nuts, ripe banana. Yoghourt may be taken with any of these, if desired.

EVENING MEAL

Soup, or apple juice. Tomato juice.

Hot Cooked Meal comprising baked potatoes, lamb, chicken, steamed fish, poached egg, nut cutlets, butter beans, baked potatoes in their jackets, French beans, carrots, parsnips, sprouts, celery, cheese sauce, or any other steamed vegetables except onions. The midday and evening meals may be reversed as desired.

ON RETIRING.

Glass of milk with one or two teaspoonful of honey in it. Dandelion coffee or tea.

By observing the above recommendations there is no reason why you should not enjoy life with a greater sense of physical security, with less strain and better emergency reserve. Do not fall out with your income tax inspector or get up to any mischief creating a background of emotional stress. The more you worry and fret about the firm's or family's affairs the less resistance will you have to deal with that emergency sprint for the bus, or to sustain the shock of bad news. Do a good day's work, but always finish the evening with a "feet-up" session for about an hour. And so to bed.

Madame Helene Ronner, Fleurey sur Ouche, Pont De Pany, France.
Thank you very much for sending me the booklet "Sincere Sympathy".
It really has done me a lot of good to read it and to try to overcome sadness. After all, we cannot forget those who have left us, and we must
keep on living despite how difficult it is at times. Best wishes to you,
and to Grace Family.

ED: *Other readers who have lost a loved one are invited to send for a*
free copy of the small booklet, "Sincere Sympathy", a Grace Gift. Send
a stamped addressed envelope (address printed, please) to Grace
Publishers, Mulberry Court, Stour Road, Christchurch, Dorset BH23 1PS.
Tel: 01202 476868. FAX 01202 480559.

Eileen Littlewood, Surrey, RH8 0LE.
On the 28th August, 1984, God gave me a very special birthday present.

My mother took me out to lunch at our favourite place – Botley Hill
Farm, now sadly closed as the two sisters who ran it have retired.

While we were waiting to be served I noticed a little magazine called
Grace on a small table beside me – sounds like "Alice in Wonderland",
and it was. I became absorbed, dipping into it. What a joy to find pure
gold within its pages.

I took the details, resisting temptation to take the magazine, and wrote
to take out a subscription straight away. I have had food for thought ever
since – not only a banquet for each birthday, but feast days throughout
the years. Just think what I would have missed if I had not picked up
Grace before my meal. It doesn't bear thinking about!

God arranged for a little (in size) magazine to be put within my reach.
I wonder how many opportunities we miss by not accepting what is there
for the taking?

I was able to obtain a copy of the back number I had seen and on reading
it from cover to cover found there was a letter from a lady I knew.

I met her. By chance? I met her on a Christmas shopping expedition
for the disabled. She admired the hat I was wearing and asked me where
I got it. She looked disappointed when I told her I had made it myself
that I offered to make her one. So we became friends.

There is a story in my book of how a Member of Parliament took
'potluck' and I became his secretary. Life is so exciting. I was a quiet,
shy child, lacking in self-confidence. I just can't believe what 'disablement' has done for me!

Samuel Butler.
The great pleasure of a dog is that you may make a fool of yourself with him.
and not only will he not scold you but he will make a fool of himself, too.

Nearly tea time. From an original painting by Stephen J. Darbishire.

Anonymous.
I would like to say how much I enjoy reading *Grace*. I appreciate reader's stories in *While the Kettle Boils* and wonder if you would like to hear how my prayers have been answered.

Sixty years ago I was born with only one hand. My mother died at birth. Such accidents seemed to be more of a rarity then than now and I was regarded as a freak. My father fought for me to attend a normal school, not a special school, but I was continually made fun of. Local boys called me "old one arm" or "Nelson". In a temper I would chase but never catch them.

At night when it was time for bed, when about nine or so, I used to pray that God would give me a second hand whilst I slept. Having heard of Jesus' miracles at Sunday-School I would get into bed far too frightened to go to sleep in case I should wake up and not know what to do with a second hand.

We were a strict Methodist family. At church one Sunday morning the Children's sermon told of a young girl, ugly and deformed, who prayed regularly to be made "beautiful within" and so to become a paragon of virtue, everyone overlooking her deformities. I decided to try this tack but it didn't work out at all; I was just as frustrated.

Some forty years later I was cooking breakfast for my husband and our two teenage children when I heard of a minister on the radio telling how prayer helped him to cope with cancer. Suddenly, like a blinding light, I knew my prayers had been answered. Not in the way I expected, but because I had been given the ability to cope. I can cook, sew, knit, crochet, type. I have always been able to earn my living. I have a good husband and two lovely children. And now a grandchild has been added. God be with all members of *Grace Family* and keep them in good health. Yours sincerely.

Mr B. M. Gray, Surrey.
We are told that we lose a third of our body heat through our heads, yet when I go out I see masses of people, many old, with no covering of any sort on their heads even in bitter winter weather!

Mrs D. M. Fisher, Redcar, Cleveland TS/O.
My new dentures were so uncomfortable. I took out the bottom ones when sewing and slipped them under the chair cushion while I answered the telephone. On my return, I found that the dog had climbed on the chair and found them. He was actually trying to make a meal of them and gave them a good mauling.

When day is done.

Our sincere thanks to an unknown photographer.

257

I picked them up, rinsed them thoroughly, and tried them on. What a pleasant surprise! The dog had chewed just the corner part which had been so painful. I now found them quite comfortable!

He expected a scolding; but he got a cuddle instead.

Harry Willis, Preston, Lanes.
I read somewhere the words: "Forget each kindness that you do . . . As soon as you have done it . . . Forget the praise that falls to you . . . The moment you have won it." I find this hard to do. The sincerity and thanks of people ring in my ears for days.

Our garden is a picture at this time of the year. I grow flowers and some vegetables, all from seed, and share them with friends. I get much pleasure and sense of real fulfilment when I see the smile on their faces as they receive them.

E. W. Marwick.
A friend of mine in the small town of Stromness had to undergo treatment for his eyes, and to face the possibility of complete blindness. Shortly after his return from hospital he sat down on the seashore to watch a magnificent sunset. After a while he saw a huge rat coming so unmistakably right up to him that he looked round hurriedly for something with which to stave off an attack. Then he realised that the animal was totally blind. He shoved his hand into his pocket and his fingers closed on a stale and forgotten caramel. The rat accepted it and walked away. "I wouldn't have hurt him for a thousand pounds", my friend told me.

A. H. Penylan, Cardiff.
I would like to recommend Fuller's Earth cream for preventing chapped lips. I have been using it for years with complete success. Yours sincerely.

Gwen Fletcher, Southampton.
I do so enjoy *Grace*. Externally, I use Feverfew oil, rubbed round and in my ear morning and night, which has helped my tinnitus.

ED: *Thank you, Gwen Fletcher, for sharing with us your experience. By the way, today's most popular remedy for tinnitus (rushing sound in the ears) is Ginkgo, taken internally. It sometimes lets the fly out of the bottle.*

Muriel Humphrey.
In my own experience, I have found that ageing means a new series of experiences. Older people will be valuable only if they stay involved. The hardest thing to do is reach out and make a new life . . . but that's what I intend to do.

Mr L. V. Phillips.
Can you beat my wife? She keeps her rheumatism under control with cabbage leaves. She pins a big leaf under her vest in the small of her back, replacing the leaves when they are dry. She swears she always finds

relief. Sometimes the leaf comes away almost black. I tell her it must be all her badness coming out!

Anonymous.
In desperation I used Comfrey ointment, purchased from a health shop in Ross-on-Wye, on my very very dry hands on which I have painful chilblains, especially under the fingernails. To my surprise the skin is getting more supple and less painful.

Jack Parr.
I have never seen a bad television programme, because I refuse to. God gave me a mind and a wrist that turns things off.

Anonymous.
Can you recommend a herbal toothpaste?

ED: *Weleda herbal toothpaste contains no synthetic fluoride, sweeteners, artificial flavouring, colourants, or foam boosters. Ingredients include Krameria, Myrrh, Sage, Peppermint and Geranium (essential oils). We like it because it has not been tested on animals.*

Those wishing to keep their teeth right through to old age may take one Dolomite tablet daily, at breakfast, for calcium and magnesium. Incidentally, one tablet morning and evening helps reduce the risk of bone fracture from osteoporosis in menopausal women.

All furred up.
In a furred-up kettle water takes longer to boil, and that costs money. How do you dissolve fur?

ED: *Save and prosper. Fill the kettle with water and add some vinegar. Bring to boil and allow to stand overnight. Pour out the contents. Again fill the kettle and bring to boil. Pour out the contents. Your kettle should then be ready for use. For your freshly boiled water, non-caffeine teas are available from every health store. Everybody's drinking them now. The range is ever-increasing. We're on Lime and Lemon now, a tropical fruit herbal tea – instant refreshment in teabags. To the stomach, grateful and comforting. You can take my word for it.*

Mrs J. B. Dyer, Somerset.
Ginkgo tablets are proving wonderful for my 92-year-old mother. They enable her to cope during her declining years. When running out of them, last week, she again became confused and unhappy. Her whole attitude is brighter. They truly are great.

I must say, in passing, how she has also been helped by Echinacea tablets. The nurse doesn't need to come any more as Mum's bad leg ulcer and pressure sore have entirely healed! They appear to help also with bad bruising she gets after the slightest knock against the furniture. We are all so grateful. Sincerely.

259

Prostate Gland

(Water Treatment)

By JOHN TOBE

THIS is commonly referred to as the "sitz bath". It is believed that cold water tones up the muscles whereas hot water relaxes them. When hot and cold water are used alternately it is claimed that they help in a natural way to stimulate the body tissues and organs.

The recommended means of operation is to sit in a tub of hot water for about 15 minutes or until the lower part of the body is heated up thoroughly. Then the hot water is drawn off and cold water put in its place. The patient then sits in this for five minutes.

There are different thoughts on this phase of the treatment. Some think that the change from hot to cold should be drastic. Others think that the change should be gradual. I, on a broad attitude, oppose the drastic method because of the effect that the severe temperature changes may have on the body. Again, that is precisely what some practitioners attempt to achieve, for they claim that under such circumstances drastic treatment is required or called for.

The depth of water need only be sufficient to cover the umbilicus.

These hot and cold "sitz baths" are considered of pronounced value for releasing obstructions causing difficulty in urination.

Where one is unable to partake of umbilical immersion in the hot and cold sitz baths, due to any one of many circumstances, hot and cold towels can be utilised. The use of hot and cold towels is the simplest form of the sitz bath treatment. This treatment should be continued for 1½ hours . . . the longer the better, according to old practitioners. The towels should be applied over and under the lower groin, between the legs. Seek to cover as much of the genital organs as possible.

The sitz bath and the hot and cold applications have been in vogue for centuries and were for many, many long years the only method of gaining relief from retention and prostatic difficulties. Therefore, even in this modern day and age, these techniques should not be laughed at or ignored.

When using the sitz bath, the temperature of the water should be as high as the body can stand it. The duration should be anywhere from 20 minutes to an hour. The accepted practice is 15 minutes hot and five minutes cold, repeated up to three times at one treatment. This procedure can be followed a few times during the day.

The above treatment is also excellent for piles and anal troubles generally.

Mr H. Bignold, Northampton.
I know a man who is always cheerful. He's been like it since I knew him at school. He is a gardener and works for the "Parks and Gardens" Committee. Out in all weathers, he never seems to complain; inquire about his health, and the reply is always: "I'm fine, couldn't be better."

On hearing he was off sick, I called at his house to ask how he was getting on. He was alone and, though breathing heavily, panted: "I'm fine, couldn't be better." What an object lesson?

Fibrositis

A practical programme for the prevention of muscular rheumatism

YES, this is the time of the year for doing an extra stint in the garden to leave it nice and tidy for the winter. Careful with that hoe. If you've been a layabout all the summer or idling with those woods on the green, early autumn exertions on the vegetable patch may result in stiff muscles or a story-telling creak here and there.

Exertion and damp are not the only causes of fibrositis, although a combination of both can often precipitate an attack. Neither are nervous strain and fatigue, which are blamed for more than their fair share of muscular spasm and pain.

Common causes often overlooked are rich, acid foods like eggs and red meat, not to mention alchohol. The treatment of this form of rheumatism is not easy. But whoever the sufferer is, he can profit much by the following:

An Epsom Salts bath twice a week to assist in the elimination of wastes from the skin. Two or three handfuls of crude Epsom Salts to your bath.

Sun and air baths when possible.

Dry friction rub every morning on rising and before retiring. Two stiff brushes, about six inches long, can be purchased and used to brush the skin vigorously to stimulate the circulation and facilitate drainage of wastes from the subcutaneous tissues. At first the user will find that "gently does it"; but it is surprising what a marvellous exhilaration of skin and spirits follows. Soon you will not wish to start the day without that lively brush-down which is one of the more gleeful aspects of keeping fit.

Three days' fast on fruit juices and water only.

This should be followed by seven days on fruits, salads and conservatively-cooked vegetables only. Starchy and protein foods should not be taken during this period.

Herbal Help – Celery Seeds.
Place one heaped teaspoonful Celery Seeds in a teacupful of water, bring to boil and simmer for one minute only. Drink cold: ½ cup morning and evening. If well tolerated, after a few days increase dosage to 1 cup.

Manipulative treatment and massage when necessary. It is within the ability of everyone to adopt these simple measures which might prove effective in keeping at bay the menace of fibrositis.

❀

Mr A. H. C., Canada.
Middle age is when everything starts to click; your elbows, your knees and your neck and back.

Winifred Spray, Kennington, Oxford.
I was taken back many years when reading in the Winter issue of the Magazine of the small children's dilemma of identifying their homes on a new Bergen housing estate until photographs of their mothers were placed on the front doors.

My mother used to relate how my absent-minded academic father once returned home shortly after a move to one of some ten identical houses in a rural area. He opened the front door, entered the hall, hung up his hat and coat and walked into the living room before realising that he was in the wrong house . That could not happen today when doors are kept locked after dusk and only a key-holder would be able to let himself or herself in. As it was, no alarm was felt by the intruded, and what better way of getting to know a new neighbour?

From the Kent Messenger.
"At the meeting of the Women's Institute, members were given advice on vegetarian cookery by Valerie Veal."

Mr J. B., Coventry.
Is there any way we can prepare for an outbreak of flu? We are told that flu vaccines are not always successful. We believe there must be some alternative.

ED: *Influenza experts have warned of an increased risk of a flu epidemic. The World Health Organisation announces new virus strains on the way.*

One of the most effective preventatives is garlic. Two garlic capsules or tablets at bedtime have a good record as a flu preventative. By the way, when taking tablets or capsules at bedtime always make sure they are not held up in the gullet, by taking them with a few sips of water. Those who can't get off to sleep easily may wish to chase them down with a cup of limeflower tea.

For an acute attack, when flu has definitely arrived; don't attempt to soldier-on in the office, factory or kitchen and give it to other people. For the sake of your early recovery go to bed and stay there until the temperature falls.

Allow yourself a 3-day fast with plenty of fluids: yarrow, elderflower or peppermint teas or fruit juices. Two Lobelia tablets every two hours until fall of temperature.

Aromatherapy: a few drops of any one of essential oils: Niaouli, Pine or Eucalyptus, to a bowl of boiling hot water; cover head with a towel to trap the steam; inhale. Hot bath or footbath at night.

Anonymous.
I have to stand all day at my work and my feet perspire terribly. Should I use an anti-fungicidal powder?

ED: *First of all, are your shoes comfortable? Have the sides cut away opening-up the toe if this is possible. This will allow more circulation of air. Before setting out in the morning try to find time to soak the feet in hot water. Follow by bathing in cool water into which two teaspoonfuls of cider vinegar have been added. Dry thoroughly, avoiding tightly-fitting stretch-socks or tights.*

Mrs L. R. Meeker, Houston, Texas, U.S.A.
I have been drinking red clover tea and I am happy to report that I no longer have chronic and continuous bladder infections. These have been plaguing me for years, and for which I have had surgery and a mountain of drugs. I have not had to take any medications since drinking the tea. I am also surprising myself with the strength to take care of my sick husband, hold down my job and take care of my household. A year ago I don't think I could have done all this.

S. B., Swansea, South Wales.
I must tell you how I got rid of my painful back. You would never believe it . . . ! I bought a pair of arch-supports and fitted them to my shoes and it has made a lot of difference. I think everybody with a bad back should try these supports. I am sure many will be agreeably surprised after a month.
    ED: *Many thanks, S.B. for information which I know will prove helpful to other members of Grace Family. I suppose they act as a kind of shock-absorber to the spinal bones, softening the shock every time your heels touch the ground. In any case, we don't have to know all the science as to why it works, the main thing is that it may relieve pain in some back cases. Good luck to them!*

The Editor.
Browsing through some record cards of my old patients, I thought to myself, "Why don't I pass on to members of Grace Family remedies which have proved unusually successful?" I pass them on to you for what they are worth.
    During my forty years in practice, I was able to rely entirely upon Blue flag root *(Iris versicolor)* for severe cases of jaundice; Black root *(Veronicastrum virginicum)* for inflammation of the gall bladder; Lobelia *(Lobelia inflata)* for stubborn coughs; Goat's rue *(Galega officinalis)* to give a diabetic a lift, and possibly effect a reduced dose of insulin; Hawthorn berries *(Crataegus oxycantha)* for weak hearts, and Cramp bark *(Viburnum opulus)* for angina pectoris.
    Painful menstruation has ruined more women's lives than bad marriages. I have yet to discover if Vitex *Agnus castus* fails to give some relief in straightforward, uncomplicated cases. Raspberry leaf tea, hot and strong, is also a woman's best friend for unpleasant menstrual troubles and pregnancy. For prostatitis in men in the second half of life, Pulsatilla *(Anemone*

pulsatilla) taken internally, and one or two garlic capsules inserted into the rectum daily, can often mount a rescue operation.

G. Wyatt, North Yorkshire.
My wife and I have made a "switch", she being the breadwinner, and myself the house-spouse. We seem to get along very well, I myself doing the shopping, washing, ironing and all the cooking (and baking!). I don't mind doing the housework, at all!

I wonder why some other couples do not follow suit. Because of tax advantages, we now have twice as much to spend, and we enjoy longer holidays than were possible when we were in reverse situations. I enjoy the cooking part, with time for afternoon tea. My wife likes my buttered scones, muffins and tea-cakes when she comes home.

Mrs K., Norway.
We continue to enjoy thoroughly your fine magazine and have proved the efficacy of your recommended aids to recovery.

I . Vitamin B, and vitamin C have given great relief from arthritic pain in the hands. Taken daily, over a long period, pain has almost disappeared.

2. The "potato" eye treatment has greatly improved our sight. Used nightly or morning, it is so soothing to the eyes.

3. The "Try the Porridge Cure" *(Grace, Spring 1982)* recommended for diabetics has really worked. Proof was shown in the latest test made by the Specialist who reported a big reduction in sugar. My husband is delighted and feels so much better.

4. "Cranesbill" tablets, too, have proved their worth and given me wonderful help over a difficult and troublesome problem. Many thanks.

Tea junction
A young woman was having her first driving lesson. Her instructor said: "Now that you are out of town and into the country, what sort of road signs would you expect to see?"

After a long pause came the reply: "The only one I can think of at the moment is "Fresh Farm Eggs" .

Mr S. Dobson, Burnley, Lancs.
I have been told that aluminium cooking vessels may be responsible for early senile dementia. The metal is supposed to have been found in the brains of people at postmortem. Is this true?

ED: *I cannot vouch for the post-mortem findings, but several books have been written on the relationship of aluminium salts with certain diseases. This metal occurs naturally in many foodstuffs. It is added to processed cheese as an emulsifier, to cake mixtures as a leavener, and to pickles and chutneys to fill out the ingredients. It is difficult to get away from the stuff, especially when "they" put it in our drinking water (along with other chemicals) to remove impurities.*

To add to these, and many other sources, it is little wonder that aluminium pans may not be as harmless as some people would lead us to believe. For one thing, the kidneys and depurative organs find it exceedingly difficult to efficiently eliminate aluminium salts and the spurious derivatives it forms in the body. The authorities have not yet made up their minds as to what allowable levels in food can be recommended.

Don't forget that many antacids (indigestion mixtures) are heavy with aluminium salts and have been known to dull the brain. Any deposits not thrown out by the kidneys are believed to be deposited in the bones thus interfering with the production of vital blood cells. Need we go further for a possible cause of myeloma and its ilk?

You have put your finger on a thorny problem, Mr Dobson, because the whole world is sold on aluminium cooking pans. The medical profession gets the jim-jams wherever the question is raised, being very touchy on this sensitive subject though, of course, both they and the manufacturers will always come out strongly with the declaration that the metal is quite harmless, "there being no evidence of toxicity."

It just shows how the world has changed!

Miss M. M., Pulborough, Sussex.
This letter is in personal gratitude for the healing powers of Comfrey which you recommended for my infected toe. The pain I have had since last September! It has gradually subsided and I am practising wearing normal shoes again. The relief makes me quite light-headed!

Grandmother.
When my daughter's little boy was asked why he got so dirty, what do you think he replied?
"Well, I'm a lot closer to the ground than you are.

Ronald Crossley, Bourg-La-Reine, France.
I am passing on to you a good anti-wrinkle lotion. Pour one litre of boiling water (spring water, if possible) on a handful of chervil leaves. Add one or two mint leaves. Infuse for 20 minutes, strain. Wash the face with a piece of cotton wool dipped in the mixture. Keep in a cool place – in the refrigerator for instance.

Edward Winckly.
It seems to me that psychiatry is blind to the nature of sin; that is to say, if the psychiatrists I have recently heard address public gatherings are typical of their profession. Of course the sinner is "maladjusted", because sin breaks into human nature, lowering physical, mental and spiritual vitality, but the jargon of the psychiatrist appears to me to be completely

contrary to the Christian faith. "Maladjustment" is a misleading term, when it is substituted for the word "sin".

I heard a psychiatrist say recently: "We assist mental sufferers to have confidence in themselves." That, surely, is what every minister of the Christian faith is constantly at pains to tell people not to have! I consider anyone who has no confidence in himself and has untroubled trust in God, that he is adjusted."

Sallie Stephens, Brighton, Sussex.
I am pleased to let you know that Hawthorn tablets, which my husband has been taking for his heart problem, have proved very good – also the 1000 iu's of vitamin "E" he takes daily instead of 2000 iu's a day (which he had previously). It seems to be just right. Yours sincerely.

North Norfolk Village
Approaching our village came a magnificent Daimler, which is something we don't see every day of the week in our part of the world. Who do you think was inside? It was the Queen, all in blue. We will never forget the happy smile she gave us, the first time I have seen her in the flesh. The sun was shining and it was a wonderful day. I wonder if the Queen realizes how much pleasure she gives us when she waves?

Mrs G. Morrell, Battersea, London SW11.
I felt I must tell you what a wonderful success Marigold cream is. I had a very nasty gash on my arm. I was passing through an open door with my arms loaded, when the wind caught it and the tongue of the new lock caught my arm. It was as if the flesh had been sliced with a knife. Of course, it bled. To staunch the bleeding I put on clean lint; then I suddenly thought of Marigold, especially if the skin is broken. I smothered the wound with the cream, covering it with a large plaster and left it completely alone for four days. There was no pain or soreness. When I had a look I could scarcely believe my eyes. It was practically healed. It was absolutely wonderful. Thanks to Marigold.

Skin care.
A beauty specialist in the town was horrified when I told her I use nothing more than soap and water on my face, followed by the briefest dab of make-up.

She warned: "If you don't take proper care of your skin you'll have wrinkles by the time you're forty." She made me so happy. I'm fifty-five next week, and dancing for joy.

Mrs H. N. B., North Walsham, Norfolk.
What's all this forecasting of a hard winter? As the nights draw-in, the country prophets get busy and predict what it is going to be like. The

age-old signs can be right. This year gives the forecaster plenty to worry about: whopping-great Hawthorn berries, an abundance of nuts and berries for the birds, bumper corn harvests, plump rabbits, swallows leaving before their time.

I love hard weather ! I often break ice crusts on my chickens' water fountains as I make my round of the hen-houses. The best time comes in the late afternoon when I go inside to a nice coal fire, bowl of hot soup, and slippers waiting. Outside, the wind can howl as much as it likes. My husband and I have few of this world's goods – I still do my own washing in the wash-house out at the back – no washing- machine – but life is far from gloomy.

My husband said, "You can't beat Nature's signs of the seasons," as we watched the tortoise furiously digging himself in, and saw how even the onions had grown thicker skins.

Mrs E. C. Weightman, Leigh on Sea, Essex.
I had been looking for some relief for the burning and irritation of my dog, Tracey's, stomach. In my search I looked-up a homoeopathic medicine of value for these symptoms. I turned-up the name, Rhus Tox, potency 3x. I   gave her a dose three times daily. So far so good, both the irritation and burning are gone. So maybe some other dogs can be helped in this way. I understand many dogs have itching which is difficult to get rid of.

John Tobe, Ontario, Canada.
The other day I twice heard on the radio a report from Toronto that they now know that cola drinks, smoking, liquor and coffee cause bladder cancer.

This the health-nuts have known for years. They also contribute to other forms of disease, as well. If you doubt what I tell you and if you don't believe I heard it reported twice in one day, you can check up on me.

You know, folks, I at one time enjoyed all these four blessings. Many. many years ago I saw the light and gave them the heave-ho. Oh, what a happy day that was . . . lucky for me.

So if you still use any of these so-called foods or what else they are named, now is the time for you, too, to give them the heave-ho . . . before they give it to you !

Mrs Sheila Smithson, Oxford.
The outside of me is falling apart. My nails are brittle and crack across the tops, crops of tiny little warts flourish on the top of my chest, and my hair is falling out in handfuls. It's no use telling me to eat wholefoods and take yeast and other supplements. I have done this for months. Something not nauseating, or painful to take, please.

ED: *There is only one kind of remedy well tolerated by all ages from babyhood to old age, and perfectly safe, and that is the Biochemic remedy. New Era Laboratories put out a very good one. Try Silica 6x, four tablets, between meals, three times daily for about two months. Remember, coffee and strong tea antidote biochemic remedies, whatever time of the day or night they are taken. If you want to get the best out of them, discontinue salt, coffee and even tea, substituting Dandelion coffee, Rose Hip and Hibiscus sachets, or other popular herbal tea from your Health Store.*

J. V. L., London N.W.2.
A recent programme on the Home Service radio described some of the "folklore" surrounding the use of Vitamin "C". Why is it that these boys fail to give both sides of the question. During the whole programme no constructive opposition nor scientific facts were advanced, at all. It was just a studied condemnation before investigation. How prejudiced can these people get?

ED: *It is now apparent from statements made on the radio, TV and in the newspapers that some scientists are getting frightened at the vitality and success of the whole natural health movement. Is it true they have something the doctors haven't got? Do the thousands of cases of improved health stem from vitamin therapy and an insistence on natural wholefoods? Or is it all just moonshine?*

The most convincing proof comes from the doctors' own ranks. To more members of the Profession, it is beginning to dawn that there may be, after all, some truth in it. Among them is Dr. Linus Pauling, winner of Nobel Prizes for both chemistry and peace. In his book, "Vitamin C and the Common Cold", Pauling advocates daily doses of vitamin C (rose hips, acerola, ascorbic acid) to prevent and treat the common cold. Those interested in this subject should obtain a copy of the book and form their own opinion. They will not only learn more about the common cold, but of rheumatoid arthritis, respiratory infections, influenza, diabetes, and arthritis.

Dr. Pauling records how Dr. A. Hoffer and Dr. H. Osmond began successfully treating schizophrenic patients with vitamins, which knowledge may be of value to those of a distressed mind. This Pan/Ballantine paperback is inexpensive and should be read by all who are compelled to take more than a casual interest in their health in order not to be a burden on others.

Drs. Willis and Fishman draw attention to investigations indicating that ascorbic acid (vitamin C) can have a beneficial effect on the ageing process, atherosclerosis, the hardening and thickening of the walls of the arteries.

It is so easy to smile down one's nose and make snide remarks about something we know nothing about. A professional man gets a dreadful feeling of natural enmity to the layman when he sees him making a success of something he regards as his own prerogative.

268

Her Grace, The Countess of Mayo, PI.D.
It moved me to read such a tragic story as "Doctors can be Wrong", appearing in this magazine. However, when she was inspired by Divine Guidance her fate changed. So it does for us all. Problems are, I think, stepping stones across our material river of life to our universal Oneness,
I woke up one day and could not turn my head. The doctor said: "You will have arthritis for the rest of your life: so you must make up your mind to live with it."
My answer was: "I am not accepting that verdict." I was told that Las Palmas, Canary Islands, has a claim to cure arthritis. I decided to go there. I lay out in the sun. In six months I was cured. Nature's sun did the trick. I also breathed the breath of divine wisdom knowing that pure and perfect oxygen was cleansing my blood and burning the dross out of my joints. I also cleansed my body by taking vegetarian foods. I am so much better.

Mrs Emma Northe, Detroit, Michigan, U.S.A.
Enclosed is my donation. It is a small gift, but it is sent with all my love and blessing. This is a harsh winter with a great deal of snow, icy streets and roads and freezing temperatures. Often, there comes over the air the song of Irving Berlin: "I'm dreaming of a white Christmas". In all the pictures I've seen of him, he was as brown as a beach boy. He didn't get that tan lolling on a snowbank. How good it is to stay inside a warm little house, put on the soup, bake gingerbread, and read. I like to step out briefly, in such weather, to smell the cold clean air. I hope the little folk are tucked away somewhere safe in the woods. I expect they, too, know it will not be long before Spring is on the way. May God bestow His blessings to you all as days come and go. Sincere good wishes to all Grace Family.

Mrs E. L. Coggan, Cape Town, South Africa.
I have read Captain Whitehouse's article about cramp in the Summer issue of *Grace*, and feel I must tell you that I have overcome this distressing complaint since I put into bed with us a magnet, many months ago.
I read on the Family Letter page of the Cape Times a hint from a reader who had done this. So I paid 30 cents for a magnet at a bazaar shop, put it into a cotton bag and placed it between our sheets. My husband and I have both been entirely free from cramp ever since. Husband says to be sure we ought to remove the magnet and see what happens, but I have so much memory of broken nights, walking about for half an hour in the middle of the night until the pain ceased, that I am prepared to let well alone.
There were subsequently several letters from grateful people who also bought a magnet and put it to good use, and I have successfully passed on the hint to others over the months since I started. With best wishes, and gratefully yours . . .

Mrs Audrey Wright, Merseyside L37 3PB
I find that a bottle of good cider vinegar, made from whole apples, has a variety of uses.

Two teaspoons with two teaspoons honey, in warm water, helps me to sleep and gives me a restful night. A tablespoon in a jug of water makes a final rinse for my hair, and leaves it "squeaky clean".

A tablespoon in a tumbler of water makes a setting lotion for straight hair, and helps it to curl. I believe it has the reverse effect and straightens curly hair, but cannot vouch for this as my hair is very straight!

Mrs I. E. Pope, Rise Park, Romford.
My experience may be of interest to *Grace* readers. I bought the little book, Better Sight Without Glasses" (Thorsons). Ten years ago I had my first pair of glasses. Since then, I had four new pairs, getting stronger each time. Then I read this little book by Harry Benjamin who wrote that you could improve your eyesight considerably and possibly discard them altogether by the Bates Method.

I was so intrigued that I started on the exercises, etc., there and then. I am thankful that such information has come my way. As the weeks went by my eyes became much stronger and I was able to discard the last two pairs of glasses very soon.

I now manage perfectly all right without glasses, even working in the office without them.

Mrs M. Hall, Princes Riseborough.
I have suffered from mild attacks of indigestion for many years. I have tried all kinds of remedies, including National Health tablets from my doctor. Some time ago a friend advised me to take half to one teaspoonful pure olive oil each day, as far away from meals as possible. So as I always wake in the night I take it then. I have found it most beneficial, well worth trying, but not with food.

ED: *Many thanks for letting us know your remedy. There are hundreds of remedies for indigestion and you have hit on yours. Sometimes we have to search until we find one which matches our own set of symptoms.*

JUST NOW

Never mind about tomorrow . . . It always is today . . . Yesterday has vanished . . . wherever, none can say. Each minute must be guarded . . . Made worth the while somehow . . . There are no other moments . . . It always is just now.

Just now is the hour that's golden . . . The moment to defend . . . Just now is without beginning . . . Just now can never end . . . Then never mind tomorrow . . . 'Tis today you must endow . . . with all that's true and noble . . . And the time for this is . . . now! *Anonymous.*

Brill windmill.   *Ronald Goodearl.*

OCTOBER ON THE HILLTOP

Joan Jensin, Calgary. Alberta, Canada.
Hello there! you dear people. Yippee! *Grace* arrived today. I can breathe
a little easier once more. We just hold our breath when it comes near
time for its arrival. As Waldo Trine says in his book *In Tune With the
Infinite* (which I managed to get after waiting three months) . . . "Nothing
is to be gained by fear. On the contrary everything can be lost". Believe
it or not: the other day a woman told me she never read the printed word.
O, what a terrible admission ! What a wasted life! No wonder she is so
at odds with life. I had *Grace* on the table when she was here. She said
it was too deep for her.

Anonymous
I have found that taking brewers' yeast makes insulin more effective. I
am interested in your occasional observations on the subject of diabetes.
I can understand how mineral properties in herbs, including infusion of
dandelion root, can sometimes bring about improvement to the point of
reducing insulin. What are your thoughts on the complaint?
    ED: *There are several causes, including severe psychological trauma.
For instance, a domestic background of violent quarrels, lack of affection
or indifference may predispose. Heredity is a factor, but not an important one. For many years the Consulting Medical Herbalist has used the
liver as his base, he believing that structural changes in the pancreas can
be brought by liver damage, in more cases than physicians are aware. It
is so easy to fail to recognise the accompanying mental deterioration.*
    *Dr. I. F. Nisbet casts some light on this brain/liver relationship in his
"The Insanity of Genius" : The connection of diabetes with the neuropathic
group was discovered by the merest accident. It was found that puncture
of the fourth ventricle of the brain produced the diabetic condition. Sugar
appearing in large quantities in the urine; and further investigation
showed the formation and excretion of sugar to be the result of vaso-motor
paralysis of the liver, the immediate consequence of the injury in
question.*
    *By the way, did you know that a diabetic can drink pure, unsweetened
fruit juices by taking a hundred grams in lieu of a ten-gram carbohydrate
portion?*

Wilfred Hadley, Devon, Connecticut, U.S.A.
Greetings, and a long overdue "Thank You" for your excellent journal,
Grace. I have learned much in many respects from your essays and com-
mentary and your philosophy. I have learned especially a very wholesome appreciation of the many small things of life which, when viewed
with an honest philosophy, make our days more enjoyable than merely
tolerable.
    I have through your influence developed a much broader appreciation
of the beauty and glory of classical music . . . never a day passes now

without at least an hour in the company of the great composers. If you can find the opportunity, listen to the *Oboe* and *String Concerto*, by Alessandro Marcello, especially the second movement (the *Adagio*).

Your frequent comments on the inspiration of great traditional art moved me to visit the art galleries and museums of our New York. I have spent an entire day in one art collection alone and been all the better for it. You have taught me the unrecognised value of so many things taken for granted, which in their own right are small delights . . . that there is much more in life to enjoy than there is of which to be critical . . . mail clattering through the letter box . . . a well-made cup of tea alongside a well-rounded fire, with music to keep it company, and so much more.

A million thanks. Best wishes to you and to all who read *Grace*. As I read of the trials and tribulations of England and its people I am reminded of a verse that I think was attributed to Winston Churchill and which is surely very appropriate, now:

> *"One broken dream is not the end of dreaming,*
> *One shattered hope is not the end of all;*
> *Beyond the storm and tempest stars are gleaming.*
> *Still build your castles though your castles fall."*

God bless you all.

Mr E. Symons, Racanville Nutritional Research Association, Saskatchewan, Canada.
Rachel Thompson, a local friend, is a wonderful old lady of 91 years, with a young mind. Interested in natural foods she has used Alfalfa for some time, but sparingly. On suggestion, she recently stepped-up its use, finding that it makes her "hungry"; in other words, gives her an appetite. At 91! What can it do for you and me?

From her scrap-book Rachel reads: "Harry Taylor's relief for arthritis: Alfalfa seed; one tablespoonful to a pint of water. Let it heat until the seeds dance up and down. Steep, cool, and drink this amount during the day. After Mr Taylor was in bed for ten weeks, this fetched him out, fit to drive his car again. You have to take it for "quite a while".

ED: *Thank you, friends, for a very useful recipe. This is the first time we have heard dosage instruction taking this form. We have heard of yellow rattle, creeping Jenny , flitweed, love-lies-bleeding, and mind-your-own-business . . . but never alfalfa doing a fandango in the pot. We imagine the whole operation must make one quite giddy. But if it fetches some folk out of bed after ten weeks we guess this is sure some gala performance!*

In a restaurant
We were sitting at a table in a crowded restaurant when my wife started kicking my ankles. I didn't get the message and carried on eating, but I noticed out of the corner of my eye that the couple sharing the table were

giving me some dirty looks.
When we came out I said, "What was all that about?"
"You were eating their bread and butter," my wife snorted.

Mrs Oliver Veltom, Llangollen, Clwyd.
I am a diabetic, and after virus flu when I had to take antibiotics, my sugar level went up to 20 (should be about 6 I was told). There was some difficulty in getting it down and the drugs given for this had little effect. I remembered reading in *Grace Magazine* that Vitamin C helped to stimulate the pancreas, so I gave up the drug and took 1,000 i.u.s a day (in Rose Hip capsules) of Vitamin C. The result was that I had no more positive tests, and have had none since. I have now reduced my intake of Vitamin C capsules to 600 i.u.s a day.

S. R. Jones, Wells, Somerset.
I have tried pumpkin seeds for prostate trouble but with no results. I am told my trouble is not serious and I have to attend again in three months time. In the meantime I feel I could be spending the time profitably by at least trying to help myself.

ED: *Diet certainly has a part in this complaint, but not an important one, as apparently the gland is already enlarged. So much can be said but space prevents mention of more than the following: For simple enlargement – cornsilk or uva ursi. Inflammation – pulsatilla. Difficult urination – parsley piert or couch grass. Constant desire to urinate – horsetail.*

A Sitz bath, or hip bath, has been known to reduce swelling where the gland is not chronically hardened. Have you tried squatting in a bath with a few inches of cold water, with the knees raised? Two or three minutes can be sufficient, the genitals and lower abdomen being immersed. Cold sprays to this area can also assist.

At night, one could do worse than pass urine on all fours. One should not rush into an operation before having tried natural drugless methods of treatment. There are, of course, some which have to be surgically removed.

> He who with swift, unerring hand
> Has oft removed the prostate gland,
> Has reaped the harvest he has sown,
> He's having trouble with his own !

George Coo, Eltham, London.
Glad to read the wacky epitaph in your last issue. There is one that reads:
> "She lived with her husband for fifty years
> And died in confident hope of a better life."

I wonder if this is any relation to the man who in 1918 recorded, "The light of my life has gone out," and who in 1921 struck another match?

Miss L. Butcher, Peterborough, Northants.
I was down on an admissions list for haemorrhoidectomy (surgical treatment of piles) and had a long wait before my turn came round. In the meantime a friend advised me to add bran to every meal: with cereals for breakfast, with "sweet" following lunch, and with stewed fruit, etc., for the evening meal. Imagine my surprise when called upon for operation it was found to be no longer necessary. Full marks for "health foods". I used Allinson's Bran Plus.

One reader to another
For three days psychologists and brother sociologists held their conference at which almost every aspect of that guileless human emotional response called laughter was discussed, in depth. How they like to create a serious study out of this expression of mirth peculiar to man! What do the experts hope to prove by this exercise? Maybe, they prefer to see it nationalized and processed like the water we drink, the air we breathe, modern education of the last remnants of personal freedom!

A team of three researchers from the University of London read a paper called "The Anatomical and Physiological Examination of the Eye Pouches", the point of which seemed to be that people with bags under their eyes are more addicted to laughter than others. What has happened to that thing called "commonsense"? How ridiculous can these social scientists get?

ED: *Robert Benchley had a word for these little grey men who are so anxious to reduce us all to the same level: "There seems to be no length to which these humourless people will not go to analyze humour. It seems to worry them. They can't believe that anything could be funny on its own hook." But there you are!*

Anonymous
I am a great believer in "companion" plants. One seems to help another when in trouble. Marshmallow I hear is a "doctor" plant, imparting strength to sickly neighbours. Another is chamomile which is regarded in some backward areas in France as a plant reviver. Part of my garden is a "surgery" or convalescent home for ailing plants which have been known to "pick-up" like magic when chamomile has been planted nearby.

Anonymous
My daughter and friends had a tea-party on the occasion of my birthday. They gave me a little gift and a colourful card which sent my spirits soaring. They formed-up beside the piano and one of the children sat at the keys. "How exciting." I thought, "special musical honours." They sang: "she's 41 today, 41 today . . ."

The Editor
Buy your Christmas gift books now, so that you can read them before posting them.

Miss G. Wright, Beedon, Newbury, Berks.
Members of Grace Family may be interested to know that our experience of the use of castor oil is that it is very helpful for bunions and the soles of the feet.

Mr S. L. Jamison, D.V.M., N.D,, California, U.S.A.
Illness is a sign that we have not lived up to the law, and is a warning signal. Pork is dynamite. I have seen cancer victims relapse on a pork binge. It happens fast.

In the body the cobalamine is combined with amygdalyn – a cyanide glucoside – by the action of the enzyme thiosulfate transsulflurase (rhodanese) to form cyanocobalamine (vitamin B12) The B12 then works with folic acid, lysine and magnesium in the bone marrow along with potassium to form red blood cells.

Amygdalyn is a cancer inhibitor, as the cancer cell lacks the enzyme rhodanese and is poisoned by the liberated cyanide. Apple seeds, green grass, apricot pits (stones) and almonds are good sources of amygdalyn.

L. Weismann, St. Paul, Minnesota, U.S.A.
I have tried several different things, including drugs, to reduce the swelling of my ankles. The doctor says it is not due to heart trouble. What have you?

ED: *Oedema, in the absence of heart trouble, may mean kidney deficiency, metabolic disturbance or other dysfunction. Have you tried-out the kidney angle? Sometimes the simplest devices get overlooked in this age of total science. Why not try pearl barley water? Nothing so soothing . . . no toxic by-products left over to irritate . . . when kidneys need a little harmless stimulation. But there . . . it takes labour and time!*

Alternative method: Place two ounces pearl barley into a saucepan and cover with one pint cold water. Bring to the boil and simmer for half an hour; strain, and add lemon for taste. Cover closely when simmering.

Anonymous. Answers to a patient's question.
My hair is coming out in handfuls. What can I do about it?

ED: *"I don't wonder," I told myself. Mrs H.C. had been "on the stretch" for the whole of the past year. First it was her husband's illness which tired her almost to the limits of physical endurance. This was followed by an expensive long-distance removal to the south, after which both children "went down" with German Measles. No wonder she felt run-down and nervy!*

Hair falls out from a number of causes, chief of which are the worries of living in the present age. Treatment can bring back "condition" to hair once the cause is known. Orthodox therapy for this condition may consist of extracts prepared from certain glands of animals. We believe no ultimate good can come from monkeying about with the endocrine glands of laboratory animals and prescribing their secretions for human beings,

There are all kinds of "fall out" problems today but the one you keep under your hat is one of the most manageable. Some hair is easily devastated by debilitating troubles such as anaemia, neurasthenia, calcium and general mineral deficiency. Excessively low protein meals can cause physical weakness, sweating, and loss of hair. Where this is the case obtain about four ounces of cut Gentian root from your nearest herbalist or Health Store and prepare as follows:

Place one heaped teaspoonful into a teacup of cold water and leave to stand all night. Next day, drink one half-teacupful on rising, and one half-teacupful before the midday meal. Cases of Anaemia and debility and feeble digestion should continue until the whole of the four ounces has been taken. Reduce from one to half teaspoonful per teacup if the infusion proves too bitter. Do not sweeten. Should you run true to type you should have the appetite of a horse within a fortnight. Good also for low blood pressure and thinness. Of value to those seeking to put on weight.

For falling hair avoid salt, salty preparations, pickles and hot spicy foods. Do not be too proud to take the brewer's yeast and crude black molasses zealously recommended by health-nut Aunt Millie.

While a bald pate may be a sign of maturity, we have knowledge of one or two over-sixty patients who preserve their luxuriant thatch of smooth glossy hair with a daily Vitamin A booster of raw cod liver oil: from one to four teaspoonfuls according ability to "stomach".

Have you tried a smear of lanolin on the scalp? This has been helpful for blonde hair whereas coconut oil is better for brunettes.

For a good all-round scalp brilliantine mix, shake well, and use once every second day: one ounce olive oil, one ounce almond oil, two ounces brandy, and extract of witch hazel to six ounces. If you are fortunate enough to add to these, from an old-time chemist, 10 mls tincture cantharides, so much the better.

If you turn up Clarke's "Dictionary of Domestic Medicine" you will find under "falling hair" Ac. phos. 6 (night and morning). To pursue the matter further this remedy is obtainable from any well-known homoeopathic chemist.

Men go bald because of the intense activity going on in their heads. It is for this reason that women seldom grow beards.

Mr P. Vance, Cromwell Road, London S.W.7.
For months I have had a small ulcer on my lips which refuses to heal, My doctor says this is Herpes Simplex (a variety of shingles), As soon as it is healed it breaks out again. I have read where even vaccination has been suggested as a cure.

(continued on page 280)

Out of Doors

WHAT A wonderful day it has been!

This is the month of harvest, with so much goodness awaiting the reapers. It may not be for us to wield the sickle in a ripened field, but we can seek and find part of all loveliness on offer out of town. The artist is abroad with his brush, the farmer with his combine.

An Autumn landscape is the most wholesome tranquillizer. Is there a lovelier sight than brown sheaves under a late summer's glowing sun? We just love them for what they are. It is difficult to say how much they mean to us.

What a wealth of things we have cause to be thankful for! We have become so accustomed to the sight of good food on our tables, that we should savour these golden moments.

From the earth we draw strength. With a return to the elemental things for a brief hour, kindlier attitudes penetrate the mind, and we enjoy a perfect antidote to the stresses of the new millennium.

Reader, something gorgeous and wonderful awaits you in the fields. There you can be thankful for sunlight, rich and warm; crops and grain; for country lanes and the benediction that hovers over every cornfield.

Could we be anything less than grateful for the scent of purple clustered grapes, for homes and families, and work to do?

This is the season when we lift our gaze a little higher. Our minds wonder on all the essential goodness that is ours — for art and science, for people loving each other, for wading with naked feet along a sandy beach, and for sitting at table for dinner with friends.

There's a beauty that never grows old — the beauty of the thankful heart, like autumn trees against an azure sky, golden as honey on the comb. When our lives are full of grace to perceive present-day blessings we are rich indeed. This is the great art of life.

In a world so full of change, it is well to know we still have everything to make us happy.

An unknown writer puts it all so beautifully:

"For all that God in mercy sends . . . For health and children, home and friends . . . For comfort in the time of need . . . For every kindly word and deed . . . For happy thoughts and lively talk . . . For guidance in our daily walk . . . For everything give thanks!

"For the sweet sleep that comes at night . . . For the returning of morning's light . . . For the bright sun that shines on high . . . For the stars glittering in the sky . . . For these, and everything we see . . . O Lord! our hearts we lift to Thee . . . For everything give thanks!"

Gentle reader . . . I leave you beneath a harvest moon in a wide sky where stars seem closer. It has been a joy to be with you again. You have earned a night's repose. May God bless you, and keep you, each single one of you. A very good night to you all.   *Thomas.*

Silence

BY ROBERT I. GRESAK

IT was borne home to me recently the great value of silence—of the need, the urgent need—in these days of modern civilization with its endless noise, its clamouring after things of the physical, its hard fast living—for serenity and peace of mind, for living in simplicity, being still, and flowing harmoniously with the currents of life, not becoming a prey to worry and fear resulting in nervous tensions and bodily ills. To live, as a tree, a flower, still and open to the sunlight, instead of trying to get, not caring what one does in thought, word, or deed to another in order to gain materially.

Recently with a few others, I went on a trip into the mountains. We camped out, and the day after our arrival set out for the top of the escarpment. It was a long tiring up-hill slog for five hours, and I thought as we forced our weary bodies ever upwards, gasping in the cold rarified air, how symbolic this was of the spiritual pathway, the gradual ascent ever upwards through sorrows, sufferings, trials and joys, always progressing towards the summit of spiritual attainment.

At last we emerged from the top of the stony pass and on to the escarpment bathed in golden light.

How can I describe my feelings then as I looked down at the clouds, the valley far below, the green hills undulating towards the horizon—and above all the deep, uncanny silence. I felt awe, wonder and a great exhilaration. The silence was so tangible, and into my mind came the words "The thunder of the silence". It was truly a stillness which thundered here on top of the world where men seldom trod.

I gave thanks, while my lips tumbled praises and adoration. In this ethereal silence I felt like opening my arms and pouring forth love to the whole wide world. How reluctant I was to leave this high place of such beauty and silence. All too soon we had to begin the descent.

Men have lost so much, drifted so far from truth. For it is in silence in turning away from the things of the world that these are attained, and yet the primordial silence which was felt in that high remote place is nothing, surely, compared to that which comes from within, "Peace I give unto you, not as the world giveth, give I unto you".

ED: *We are sorry to learn of your complaint. Herpes Simplex is a localized disturbance caused by a virus latent in certain tissues of the body, especially the lips. It is due to Herpes antibodies in the circulation. It is dormant in most people but can be activated by a number of stimuili.*
One of the first things springing to the mind of a practitioner would be a deficiency of vitamin B. It would therefore be "a source" to commence with this and some preparation of vitamin B12. A source food of the latter is liver.
We were surprised when a long-standing case cleared-lip on Brewer's Yeast tablets supported by Chamomile flowers (six dried flowers to a teacup of boiling water), half-teacupful morning and evening. We use deeper-acting remedies in the usual practice, but it is the beauty of herbs that you never know when the simplest and humblest plant will supply just the necessary stimulus to the vital recuperative forces of the body. Plenty of fresh fruits and green salad materials are advised and the irritative lesion can be smeared with castor oil if hot and dry . . . witch-hazel if moist.

Anonymous, South Africa.
Fifteen years ago, I was a normal hearing person, but rarely went out. I had few friends and life just didn't have any meaning. How selfish I must have been.

Now, after ten years of total deafness, I am honorary secretary to our local deaf and hard-of-hearing club. I have more friends than I can count. We hold parties and have holidays together. We had a tour of the Trossachs this year and next year we hope to arrange a holiday in Switzerland. I help organize all these and I've never been so happy. My motto is: "Do all you can, and give all you can to others. It's surprising the results you get!"

Miss A. S., Minerva, Ohio. U.S.A.
I am very pleased to renew my annual subscription to *Grace*. I am a bed-fast arthritic and have dozens of magazines coming, but *Grace* is the only one that makes me forget my pain. It's the only magazine I read from cover to cover without setting it down (even for meals). And when I've finished with it I'm sad because there isn't any more. Wish it came every month. Bless you for the joy *Grace* has brought me.

Stephen Sagamang, age 4, Sogada, Philippines.
"I tell God, 'I am sorry. Please let us be friends again.' Then He give me peace. My teddy bear has peace because he is good."

George Taylor, Fort Worth, Texas 76119, U.S.A.
Yours must be a good magazine when it is mentioned on 27 radio stations.

I know John Tobe of Canada, and Dr. Joe Nichols and Carlton Fredericks over here speak highly of you all. Your magazine gets good road use –

it passes through 50 persons and ends up in Guadalajara, Mexico. I would like to have a cassette tape exchange friend or friends – cassettes beat writing. So many people can get in on the play.

Miss E. Barbara Manning, Fulwood, Preston.
1 find I sleep well when I take hot milk last thing with a dessertspoonful of honey in. I healed a nasty septic spot (which I hardly ever get – having a good complexion) on applying honey as a sort of ointment for two nights only. I am beginning to always put honey down on my shopping list!

ED: *Thank you for a helpful contribution. Had you heard also of other uses, including athlete's foot. Soak a bandage with honey and bind affected parts before going to bed. Use old sock to prevent soiling linen. Persevere until successful.*

Miss C. Marjorum, Belle Vue, Manchester (34 years).
To all my dear friends of the Grace Family I say, "A Merry Christmas" and send them the following words of Charles Dickens:
I have always thought of Christmas time, when it has come round, as a good time; a kind, forgiving, charitable, pleasant time: the only time I know of, in the long calendar of the year when men and women seem by one consent to open their shut-up hearts freely, and to think of people below them as if they really were fellow-passengers, and not another race of creatures bound on other journeys. And therefore, though it has never put a scrap of gold or silver in my pocket, I believe that it has done me good: and I say, God Bless it!
"God bless us, everyone," said Tiny Tim.

Mr Jerry Kerr, St. Leonards-on-Sea Sussex.
We are told that fewer potatoes will be eaten in future in Britain. Economists at London University predict that in 20 years consumption will drop from 200 pounds to 145 pounds per person, and two in seven of the present growers will cease production. What are your views on this?
We are sorry to learn of this forecast which we trust will not prove true. We regard the potato as a real friend of man. The number of famines it has averted has been legion. In Europe, Russia and China it has sustained life when grain has not been available because of poor harvests or devastation. We never really appreciate the potato until we are up against it. After their terrible famine in the 19th century, the Irish said "Never again" and started planting potatoes. They are now the backbone of that country's agriculture.
Potatoes are a good source of low-cost vitamins and minerals, especially when cooked in their skins. An average helping of potatoes contains as much vitamin B as two slices of wholemeal bread, it also supplies iron,

as well as traces of copper. Some time ago scientists exploded the notion that potatoes are unusually fattening. Bread is acid-forming, and sometimes proves more fattening than potatoes.

There is a story told by that wonderful old doctor, Valentine Knaggs, which bears repetition. Dr. Hildhede of Denmark, world-famous as an authority on nutrition, tested the value of potatoes on his gardener who volunteered to eat nothing but potatoes for a whole year. The gardener took no undue risk as he was suffering from an incurable disease from which he didn't expect to recover. He recovered on his potato diet. After the year, the gardener was found to be well nourished on nothing but potatoes, which suggests not only their hidden healing virtues but their adequate source of protein.

C. H. Wickett, Rotorua

I was in hospital with cancer in the bowel. After an exploratory operation I was told that it would be too big a job to remove the tumour at my then age (72 years). Two days later I collapsed with pneumonia and an abscess on the lung, but was revived with oxygen.

A colostomy was then performed, and after four months in hospital I was sent home. My weight reduced from 12 stone to 10 stone.

I was given from two to three years to live: but one day I picked up a book by Godfrey Winn, *The Quest for Healing*, in which I read about the spiritual healing work being done at Cavendish Congregational Chapel, Manchester, by the Rev. Alex Holmes, so I wrote and asked for their prayers. I was told to report by airmail once a fortnight to keep my name on the prayer list.

Mr Holmes' replies increased my faith and in less than two years I felt sure that I was being healed.

I was an outpatient of the Hospital for four years, during which time I had several check-ups and finally a barium X-ray which proved that the tumour had gone. The colostomy was then closed; and now nearly three years later, with my weight restored to 13 stone, my doctor can find nothing wrong with me. He said, "You have been through a lot but don't show it." And I am still active in my eightieth year.

Mrs Oria Cartwright, Modesto, California, U.S.

A friend of mine sent me a copy of *Grace* and it is a pleasure to read. I cannot subscribe now as my husband is in hospital and I have to see him every day. It costs me five dollars to hire a car. I have had two accidents on my way to see him, but I was insured with our Omnipotent invisible Father who saved my life.

In your magazine I read of peppermint. I bring it to the boil and drink it for gas (wind) trouble. I am now almost well. I also use it on sandwiches of rye bread, lettuce and tomatoes. I make my own bread-crackers, and here is the recipe:

2 cupfuls Whole-wheat flour. Two-thirds cupful of water.
1 tablespoon of wheat-germ. 1 teaspoonful Kelp salt.
2 tablespoons Olive Oil.
Pour the water slowly on the flour. Add all ingredients. Make a dough for ten minutes or longer. Cut it into small balls. Spread each ball on the table and roll with a rolling-pin until it is shaped like a little plate and thin. Put it in a frying- pan without any fat. Let it stay for a few minutes until brown. They look like crackers but are soft and delicious.

I am 87 years and eat only fruits in the morning, and vegetables for lunch. I never eat meat, or drink coffee or tea. I grow my own fruits and vegetables, without sprays. God bless all members of the Grace Family from His superabundance.

J. Edmunds, St. Leonards-on-Sea, Sussex.
I have suffered from kidney trouble for many years which has altered the look of my face. When a joking relative said my eyes were as baggy as Mr Wilson's trousers I thought I would try to find something in place of the constant drugs. What do you say?
Clivers. Clivers, every time. Also known as goosegrass or cleavers. When we were boys in the country it was called 'sweetheart'. Square-stalked, its lanceolate leaves were about half an inch long, in rings of six, and with backward bristly hairs at the edges; so when playfully flung on your coat they clung like glue.

I shall never forget the sheer delight of the day when I learned of its medicinal virtues – out in the field – the proper place to learn of God's medicines and true healing.

Here is a fine diuretic (promoting the flow of urine), and alterative (blood cleanser). Place two teaspoonsful of the dried plant into a teacup and fill with boiling water. Allow to cool. Strain. Drink cold,' one wine-glassful after meals three times daily .

Mr E. Wilkinson, Wellington, New Zealand.
Have you anything to recommend for over-weight?
1. Three days' fruit-juice fast.
2. Follow with three days' diet of nothing but raw fruits.
3. Follow with three days of fruit and milk diet.
4. Epsom salt bath (hot) twice weekly. (Place two heaped handfuls of commercial epsom salts in your bath). Go straight to bed afterwards.
5. Conscious breathing exercises.
6. When the fruit and milk diet is finished go back to ordinary foods cautiously. Drink no coffee; less tea. Drink herb tea once or twice daily.

Mrs W. A. Forster, Harpenden.
I have been wearing a Copper Bracelet and feel you might be interested to know that I had a brown freckle mark on my hand, which developed

into a kind of wart. Since wearing the Bracelet it has completely disappeared. It was on the right hand – the side on which I wear the Bracelet.

Mrs Hilda Scott, Weston-super-Mare, Somerset.
Can anything be done for brittle, splitting finger-nails?

ED: *Brittle nails may be caused by a number of things, from faulty internal nutrition, or to external contact with detergents, cleansers and sol-
vents contained in nail-polish removers. Nail brittleness increases as a
person gets older.*

*Many find a cure in the use of Tincture of Myrrh used as a paint. Readily
obtainable from your nearest chemist. In most cases internal treatment is
the only answer. The Biochemic tissue-salt, Silicea 6x, has many cures
to its credit. Obtainable from your nearest Health Food Stores.*

Cashing in on Chickweed

CHEMICAL analysis of some
of our common plant medicines
reveals the presence of one or
more earth elements like silicon,
magnesium and aluminium,
assimilated and broken into a
form that supplies life energy to

Chickweed. Stellaria media.

the plant. The above three elements are believed to be coincident to
each other, because of their close atomic weights. Present in
Chickweed, their effectiveness has been proved when energy is
released by long trituration and succussion. Sooner or later scientists
will be forced to recognise different forms of energy—from what we
have considered as inanimate elements present in plants.

It has been helpful in the granulation of ulcers which refuse to heal—
as a poultice of the fresh leaves. Two or three drops squeezed from
the succulent stems into an eye bath, and half filled with warm milk
make a beneficial eye-bath for eye troubles. For skin eruptions and
rashes and kidney disorders 1 oz. may be boiled in 1 pint of water for
two minutes. Dose is anything from a wineglass of more according to
severity of the case. Being safe there is no fear of over-dosing. Stubborn
rashes sometimes get a little worse before improvement. A common
plant, growing anywhere in moist places.

The Nutritious Walnut

MRS. P. SOUTHWELL

A Woman, a dog, and a walnut tree
The more you beat them, the better they'll be.

Anonymous.

IT seems a pity to me that so often walnuts are used merely as a decoration for a cake or trifle. The walnut is a wonderful source of protein. Why pay steak prices when, weight for weight, the walnut contains almost as much protein as sirloin steak? It is such a versatile nut too, being equally at home in a savoury or sweet dish. It contains as much fat content as an equal weight of bacon and has almost as many calories as butter—two more facts to help me persuade you that walnuts should be on you shopping list.

In these days of Women's Lib the above quotation is, perhaps, not a very appropriate one. But if you are lucky enough to have a walnut tree in your garden, even the leaves can be used. A "tea" can be prepared from the chopped up leaves, using about 2 teaspoons in a pot of hot (not boiling) water. The infusion makes a complexion wash as well.

Indeed, in times gone by, many ladies relied on the walnut as a form of hair dye. I recently came across this old recipe for those not wishing to go grey: "This is well known, and, of course, is harmless. To make, take half a pound of mixed walnut leaves and husks, bruise and soak in a gallon of water for twenty-four hours. Boil until the amount is reduced to half, strain and add a tablespoonful of gin. Unfortunately this preparation dyes the scalp as well as the hair, but if it is applied carefully no harm will be done. And certainly it changes grey hair to a very beautiful and glossy brown." It must have been hard luck on those who ran out of walnut leaves and husks and could not keep up the deception. How much easier is life today.

My family's favourite nut dish is a cheese and walnut roast. It is particularly palatable served cold, thinly sliced, with salad. I find it ideal for picnics. This is the food which, each summer, accompanies us on the long drive to Scotland to see relatives. As vegetarians we even eat it on Christmas Day, and the easy recipe allows me to stay snugly in bed instead of being up at some unearthly hour to stuff and prepare an enormous turkey. Here it is:

Mix together
   12 oz. breadcrumbs (brown)
   8 oz. grated cheese
   4 oz. chopped walnuts
   1 chopped onion

then gently melt 2 oz. margarine in ½ pint milk, without getting it too hot. Add salt and pepper, 1 heaped teaspoon mustard powder, and beat-in 2 eggs. Stir this into dry mixture and mix thoroughly. Turn into greased oven-proof dish with lid and bake at mark 6, 400 degrees, for about 40 minutes. (I divide the mixture into half and use two round pyrex casseroles.)

Another firm favourite in my household is Date and Walnut Loaf. This improves with being kept in a tin for a few days, and is delicious when sliced and buttered.

   1 cup (8 oz. measure) All Bran
   1 cup milk
   1 cup brown sugar
   1 cup brown S.R. flour
   1 cup chopped dates
   ½ cup chopped walnuts.

Soak the All Bran in the milk for a little while, until soggy. Then stir in all the other ingredients and mix really well. Turn into a greased and lined 1 lb. loaf tin, and bake in a moderate oven for 1½ hours, or until done.

What a beautiful picture comes to mind when we read in The Song of Solomon, chapter 6 verse 11, "I went down into the garden of nuts to see the fruits of the valley, and to see whether the vine flourished, and the pomegranates budded". The nuts doubtless included walnuts. We can still enjoy their rich flavour and fragrance today.

285

honey and your health

DR. BECK quotes a correspondent on the curative value of honey in pulmonary troubles:
"In 1925, I became ill and consulted several doctors, all of whom gave me the verdict of active tuberculosis. After several months, two doctors gave me up, and said that my only chance was to go west, which I could not afford to do. At a later date, they frankly informed me that I had only three months to live and insisted on sending me to Colorado. I was then living in Kansas City, Missouri, and had previously been engaged in cement and paving work.

"I managed to land a job in Nehema County, Kansas, about 140 miles west of Kansas City. My work was to establish an apiary (bee farm) of one hundred colonies for a commercial orchard. I was to 'batch' in a room in the apple house, which had a cement floor. Often it took all my strength to carry a gallon of water from the well, which was one hundred feet away.

"In studying bees, I had learned the value of honey in driving out and destroying all germs in the human body. I used honey regularly and worked to the limits of my strength. Three years later the same doctors examined me and found only a few spots on my lungs. They absolutely refused to believe that I was the same person.

"Today I take my place as an average man. I take care of two hundred and fifty colonies of bees and a farm of twenty-five acres of land. The only help I have is about one month during the honey harvest. I don't know whether the honey cured me, or it was the fact that I was too lazy to crawl into my coffin, but I believe that the honey and possibly the raw diet were the major factors of my recovery."

From the book by Bodog F. Beck, M.D., and Doree Smedley
(Published by McBride & Co., New York)

Dandelion Wine

(Useful method for disposing of unwanted weeds in the garden)
BY CRAGGY MAGGIE

Ingredients: 2 lb. Raisins; 2 lb. Yellow Dandelion flowers; one lemon in thin slices; 4 lb. Demerara sugar; one orange cut in thin slices; 2 lb. rice.

Method: Bring the rice to boil in 10 pints of water and allow to cool. When tepid, empty other ingredients into the water and set aside. After four days strain well. Select a warm corner of the kitchen to allow liquor to ferment for another eight days. Strain. Bottle. Keep it dark . . . for one year . . . if you can wait that long!

> The man who drinks good home-made wines
> And goes to bed quite mellow,
> Lives as he ought to live
> And dies a jolly good fellow.

(nuff for now . . . Craggy)

Mrs L Whitton, Weston-super-Mare
Another bit, in case there is room. There must be magnetism in tulips. Have you ever noticed? Placed six in a vase as far apart as possible, and by morning you will find at least two with their heads together. Sometimes two pairs cuddling up! How is it done? My warmest wishes to you all.

Mrs Helen Price, County Down, N. Ireland.
There is a lot of nonsense talked about 'self-medication' . Provided one knows what one is about, it can save a lot of waiting-about at doctors and help get-better without drugs.

Now it seems to me the newest 'miracle-drug' is vitamin "E" which is of particular benefit to old people. My books tell me it keeps arteries young and is good for the heart, varicose veins and chest pains. All this I have proved for myself. That suits me.

Mr T. Thomson, Melbourne, S. Australia.
Biochemic remedies are arriving from England and are on sale in our Health Stores. I have obtained great benefit from Nat. Phos. 6x., for acidity. Even my sleep was affected. Now I am getting off to sleep and staying asleep, and I am able to eat things I could not touch before.

G. J. Jones, Roath Park, Bristol, Somerset.
Sitting round the fire one night with friends the conversation turned to home cures of our young days. Why is it that so many old chestnuts, like a cold wet cloth at the back of the neck for headache, are forgotten?

One said he was convinced that a sprinkle of sulphur in his socks took the pain out of his gout. Another asked why Spanish black liquorice was not easy to get, for winter coughs. Another said it used to be the belief that the common herb, Garden Rue, strengthened the optic nerve, and was of value for dimness of vision. Another had a wife who wore a copper bracelet for rheumatism; and the last man capped everything by swearing by the shrivelled nutmeg he fished out of his waistcoat pocket . . . 'Haven't had fibrositis for eight years," he crowed.

Mr T. H. Harris, Ryde, Isle of Wight.
Might I add recollections of old remedies used by my mother when I was a youngster some sixty or so years ago.

We lived in an area where the fields were often divided by dry stone walls. Out of these grew plants whose leaves were fleshy and slightly larger than pennies. We called them Pennyleaves. These were gathered during their season, pulped and mixed with lard. This was used as a general-purpose ointment. Very effective for skin troubles and abrasions.

When I had pneumonia, the old Doctor prescribed diluted Creosote. Instead, my mother gave me liquid Elderflower and Peppermint which soon got me over the 'crisis'.

(continued on page 290)

An Apple a Day

For thousands of years, apples have been associated with good health. The ancient Elysium of Celtic heroes, Avalon, where King Arthur went to heal his wounds, was an island of apple trees. Pagan Gods, old folklore and ancient myths all associate apples with good health. Gerard, the famous 16th century herbalist, wrote of their virtues, including 'apples be good for a hot stomach'. Apple pulp mixed with rosemary and sold as Pomatum, was a 16th century beauty cream.

10,000 year old apples

Apples were probably the first fruit ever to be cultivated by man. Carbonised samples some 10,000-15,000 years old have been found among prehistoric Swiss and Italian lake dwellings. However, they were not like the apples we know today.

Apple trees existed in England long before even the Romans arrived. They grew wild in forests when our ancestors wore animal skins, and were as small as crab-apples. It was the Romans though, who first introduced the cultivated fruit to our shores and, when they left, the monks kept up their traditions of cultivation. Later on, the Normans also brought apples to Britain.

Among the earliest cultivated varieties on record are the permain and the costard, and indeed it could have been the costard that set Sir Isaac Newton on the road to meditating on gravity when, as the story goes, an apple fell in front of him in his orchard in 1666.

'Costards' were our oldest cooking apples and they still live on in our memories, for from them we get the word 'costermongers' named after the men who hawked fruit in the streets.

Saved by King Hal!

It was Henry VIII who saved the English apple! By an uncanny coincidence he didn't like so many foreign apples being imported, either, and it was on his orders that the first orchard, as we know orchards, was started at Teynham, Kent. By the end of the 17th century, fruit growing had reached the standing of an industry, and during the 18th century, apple growers received professional status.

English apples colonise

With apples popular so long here, it is hardly surprising that when the first settlers set sail for Canada, Australia, South Africa and New Zealand, they took the fruit with them. Captain Bligh of the *Bounty* took the first apples to Australia; Jan van Riebeeck, the founder of Cape Settlement, took them to South Africa, and the *Mayflower* carried them to America.

But, even though all these countries eventually began their own orchards, Britain has remained second to none as far as cultivation, research and selection of varieties are concerned.

Apples for health

Eating an apple 15 minutes before consuming a meal is a way to lose weight. Tests have shown that a single medium sized apple, which contains about 40 calories and a lot of cellulose bulk, can give a 'full up' feeling and so reduce calorie intake at mealtimes.

Healthy Living.

Ed: It is always the way. The apples that are easy to pick are hardly worth picking. The apples that are worth having are always at the end of a branch or at the top of the tree.

"LADY much too stout. Also suffering from a complaint which necessitated her having to relieve her bladder at very frequent intervals. Cider Vinegar got rid of her surplus fat in a matter of weeks, and at the same time cured her bladder trouble."

Cyril Scott, in Cider Vinegar.

289

Being an haemophiliac, I was subject to haemorrhages, especially in the joints. These were accompanied by intense pain and swelling. As a treatment my mother made a poultice of Comfrey Root which reduced the swelling and eased the pain.

Mr G. Richards, Toronto, Canada.
Of all the good laughs we get from your magazine can anyone cap this? The following appeared under the 'Situations Vacant' column of the Vancouver Daily Province: "Fountain Lunch Combination man with experience preparing and serving salads, sandwiches, light lunches, fountain drinks and sundaes. Must be a conscientious, willing, efficient, honest, obedient, polite, tactful, courteous, clean-living young gentleman residing in Vancouver who can satisfactorily cater to a higher class trade. Of good family training, atmosphere, background and environment, that will keep place spotless; 17 to 22; of high morals, principles and ideals; tall, thin, good-looking, engaging personality, sensitive to customers' wishes , giving personal, interested and understanding service. Write fully, giving age, height, weight, education, references, experience and nearest phone number. Please don't waste our time or yours if you can't fill all requirements.

Mrs F. H. C., Dublin, Eire.
I suffer from thick, rough dry skin on my heels which even pumice stone fails to rub our. What would you recommend?

ED: *in an absence of cracks apple cider vinegar has been successful in a number of cases.*

---

*L**ife is an opportunity – benefit from it,
Life is beauty – admire it,
Life is bliss – taste it.
Life is a dream – realise it,
Life is a challenge – meet it,
Life is a duty – complete it.
Life is a game – play it,
Life is costly – care for it
Life is wealth – keep it.
Life is love – enjoy it,
Life is a promise – fulfil it.*

Mother Teresa.

Mrs Nora Ford, Wolverhampton, Staffs.
I must tell you a "wart" cure given to me by gypsies in Yorkshire when I was a child. I had a huge one on the side of my thumb. It was a bit of a nuisance. I was told to gather dandelions during spring and summer and dab the milky fluid on my wart as often as possible during the day, leaving it to dry on. It soon turned black, went like jelly and dropped off in about two days. The juice becomes scanty in the autumn and winter and does not have the same power.

An old Romany remedy for an abscess is to bathe it with the water in which a good sized parsnip has been boiled to a pulp. Afterwards apply the pulp itself as hot as can be borne.

Mrs J. Newbold, Burton Joyce, Nottingham.
For many years I have been a grateful subscriber and avid reader of your beautiful and "down-to-earth" magazine. I would like to say a very sincere "Thank You" for all the help and pleasure we have derived.

My husband has angina and has derived particular benefit from Hawthorn tablets and vitamin E capsules.

Miss Celia Effer, Ringwood, Hants.
I am writing to say that after a few years of constant reading of *Grace* I find it increasingly helpful and interesting.

I am the secretary of a thriving "Silver Threads'" Club and when I give my talks on honey, yeast, cabbage water, etc., there goes up a laugh and "Oh. Miss Effer's Commercial."

Several members of my "Silver Threads" Club have spoken of its benefit and one lady's cough cleared up very quickly after use of honey and lemon.

My friend who accompanied me on a tour recently had a very sore and painful arm following her vaccination. She applied honey to the wound and it was very quickly relieved.

C. H. Nelson, Park Place, London, N10.
Seeing that it cost the nation over £5 million last year to maintain our children's teeth, and since sweets are the main cause of early decay, should there not be a tax on sweets? The dentists consider themselves underpaid; is there any reason why the revenue from such a tax should not go to improved dental services?

Notice outside a church in Beckenham:
"Prayer, the only commodity that isn't going up".

Mr John Balfour, Worcester Park, Surrey.
My trouble is anaemia and chronic catarrh; I am also overweight. I have tried a slimming diet but results were not very good. I have to take aperients.

ED: *We are sorry to learn of your trouble. Have you tried adding to your breakfast meal two tablespoonfuls of bran, and one of wheat germ? Have plenty of cooked and raw beetroot to improve the blood. You should have at least one salad a day, summer and winter, containing grated carrots, lettuce, cucumber, celery, pulses, to which may be added a few grated nuts and cheese.*

Do not overlook the importance of molasses to sluggish bowels: it is also a source of iron. Kelp has something to offer, as also would the vitamin B complex.

Do not forget deep breathing exercises, and the simple action of retracting the abdomen, releasing, retract, release, and repeat the movement a number of times. You are, of course, not likely to rush your food. Chew all food thoroughly, and do take time over your meals.

Mrs P. Collins, County Cork.
I have never yet seen a remedy for agoraphobia (fear of open spaces). I rarely venture out of my house, only going out a few times in the past five years. It all started after my fourth child. I was told to pull myself together and given tranquillisers. I am told this comes mostly to women.

ED: *It is a vast subject, demanding more study. There is, however, a homoeopathic remedy which has resulted in a number of successes. To the homoeopathic practitioner the remedy, Argent Nit, is known as the 'funk pill'. It might prove helpful for the woman who wants the end seat in a pew, to be nearer the door in a church or theatre, and who needs an easy escape. Kent writes: "in the street the sight of high houses always makes the patient feel giddy and causes him to stagger. Cannot look down – cannot look up."*

Anne Edwards
Nearly every wife ought to get a bonus for being beautiful or elegant, plus a percentage increase for the work she puts in on staying up when she'd rather go to bed, going out when she'd rather stay in, making up to her husband's contacts, working hard in his interests, and listening . . . listening . . . listening . . .

Member of Parliament, in the House of Commons.
I would like to invite all M.P.s suffering from rheumatism, arthritis, lumbago and nervous disorders to be stung by bees.

John G. Clark and Betty Morales, California, U.S.A.
Hydrotherapy, a natural method of healing, is having a revival. This is a treatment by application of wrung-out cold-water packs.

Dr. R. Lincoln Graham is an authority on this science and has written a book in which is reported that during the outbreak of swine flu which swept the States, over four-hundred cases were treated, without loss of a

single life. This flu was said to be as deadly as the 1918 variety.
His technique for treating this kind of flu is basically four points:
1. No food until the disease is over.
2. A glass of water every hour, preferably spring water.
3. An enema or high colonic irrigation every day.
4. A cold, wet pack around the chest in case of symptoms of pneumonia.

A reviewer of this book writes: "I could scarcely believe the astounding results reported, but since I have been putting his methods into practice, for flu, in my own practice, results have never once been disappointing.

"I shall never forget the first time I tried this method. I was called to the home where a six-year-old child lay dying of pneumonia. The attending physician told me: "This child will die before morning. However, I began hydrotherapy treatment. Within an hour the most remarkable change took place. She had been extremely constipated, was too weak to cough up the mucus that was choking her, and constantly moaned in pain.

"Soon the moans stopped. Her bowels moved three times normally. The straggling mucus poured out of her. Her temperature gradually dropped from 104.5 to 97. Next morning the dying child was well. Completely well. It taught me a great lesson. It reinforced my belief in Dr. Graham's methods, which I have continued to use.

"Observer", in "Financial Times.
At a market stall selling jars of rejuvenating cream, one woman asked, sceptically: 'Is it any good?" "Any good?" echoed the stallholder. and turned to a young girl beside him, "Hand the lady a jar, Mother."

Mrs H. S., Glasgow.
What would you recommend for napkin dermatosis. My baby's buttocks are always red and raw and zinc oxide creams do not seem to help.
ED: *Have you tried Marigold cream? Comfrey cream? Castor oil? Maybe, the irritation is being kept up by irritation from a strong acid urine. Make sure your doctor has ruled out candida albicans, which may well be the cause. The widespread increase in thrush, particularly vaginal thrush, places some babies at risk, and the rash can be most distressing.*

Do not overlook the practise of bathing the affected area with a simple infusion of chamomile flowers: 5 to 10 flowers to a teacup, allowed to steep for ten minutes.

Mrs L. C., Oswaldtwistle, Lancashire.
I've taken every *Grace* ever since it first came out. I find great comfort from it as I am a widow of 72, and an invalid with arthritis, and live alone. It takes away much of my loneliness.

Mrs D. Adams, Pennsylvania, U.S.A.
What foods can help me to get a better circulation of hands and feet'?
(I am sorry we have not space to go into all foods for this purpose.
Dates, raisins, honey and figs are important ones. – ED.)

Alan Woodhouse, Adelaide, Australia.
I have read that raw cabbages are good for rheumatism and fibrositis, How
do you take them'?
ED: *One way of eating raw cabbage is by making a raw vegetable salad.*
Take a quantity of white cabbage, red cabbage, a few carrots, a root of
celeriac, and salad dressing.
  Wash red and white cabbage in warm water. Slice or chop finely. Grate
the carrots and celeriac. According to season, garnish with lettuce leaves,
radishes, mustard-and-cress, or watercress. Salad dressing is made by
taking three tablespoons Olive Oil, and adding 1-2 tablespoons lemon-
juice. With a little salt shake well to emulsify. Add chopped chives or
parsley, or culinary herbs of any kind according to taste. Addition of
white of an egg makes a very satisfactory dressing.

Miss R. Lupton, Hatfield, Salisbury, Zimbabwe.
Must tell you about the rats. I cannot have cats here because of Tuff.
He's hot stuff on cats! Some rats made holes and nested under the house
and were getting up into the roof night-time, making a dreadful noise as
they thundered along overhead playing hop-scotch. The honeysuckle
creeper is their method of getting up into the roof. Have seen them up
and down the creepers. Normally I hate rats – am scared stiff at them –
but being loathe to kill any creature (and also because of Tuff the dog
nosing around) I did not want to set traps or lay poison bait. So I decided
to follow Lady Muriel Dowding's example and methods of dealing with
unwanted fauna.
  Whereupon, firmly shutting Tuff inside one night around 7.30 p.m. I
went out and round to the four rat-holes. Standing a respectful distance
away, I called out for the chief rat to come up and listen as I wanted to
talk to him. Sure enough, as I went on talking aloud after a few minutes
a big rat popped up out of the biggest hole and sat up on his haunches
behind one of the cotyledon bushes, his eyes glittering in my torchlight.
During this session some more rats emerged from the holes until there
were quite a number of them squatting on their haunches in a long cres-
cent formation beside the house.
  I talked to the King-rat and all of them, explaining that as they were
all part of God's creation I sent out love and loving thoughts to them. I
wished them well in all ways but I must ask them to remove themselves
completely from underneath the house as their holes and tunnels would
undermine the foundations and when the rains came, as they would do
soon, the water would pour down the holes and they would all be drowned

in their nests. I did not want that to happen. Pointing out that they were creatures of the wilds they must move away from the house altogether and must refrain from getting up in the roof, holding races and rodent football matches up there on the ceilings because they made a lot of noise and were doing damage.

I was requesting them politely and nicely to vacate their underground nests and tunnels and to move off down to the frontage amongst all the trees where there was plenty of food and water for them. I did not want to have to set traps or put down poison. So would they please be nice, good rats and move off *en masse* to the untouched and unused parts of the ground where they would be quite unmolested? Wished them well and thankfully departed indoors.

Believe it or not. They moved that same night! Yes sir! There's not been a sign or sound of rats since and the holes are quite definitely empty. Not one has been up to the roof either! Lady Dowding swears by this method. So do I now. I was rather sceptical about it at first. This was over a month ago – and have not seen a whisker of a rat since that night. Love to all the readers.

Harold Chambers, Liverpool, 11.
I have had recurrent attacks of severe colicky abdominal pain and distension. I have had all the usual tests but am told there is nothing really wrong. I have had drugs. Is there a herb?

ED: *If nothing has been found to be wrong, you probably have 'irritable bowel' trouble and doubtless have tried adding bran to your diet.*

Avoid: pickles, condiments, salt, white bread, white sugar, starchy and cream pastry, confectionery, vinegar, alcohol, etc. Try to keep to three substantial meals a day, with no snacks, and a minimum of tea and coffee.

You should find oil of peppermint helpful: either one drop on a teaspoonful of honey or, better still two drops placed in an empty gelatine capsule. One capsule may be swallowed before meals, three times daily. This enables the peppermint to be released slowly. By the time the capsule is dissolved, it is well past the stomach and duodenum, and on its way through the intestines where its influence is required.

Wild Yam, (dioscorea villosa) is a sovereign remedy for this condition, including appendicitis, diverticulitis and liver troubles generally.

Mr J. C. Langley, Leeds.
My wife and I are not ones to take drugs or any kind of remedies, usually being very fit. But we read of cholesterol which can get out of hand in the veins. Is there any simple thing we can take? We are both a little on the heavy side, and my wife had liver trouble early in life, but has now been free of it for many years.

ED: *There are a number of things which come to mind, but I think perhaps one of the simplest would be to take Contrexeville water, or*

Vichy water, instead of tap water. These two have a long reputation for weight- reduction. More than that, recent work shows how these waters are good for keeping veins and arteries reasonably free from cholesterol deposits.

Experiments on women with hypercholesterolemia have proved satisfactory. This is a simple drinking cure, whereby a person's daily pattern of living is not altered.

John Fuller, Devizes, Wilts.
Along the path. Clinging to my trembling hand the child said: "It's great to be able to look up to you for help."

I, myself, looked up; softly repeating these words.

Mrs V. Williams, Oxford Road, Southampton.
I have had Raynaud's disease ever since I was 43 years old, and am now 67. I have had hospital treatment and was taking 16 tablets a day from my doctor which were not successful. In the end they said I must learn to "put up with it" .

So, when I read about vitamin E helping the circulation I started taking them. I can say there has been great improvement. My fingers and toes do not go white and blue any more. They are still cold, but these are early days. I feel that before long I shall be able to go out and not to have to take a hot water bottle with me. Many thanks again. Very sincerely.

Mr K. L. Mason, Oadby, Leicester (42 years)
It's nice to gather together around the teapot, in *Grace*. Where would we be without tea? John Wesley included it in his attacks on strong drink. He declared it harmful to body and soul, an extravagance for the poor and a needless indulgence of the rich. Later in life he realised his error and became a confirmed tea-drinker. So much so, that his friend Josiah Wedgwood, the famous potter, made a special half-gallon teapot for him which was used at his Sunday morning breakfast parties.

Dr George Gemmill, Manchester Road, Burnley, Lancs.
I agree with Mr C. H. Nelson (in a past issue of *Grace Magazine*) that there should be a tax on sugar: ("Pure, White, and Deadly," as Prof. Yudkin describes it.)

Television advertising of sugar, sweets and white bread should be banned. The widespread consumption of artificial, chemicalized, processed, refined and bleached "foods" continues unabated: shelf-life being more important than human life.

The so-called National Health Service is a danger to the national health. Vast sums of money spent on health merely produces more illness.

Autumn leaves, Witham, England   *Photo: Dennis Mansell.*

Drugging is widespread. If there is such a thing as health-education in this country, I am still waiting to see the results of same. Keep on with the good work in *Grace*. Yours sincerely.

Gwen Oxberry, Wickford, Essex.
Over 50 years ago my mother had large warts covering her hands. Having a persevering nature, she tried many remedies. Then she tried castor oil. This was applied several times during the day. They started to diminish. Finally, "All Clear."

A salt-water mouth-wash for healing and relief of mouth ulcers is very effective. Held in the mouth for ten minutes it can end them.

Mrs M. Chapman, Winnipeg, Canada.
How shall we ever be able to thank you for the wonderful improvement in my varicose veins, and for help for my husband's "nervous exhaustion" and bad circulation. All due to Vitamin "E". There ought to be a packet in every home.

Anonymous
While on holiday, I went to buy our meat from a mobile shop. "Excuse me," said the butcher. "I must serve my old regular customer first, otherwise he is likely to get impatient!"

Somewhat taken aback, I looked round expecting to see an elderly gentleman. Instead, there stood an aged mongrel dog with his front paws on the running board.

The butcher handed him the bony end of a breast of lamb. "What do you say?" he asked. There came a muffled bark, and the dog was off up the lane. "Nice old chap," said the butcher. "Always does his own shopping. He'll bring me the money in a paper bag on Friday."

Press notice.
Hew broke the underwater record by staying underwater for three hours and twenty-five minutes.

The funeral will be held tomorrow.

Mrs O. E. Thurlow, Waiheke Island, Auckland, N.Z.
A letter from a London reader to you, about the remarks made by some doctors, brought to mind an instance in my family. My father lost his wife suddenly and was left with a family of six children. Times were hard. The doctor who attended him for heart trouble told him his condition was such that he only gave him 6 months to live. This had the effect of making him take a grip on himself. He got better, lived to marry again and bring up another family. He died at 86 years. He was beloved by all who knew him; believed in moderation in all things. I sometimes won-

der whether doctors say these things with that object in view in some cases, as it certainly had a beneficial effect in this case.

ED: *It's like so many things in life, isn't it? It's not brains but persistence and the will to live that wins.*

Nancy Walmsley, Bristol.
Two young girls were walking along a street in Bristol. Something from a passing car hit one girl's leg, and on inspection found a large hole in her stocking. It was on a Friday, 13th.

Her friend was sharp enough to take the number of the car, and so traced the owner. The young man received a letter from the owner of the damaged stocking, in which it was suggested he buys her a new pair. He replied with apologies and said he would bring them.

They met. You've guessed the end of this true story. Yes, they are now happily married. He said he left a spanner on the running board. Girls . . . you can never tell your luck!

ED: *Who said thirteen was unlucky?*

Epitaph, North of England.
On the twenty-second of June . . . Jonathan Fiddle went out of tune.

Member of Grace Family.
On return from the Holy Land I have brought back with me the knowledge that sea salt is good for you. Unlike common salt on sale, it contains valuable minerals: magnesium, potassium, bromine and iodine (for the thyroid gland). Besides this, there is the added benefit of a more acceptable flavour. It is not too bitingly salty.

Epitaph.
Eliza, sorrowing, rears this marble slab . . . To her dear John, died eating crab.

Mrs E. M. Hill, Ealing, W.5.
I thought you would be interested in this little episode:- Our workroom over-looks a small cemetery adjoining a 14th century church. One is saddened by the sight of the service and the grief of the mourners. After the service is over one has the beauty of the floral tributes to view. Imagine my surprise on looking up from my work, to see four little girls with their hands clasped together, offering up a silent prayer for the departed one. This is something that will live in my memory for a long time to come.

Mrs A. V., Norfolk.
My daughter, three years old, manages to find an excuse for almost everything she doesn't want to do. Her latest: "I'm really far too young . . ."

Mrs Florence K. Mansfield, Southend-on-Sea.
Early in August I had a shock which caused me to have a considerable amount of pain in my right leg and thigh. Having read the articles on Vitamin "E" I visited our local Herbalist and asked his advice. He agreed it could assist my difficulty and I procured a supply. He also suggested I needed more pure sugar, i.e. honey, so I've been having about 1lb a week and have improved greatly. I also followed the advice of your reader and put flowers of sulphur in my shoes to ease the pain. This worked wonders as well! What a lot I have to thank *Grace* for!

Card in a Lancashire shop window.
Reluctantly forced to find a good home for large shaggy mongrel dog. Disobedient, impossible to house-train, gluttonous and has unpleasant habits, but has bitten an unwelcome visitor.

Anonymous.
Mrs T. reported that during her last two months of pregnancy she massaged her abdomen nightly with castor oil. She attributes to this activity the fact that she had no stretch marks at all after her pregnancy was ended. The child born then received the same treatment. The castor oil "works very well on his bottom when any redness appears."

Mrs May Howard, Whitby, Ontario, Canada.
It is too bad that so few people know of a simple home cure that checks gangrene if used in the early stages. The large toe on my Mother's foot had turned black, and at that time she had not heard about ordinary white vinegar, used externally, as a cure for gangrene.

However, as her feet ached and burned, she started bathing them every day in vinegar, slightly warmed, and in no time her toe was completely normal, and she lived to be eighty-seven years old, with no return of the trouble.

ED: *I understand this was sometimes used by old-time nurses. Isn't that something!*

Stanley Hickman, Easthourne.
My wife was putting to bed our three-year-old grandchild, Caroline, having read to her the favourite nursery rhyme, "Humpty Dumpty."

"Now," coaxed Granny, say your own prayer, "Gentle Jesus". Very sleepy after her energetic playtime, she knelt beside her cot and folded her little hands in prayer.

"Gentle Jesus . . ." Then came a pause followed by a tired sigh. Making a second attempt, she began:

"Gentle Jesus sat on a wall . . ."

We wonder if even He could not suppress a smile as He softly hushed this sweet innocent child to sleep.

Mrs B. L., Inverness-shire, Scotland.
I discovered an absorbing pastime – planting pips and fruit stones and wondering what is going to come up. I set almond stones in the garden and now have some interesting plants. I may not be here by the time they bear fruit – but that doesn't matter. In the house one of my successes is an avocado plant, with lovely leaves. A lemon plant got so big I had to turf it out, but it didn't survive in the garden.

My 'pip' plants are the first things my visitors go for. Next, I think I'll have a go at a cashew nut tree until it gets too big for home comforts.

ED: *Thank you for the knowledge of something even we without green fingers can do.*

Mrs Penson, Hampshire.
In the Spring 1998 issue I read of a reader who finds Lavender oil such a help. I thought I'd pass on to you how much it helped my family. My husband had skin cancer which meant he had to have an operation on his forehead with 13 stitches, a nasty scar, and much pain. My youngest daughter, who is a nursery nurse, said, "Why don't you try Lavender oil or gel? At least, it won't hurt, and it can only take the pain away." Which it did.

When my husband again went to the doctor's to have the stitches out, both doctor and nurse said: "What have you done – it's marvellous! How it has healed!" Praise the Lord! Doris.

Mr K. Wilson, Chelmsford.
Two dogs were watching the latest dance craze at the Leisure Centre. After a while one dog looked at the other and said: "When I act like that they give me worm tablets."

Anonymous, Leigh, Lancashire.
We know of a friend's daughter who is said to be autistic. She is at times quite withdrawn, and at others very angry without cause. I have read where magnesium is related. What do you say?

ED: *Yes, there appears to be a link between magnesium deficiency and this strange disorder of the mind. Some improvement in emotional response has been observed following supplements of vitamin B6. It is interesting to note that magnesium is essential to the body's use of vitamin B6.*

It would appear that Chamomile tea might be helpful for young women. Also, the homoeopathic remedy: Pulsatilla.

Did you know that some autistic children are said to improve when milk, wheat and sugar are cut out of the diet? A Gluten-Free diet has been advised by one authority. Why not visit your nearest Health Store and enquire about the Gluten-Free Diet?

Members of Grace Family, WA 98221-9720, U.S.A.
Pour a little vinegar into the palm of your hand and rub hands together.
They will feel like velvet. You don't even have to wash off the vinegar
before working in the kitchen. Be sure this is the last thing you do before
bedtime. Your hands will stay soft all winter long.

Member of Grace Family.
Did you hear of the incident when a family was bombed out in the last
war? From an East End tenement during the worst night of the Blitz, a
woman was seen struggling with a bird cage containing an unruffled
budgie which was overheard to remark: "This is my night out."

Letter received in a dress shop.
Dear Sir, You have not delivered the maternity dress I ordered. Please
cancel the order. My delivery was faster than yours.

Anonymous, Loughborough, Leicestershire.
From a teenager I suffered severe menstrual pains that got worse over the
years. Now at 33, I feel I don't want to go on like this for ever. It is no
good me taking remedies. I've taken them all! No-one seems to be able
to get to the bottom of my trouble.

ED: *You may not be aware that one of the most common causes of
menstrual troubles is an under-active thyroid gland. This is not the kind
of thing the doctor will be looking for. Self-help is the best help for your
condition. Ask the assistant behind the counter of your nearest Health
Store for a paperback on thyroid disorders. Talk to him/her about low-
thyroid conditions. For one thing . . . there is of course Kelp (for its
iodine content). It is not generally known that Vitex Agnus Castus also
assists the thyroid.*

*There are dozens of remedies for menstrual pain, and you can spend
an awful lot of money seeking relief. First of all, top up the gland with
Kelp; yet do not overlook the importance of diet rich EFAs (essential fatty
acids) from seeds, pulses, nuts, nut oils and fish. Some sufferers find
Evening Primrose capsules helpful, but plain old-fashioned Cod Liver Oil
is better (1-2 teaspoons daily). Mix with honey for palatability.*

Mr R. Baldwin, Dorset.
Like an unfortunate fellow in the news, I had a serious attack of hiccups,
which baffled the medical men. So I tried placing my finger at the back
of my mouth and keeping it there as long as I could. It worked.

ED: *Cures for hiccups are legion. Nearly everyone has his or her
own cure. Some try drinking water on the wrong side of the glass.
Others hold their breath until they go puce. The longest recorded
attack of hiccups was that afflicting Charles Osborne, Iowa, USA from
1922. Until the 1970s he was still going strong. He was never able*

WHILE THE KETTLE BOILS

to keep in his false teeth. Thank you, Mr Baldwin, for your letter which will be helpful for readers of the magazine when hiccups become a problem.

Mrs H. J., Essex.
My granddaughter had just finished arranging her dolls the length of the settee for my usual compliment on how nice she keeps them. I don't know how I manage with such a large family," she sighed. Then, giving me a meaningful look, she concluded: "And I'm expecting again at Christmas."

Miss B. Chantrey, Kidderminster.
I had some thyroid trouble two years ago which left my hair very brittle and thin. I have got over this trouble now but my hair has not yet caught up with my general improvement. What can I do for it?
ED: *Few things revitalize hair more than castor oil. It can be used as a conditioner before shampooing, or a little rubbed into the scalp with fingertips. Do not use too much as it can be greasy. If you have had low thyroid disturbance your eyebrows could be thin and feeble. Try a smear, daily, on eyebrows and eyelashes, you should be surprised at results. Steep a piece of lemon peel in a small bottle of castor oil for two weeks. A neglected hair strengthener. Massage into the roots with finger-tips.*

Mrs O. Holman, Bideford, Devon.
I read an article written by Jon Evans, herbalist, who advised the olive oil and lemon treatment for gall stones.
I passed a copy on to a friend whose co-worker, a woman of 34 years of age, suffered considerable pain and whose doctor gave her Bismuth to relieve it. The trouble had been there for 14 years. She took the remedy, was unwell with sickness, but passed 47 stones. She now feels a new woman!

A. H. C., Brighton on Sea.
Shingle bells, shingle bells, shingle all your hair! Don't forget to wash your neck or else don't leave it bare. Shingle bells, shingle bells, right up to the dome. Ain't it fun, the more you cut the less you have to comb!
ED: *Going grey? Keep it dark!*

Anonymous.
I suffered many years from depression, and articles that try to 'jolly you up' are very frustrating. It is absolutely impossible to smile, even were one given a million dollars.
However, I was one of the lucky ones who by chance discovered that vitamin B complex made all the difference. Now I can be more cheerful like anyone else. Very few writers on depression understand the role of the B vitamins. One was dear old Gayelord Hauser, who said: "It is use-
(continued on page 306)

Do you suffer from Tension?

*"However strong our faith . . .
however strong the spiritual antidote . . . pain
sometimes catches us off our guard, and we
perceive how frail and weak we really are.*

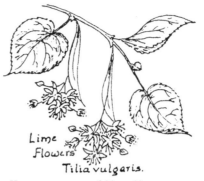

Lime
Flowers
Tilia vulgaris.

MAYBE we cannot sleep at night from an over-active brain. Whether you are a school teacher still "taking" a maths class at 3 o'clock in the morning, or a cashier still trying to trace a discrepancy in the day's "balancing-up," when you should be miles away in natural restful sleep, Lime Flower Tea is what you need.

Few hypnotics are as harmless as a congenial cup of *Lime Tea*. Did you know it is strengthening in *nervous exhaustion?* It is believed to contain valuable trace-elements of potash, phosphorous and other inorganic salts in short supply in artificially prepared foods of today.

A French specialist discovered that if you aren't sleepy o' nights, salt may be the cause. Try leaving out salt from the evening meal. For those insomniacs who are simply baffled by their inability to "get-off," the writer would like to remind them that maybe the head is too cold! Many a time a little woolly cap has solved the problem.

Or perhaps pre-menstrual tension is a monthly ordeal to be suffered, when all fingers are thumbs and the rhythm of life is upset. We all know those brave little women fighting a losing battle against rising tension with its general jitteriness, irritability and inefficiency.

Have you tried a simple infusion of Raspberry leaves? We are aware they are excellent to facilitate easy delivery in child-birth. Their use for menstrual pain can make all the difference between a day at the office or a day in bed.

However strong our faith, and however powerful the spiritual antidote we seek, pain sometimes catches us off our guard, and we perceive how frail and weak we really are. I suggest it is at such times that we are permitted to seek a little material aid from "herbs of the field which God has placed there for our use; and he who is wise will not abhor them."

King Solomon knew of the virtues of the hyssop that grew on the wall. It was a clump of figs which cured Hezekiah's boils. Rachel requested mandrakes.

Before the days of wonder-drugs, simple herbal remedies were the main material means of overcoming ills of the body. The sweet influences of balm, basil, pellitory-of-the-wall, chamomile, bergamot and betony are still available to those who turn to them. Who knows how many chronic incurable diseases have been avoided by the timely use of a harmless remedy?

For common colds, influenza and early stages of fevers, it is surprising how two teaspoonsful of a mixture of Elderflowers and Peppermint in a teacupful of boiling water can have you back again to work in good time. This simple combination is also a fine relaxant.

Drinking Black Grapes

CLARET is made from black grapes picked when fully ripe, pressed as soon as they are picked, and left to ferment – that is to say, to pass from the unstable state of turbid grape-juice to the more stable state of clear wine, without help or hindrance. No brandy is added to make the wine stronger, no lime to make it fall bright sooner, no sugar to make it taste sweeter, no artificial heat or cold resorted to, nor any other artifice to hurry or retard its fermentation, as happens in the case of many other wines . .

The excellence of claret is due not solely to the grape-bearing vines; it is due in an even greater measure to the soil and subsoil of the Bordeaux vineyards—that is to say, to the mineral salts which the roots find and pass on to the fruit; it is due also to the exceptionally suitable climatic conditions prevailing in the Bordelais, not every year, of course, but in many years: great heat tempered with sea-borne moisture. *André L. Simon (President, Wine and Food Society)*

Sun-filled autumn days.   *Horace Knowles.*

God knew we needed something more
  Than budding earth and sky;
And so He sent us friends to love
  To lift our hearts and spirits high.

God chose to teach love's wond'rous art
  Of Comfort, cheer that never ends
By giving to the thankful heart
  The dear, good gift of faithful friends.

less to tell a person to pull himself together. Unless his brain is getting the proper nutrients he cannot pull himself together."

When low spirits were on me, for many years, I really tried hard but to no avail and I must say that I found that some writers made me even more depressed. They have most certainly never looked at vitamin B or they would realise how impossible it is to think positively without it. There are other nutrients that have the same effect when they are lacking, but I can only write about vitamin B.

Mr J. E., Chatham, Kent.
My wife is on tranquillizers and wants to come off them. The doctor says it is all due to stress. The least little thing worries her. She has indigestion.

ED: *There is nothing worse for your looks and health than the wear and tear of constant stress. Chronic problems may follow: headache, low back pain and indigestion are a few.*

Your wife should eat little and often. Revise the diet to cut out white sugar, white flour products; and not too much salt. Go easy on coffee and tea, both stimulants, and experiment with herb teas. Lime flower tea and Lemon Balm tea are gentle relaxants.

Of course, she will be wise enough not to burn the candle at both ends, and never to cut down on sleep. It is the sleep before midnight that does most good.

Mrs Sally Haines, Boksburg, South Africa.
In 1975, being a keen gardener in Rhodesia, and of a very fair skin, I developed a nasty red, stinging, itchy sore on my forehead which I didn't know was a skin cancer. I kept it under control with a vitamin E cream.

In 1981, I moved to South Africa and in 1990 found it getting worse. A friend told me to put urine on it daily, which kept a scab on it. In 1994 my new neighbour told me to use Aloe Vera Skin Gel. In four months it was completely healed – with no scar. Now my skin is nice and smooth again, as I use it day and night.

ED: *Thank you, Mrs Haines, for a welcome contribution. We, too, have formed a high opinion of the ability of Aloe Vera to heal skin lesions proving intractable to other methods of treatment. Aloe Vera is obtainable from all Health Stores.*

Mrs Helen Edwards, Swansea, W. Glamorgan, Wales.
My life began at 51, when I fell in love for the first time with a fine man, and we were married. He has taught me all kinds of things – to garden, and play tennis. Since then, I have turned a rubbish dump into a colourful flower garden at the front of the house, and a vegetable patch at the back.

He encouraged me to do something I haven't done since schooldays – to paint. I soon picked it up again and have sold many pictures, which has enabled us to enjoy a holiday abroad. I love to knit, and my husband is so appreciative of my efforts that he buys all the wools and lots of other accessories. I have gone back to the piano as well. Now my husband is teaching me to drive, I feel years younger. I am so glad I said "Yes" when I did.

Joyce Sibbick. (Submitted by Mrs M. Leckebusch, resident of Livesey Lodge, Livesey Drive, Sapcote, Leicester.)
My father was called to serve his country in 1914. It was while at Gallipoli that the breast pocket of his tunic which contained his prayer book was hit by a bullet. This saved his life as the bullet landed three quarters through the book.

However, he had no wounds and lived to be a great age. I often read his account of this written in the trenches. I wonder how many of us are saved through our prayer book?

Another trip was made by father in 1940 – this time to the Dunkirk beaches where his small cargo-boat ferried men out to deeper waters to the larger ships to route home.

He wore his medals with pride. The Dunkirk medal was different – won for saving lives. How we should all love one another, and have faith.

Barbara Lister, Worthing.
In response to the request from your Australian correspondent for a remedy for vertigo. I offer the advice which was given to me when I became ill with Ménière's syndrome about 4 years ago.

A friend of mine fell victim to Ménière's when few people had heard of the complaint. She consulted the original Dr Allinson in Harley Street. As soon as she described her symptoms, he advised her take the lobes of the ears firmly between thumb and forefinger and rotate the ears vigorously clockwise and anti- clockwise about 20 – 30 times when getting out of bed each morning. This helps to stimulate the supply of blood to the brain. She was also told to take Vitamin B3. This vitamin should be taken with care, not in large doses, as an excess of the B group can upset the liver.

I derived great benefit from the ear massage. It is a simple enough remedy, and costs nothing. Sincerely.

Mrs R. Thompson, Middlesex.
My children used to groan: "Oh, not rice pudding again!" Now they're grownup and married, I've thought about rice. Lack of it in China can mean a famine.

It is more than food. It still makes, in some parts, a hat for a man's head, sandals for his feet, and straw mats for use underfoot. Rice-straw is used to light fires, feed beasts, and provide beverages in the home. What potatoes were to the Irish and oatmeal to the Scots, rice is to the East.

Tom Kent writes: Organically grown brown rice has unique nutritive qualities making it a most healthful food for all purposes. Natural brown rice has all of the germ-bran and oil of the natural kernel. Milled white rice, the most prevalent on the market today, is rice from which the germ and outer bran layers (with the vital B group vitamins) have been removed and has very little food value. The coating that is taken off to make it white, takes away 99 per cent of the food value. A spoonful of starch would provide equally as much nourishment.

Nursing howlers from hospital examination papers.
The child obviously had hoping cough.
Owing to coughing the patient may become a little horse.

Mrs Myra Watkins, Brixham, Devon.
Reading in the Spring 1995 issue *"Yoghurt, its use in thrush"* I thought it may help some of our Grace Family to know this can also help in fungal infections in the mouth.

After a visit to the dentist, I suffered from this complaint for two years. My dentist tried many different treatments, all unsuccessful. My sister suggested live yoghurt, which I used as a mouth wash after food and at bedtime. In three weeks it had cleared. Thank you for many joyful hours of *Grace* reading. God bless you all.

Mr John Anderson, Canterbury.
I have been troubled with insomnia for months since losing my hair. I get to sleep all right, but awake as lively as a cricket and want to be up and doing. I don't want to take sleeping tablets. My wife thinks you should know.

ED: *I am reminded of a book I have always valued entitled "Wind in the Sahara", by R. V. C. Bodley, (Pub: Robert Hale). I, too, am losing some of my once luxuriant hair. I had the same problem but have found the answer. The following was an experience of Col. Bodley:*

"After dinner I wanted to go to bed. Once in bed, I could not sleep. At first I could not make out why I would drop off almost as soon as my head touched the pillow, but I would be wide awake in an hour and tossing round most of the night. It was not because of the bed or being covered up or the lack of air . . . It was not indigestion or nerves. It was something quite unexpected. If I had not mentioned my insomnia to Daylis, I might never have found out the cause.

"He said: "Your head's cold . . unless I have something on my head, I can't sleep."

So, John, it looks as if you will have to get your wife to knit you a nightcap − a perfect sedative for an over-active brain.

John.
Q. Why do barbers make good drivers?
A. Because they know all the short cuts!

Miss Audrey Browning, Warnham, Horsham, West Sussex.
I always especially enjoy reading *"While the Kettle Boils"*. A letter from
Mr & Mrs Baker in the Autumn 1994 issue mentions their simple remedy for scalds. It made me recall vividly the day when I was badly scalded
52 years ago when I was ten years old.

I had taken the kettle off the kitchen range and lifted the lid to see how
much water it contained but the rush of hot steam to my hand made me
drop the kettle, and the near-boiling water scalded one of my legs from
knee to foot. My mother sprinkled bicarbonate of soda on my leg and
bandaged it. I can't remember much discomfort subsequently and when
the large blisters had gone, there were no scars. Needless to say, there is
always a good supply of "bicarb" in my house. Yours sincerely.

Teresa Waller, Cranford Heath, Poole, Dorset.
I have been using Zinc and Castor oil cream on my varicose eczema; the
irritation has stopped and the skin looks healthier. Also, for eczema, I
was told by a friend to take two tablespoons, daily, Safflower or Sunflower
cold-pressed oil. I feel this is helpful.

Miss D. A. Roth, Benoni, South Africa.
The article on page 28, *Grace, Winter, 1994* issue, evokes a lot of thought.
How we treasure our trees. Here, at Eddy House, we had a huge tree cut-
ting off the light from many of the flats and taking up much space. So,
it was chopped down. You can't imagine the effect when all the birds
who had their homes there, returned at night. It had one of us in tears.
However, smaller trees have now spread out and the birds are back again.
Their song, towards evening, cheers the heart.

F. A. Stoughton, Farringdon.
What I have to say may cause some of the medical profession to be rather
sceptical. But the proof of the pudding is in the eating. I have had a very
bad hiatus. In 1991 I was very ill and in hospital with it. But since taking white heather honey twice a day for 5 months the progress is fantastic. I can eat anything now. I could not before. But when I tell hiatus
sufferers they don't seem convinced.

Nursing howlers from hospital examination papers.
Sit the baby up in the middle of a feed and then break his wind.
A patient must be given a well balanced stable diet.
A small doss is sufficient to settle the patient for the night.
A change of heart can be produced by giving Digoxin.
Suppositories are made of jellytin or cocoa.
Castor oil is given to loosen the patient up.

Mrs Tucker, Treforest, Mid. Glamorgan.
For the past 40 years I had suffered defective eyesight, such as double vision or haloes over every person I met, or blurred vision. I underwent various tests at General and Eye Hospitals, only to be given drops to put into my eyes twice daily, which only seemed to dull my vision more so. I feared blindness some 3 years ago. A friend was staying with me and gave me a *Grace Magazine* to read. Therein I read of sunflower seeds to strengthen muscles of the eyes. I have been eating them ever since, in my breakfast of fruit and cereal: Also I take one Vitamin E capsule and between them I have found a big improvement in my general health and vision.

Ryan Gibbs, age 9.
The greatest present I've ever had is your tender loving care. And in the pain you took in having me. Thank you for the wonderful life I'm having and for our house and home.

Ruth F. Julian, Cinda Park, South Africa.
I would like to thank Joan Gross who wrote in the Spring 1993 issue of *Grace*. Soon after I became a widow I decided to take a trip to Texas, USA. From Zambia it was a very long journey. I had to change planes often, Ndola to Lusaka, Lusaka to London, London to New York, and New York to Texas.

Standing at these airports I felt so alone. When at London Airport a lad came up to me and said, "Don't you remember you nursed me after my operation?" This warmed my heart and I felt the world was not such a bad place after all!

On arriving at New York, I really felt lost in that crowded and busy airport, when suddenly a couple came to me and said, "You look so alone, can we help?"

Yes, Joan, with "fear and trembling" I really "had a go". This helped me to overcome the fear of travelling alone and meeting people. It gave me fresh confidence and as you say, "Going it alone has not been quite so hard again, though life is always lonely without one's 'other half'."

Thank you, Joan Gross. And thank you *Grace* for printing "Singleness of Purpose". Yours very sincerely.

Anonymous.
. . . reaching retiring age, I have been considering taking up a hobby, as is so often advised in *Grace*. My wife suggested wood carving or pottery, but I am not very good with my hands. I had wondered about painting – the only thing is – I wouldn't know where to start!
ED: *When racking our brains for an answer to your question we came across the following extract from The Irish Digest:*

'A firm which produces painting boxes for amateur landscapists encloses the following instructions with every kit: 'Take the palette from the box, squeeze some paint on to it from the tubes, dip your brush into the paint and daub the canvas with it. Rembrandt, Titian and all the great painters used this method'
Just the job!

Joyce Parsons, member of Grace Family.
I read in a past issue of *Grace* of someone wanting to know how to stop biting nails. Most of my life I've bitten my nails. I hate to see bitten nails but couldn't stop. Then I started to take vitamins and minerals, always trying something new. I have now found that if I don't take my B vitamins I start biting again – after not biting for months. It took me years to discover this. I'll bet almost all I have, that it was a lack of vitamin B that made me bite.

I'm sixty now. Everybody says I do not look my age. Even when I was 50, my mother used to say stop biting' . So, you see what relief I obtain from my vitamin B complex! Yours Sincerely.

Classified advertisement in the Cleveland Plain Dealer.
Secondhand tombstone for sale. Bargain for family named Perkins.

Mrs P. Smith, Stoneygate, Leicester.
I have tried all kinds of remedies and diets to tighten-up parts of the body to rid myself of stretch-marks, but they still persist. Do I have to put-up with them for ever? My skin was over-stretched in pregnancy.
ED: *Stretch marks are small purple lines that fade into silvery streaks. Their presence can be associated with lack of protein, and especially with deficiencies of vitamin B6 and Zinc – elements essential for production of sound collagen tissue. Comfrey Cream is believed to improve the condition.*

Miss J. E. Reid, Fordingbridge, Hampshire.
So many people suffer from corns. At one time I did. Nothing could be found which would help. Then I painted on Castor oil. From that day corns have held no discomforts for me. It softens up a corn wonderfully. In these days when so many chemicals are used on the body, this must be one of the cheapest and least harmful things to use.

I also find it very effective for styes on the eye. With me, a stye only lasts a few days when anointed with castor oil. A friend of mine had a bad stye. I advised her to use this oil. She did so. She was amazed at its disappearance within two or three days. She passed on the information to another woman whose eyes were troubled in this way, and that lady, too, was surprised at an almost immediate response.

Margareta White, London SW14 8BQ.
My latest experience: coming out of a shop a few weeks ago I stumbled over the step outside and fell flat on the pavement. Kind passers-by helped me to my feet.

I must have had my guardian angel, as I am 86, and a fall at that age can have serious consequences. However, I walked to my car, drove home. My right knee and foot hurt badly. I wanted to make sure that nothing was broken, consulted my doctor-friend who assured me that my knee was only badly bruised and muscles and ligaments strained.

I treated the parts in question with hot and cold water, and used Arnica cream on the bruises and foot. Now, I am grateful to say, I can walk perfectly. With very best wishes.

Epitaph in a pet cemetery.
No heaven will not ever heaven be . . . unless my cats are there to welcome me.

Mrs R. F. May, Brighton, Sussex.
In the autumn issue of *Grace*, Mrs Evelyn Packman, Dorset, wrote regarding her husband's digestive trouble – losing his food without it being digested and fast losing weight. Fenugreek tea was advised. This tea stopped the digestive trouble almost immediately. How is it prepared?

ED: *Two teaspoons Fenugreek seeds to cup cold water; bring to boil, simmer 5 minutes. Cool. Drink one cup morning and evening, consuming the seeds.*

Mrs Jeannie Peck, Legbourne, Louth, Lincs.
As with Barbara Charles' first poodle *(Grace, Autumn 1993)* our Muffin was a quiet happy soul until his death at 12½ . . . we felt then that we would never dare to have another dog, never again face such heartbreak of loss. But somehow life to us seemed that much poorer without one and not too long afterwards we chose Bella from the local poodle kennels . . . well we had planned just to have one but Coco the last of the litter seemed to be so pathetic being left on her own that we arrived home with both.

They proved, even as tiny creatures, to know their own minds and were sure right from the beginning that we belonged to them; unhappy when left in the car for even a short time and only really content when my husband or I were within reach.

Holidays could be a problem, but are not because we own a small touring caravan and cook most of our holiday meals in the microwave . . . over the years, they are just over eight now, we have found many places where dogs are welcome, open air events of course and outdoor restaurants where they sit happily under the table while we enjoy a meal. Yes, it would be good to say that we have cured them of their neurotic ways. Alas, this is not so. But we find it impossible to be too impatient in the presence of so much endearing love and affection.

Irene Stockley, Exeter, Devon.
I was especially interested in the Spring 1993 issue which included an article by Anne Baggott who traced her brother, Peter, after 55 years separation. I, too, believe in miracles, and praise God for His loving kindness. Six years ago I found my sister Joan after 63 years; she was adopted when 2 years of age before any records were kept; I was 5. We have since visited each other, and needless to say, I have introduced her to *Grace Magazine*. She loves it.

Eileen Kelly, Edinburgh.
In these days of rampant feminism I think that *Grace* stands out in propagating real values and real family life. As an elderly woman, I think it is sad that so many women do not understand the special gifts they have which in the past kept families together.

There seems to be a determination to compete with and copy men rather than be home-makers. Women can pursue careers in their own right, but without neglecting the family. I see many examples of strong family life where Mother is not just a drudge, but by putting her family first gets their support so that she can attain her own ambition.

Most people of my generation had a great respect for their parents and realise the unique power which a dedicated woman has in making a home in which talents can flourish and children develop in a secure environment. I feel that so much has been lost to many children because women have lost something precious. Sincerely.

Anonymous.
As a long-term member of Grace Family, I wonder if other readers would have any useful information on the following:

I went for a cystoscopy because of a persistent bladder infection and, although this was clear, a blood test revealed I have lymphatic leukaemia. I have to go every two weeks for a blood test. The white cell count has gone up from 35 to 50 in the past year.

Maybe, there is a reader, somewhere, who has had a similar problem and who has had some success with alternative medicine by way of primary or supportive treatment. I am a very active seventy-year-old.

ED: *We would not recommend self-treatment for this condition. It should be treated by or in liaison with a qualified medical practitioner. Encouraging results of trials in orthodox medicine support the belief that*

313

the condition can be controlled, after the manner of diabetes by insulin. Successful results in such control have been reported by Dr Hartwell, National Cancer Institute, Maryland, USA, with an alkaloid related to Autumn crocus (Colchicum officinale).

Vinchristine and Vinblastine, both preparations made from Madagascar periwinkle (Catharanthus roseus), are now established routine treatments in some hospitals, and which have been known to prolong remission of leukaemia to more than five years. You should enquire further from your GP or local hospital.

One dog to another.
1st Dog. "Hello, my name's Rover, what's yours?"
2nd Dog. "I think it's Down Boy."

Mrs Olive Harris, North Lancing, West Sussex.
My small grandson aged four was absolutely delighted when his Mum pointed out to him that the Spring issue of *Grace* contained both the table grace they sing each meal and the evening hymn they sing at night. Thank you for all the hard work that must go into the production of our delightful magazine. How we need good literature these days. Satan knows his time is running out and is doing much to corrupt minds through press and television, but praise God – our King is coming and He shall reign. May God richly bless all associated with *Grace Magazine*.

Elsie Watkins, Strand, South Africa.
Thank you for *Grace*. Now we are filled with joy. *Grace* is full of love and upliftment – some must rub-off on me. Our copy arrived yesterday . . . Tra, la, la! Now I don't care if it snows!

A. Marshall-Taylor, Bucks.
I began a little dizziness in August 1993, of a few seconds duration on each occasion. Your reference twice in the autumn issue to Ginkgo prompted me to obtain tablets. Thankfully. I am now quite free, and just take one a day. I'm 82 years young! Kind regards.

Joan S. de Boisy, Argentina, S. America.
I am writing to tell you I think the Spring 1993 issue of the magazine is the most beautiful I have ever received. Your article to readers is most refreshing in this stress-filled world where people seem to have lost the joy of living. The photographs of famous paintings are a joy – and all the stories have a positive message. As for the 'Biscuits and Buns' – a sheer delight!

I do not know how to thank you: except to say "Thank you" for all the pleasure you give your readers. God bless you and the work you do. May He illuminate you for many many years to come. With sincere wishes.

Mrs Norah Jeffery, Devon.
Regarding the letter from Harry Everett in the Spring 1994 issue for treatment for an enlarged prostate gland, pumpkin seeds and pulsatilla tablets are good.

Also, regarding the letter from Helen Holland, cider vinegar is known to relieve the pain of shingles.

Member of Grace Family.
I read somewhere in a magazine that:
"Happiness is the only good . . . The time to be happy is now . . . The place to be happy is here . . . the way to be happy is to make others so."

Winifred Pettitt, Near Aldershot, Hampshire.
For a large part of my life, I could eat no fruit except bananas and grapes. I am very allergic to acids.

I have fruit in my garden and make quite a lot of home-made jam. One year, when I had an extra large crop of Bramley apples, I decided to chop up some root ginger and make apple and ginger jam. It was delicious. What a joy! I could eat it without ill-effects. Now, I put a little ginger (chopped root or powdered) in all my jams and I can eat them all – with a few exceptions. I can also eat fruit in yoghurts – another blessing.

The exceptions: I cannot touch raspberries. I haven't dared to try rhubarb. Tomatoes, for me, are definitely taboo. They taste sweet and enjoyable but are extremely acid and make me really ill.

So, for readers allergic to acids, enjoy your fruit with ginger and live yoghourt. Sincerely.

Gennen Roth, (Quoted)
Once upon a time I was so beautiful. My hair was thick and dark and glossy. My skin was smooth and soft as a ripe peach . . . My mouth was dark pink . . .

My eyes were large and clear . . . I was four years at the time.

It's been downhill ever since.

My husband gave one teaspoon Cider Vinegar daily to our cat for nine weeks, and we now realise that the cat eczema went into remission. When we discontinued the vinegar there were signs of the eczema returning. It may be a coincidence, and wonder if any other readers have tried this with any effect. Yours very sincerely.

Your Prayers are asked for members of Grace Family.
. . . For members of Grace Family everywhere that they may be enriched in the knowledge that they are the centre of prayer . . . that those among them who have lost their former good health may be restored to strength and vitality . . . that all who work with nursing and medical skills may be

blessed in their ability to relieve suffering . . . and that those who sit in the council chambers of the world be given wisdom and statecraft to preserve peace on earth and good will among all men.

Mrs A. C. W., Norwich.
My sister who lives in Australia had Ménière's disease diagnosed six months ago. She is 47. She found an article in a health book about the disease and a salt-free diet was recommended. Since going without salt, my sister has not had any more 'turns'.

Laurence Peter. (Quoted)
'Don't worry about middle age: you'll outgrow it."

Caroline Espey, aged 9. Quoted.
Daddy, I will always love you, I will always love my family as well, but there is something special I want to say about you. If you are not working for my education and many other things you are at home listening to my troubles and caring for me. Daddy, I'm sorry for when I have done wrong and Daddy, I love you.

Neville & June Wellington, Chirton, Wiltshire.
Few people can claim that they have never been button-holed. Dr Johnson relates his experience.

A particular friend would march up to him in the street, grab his top waistcoat button between finger and thumb, raise his closed eyes to heaven and then start to pontificate on the affairs of the world.

One day Johnson saw him coming and was soon truly "button-holed". Mischievously, while bombarded with a deluge of words, he silently took out his pen-knife and craftily cut through the cottons and withdrew, leaving his friend earnestly addressing a "disembodied" button! Imagine his surprise when he returned half an hour later to find his friend still conversing with the button, unawares.

An apochryphal story? Maybe – but it brings to mind the old nun's prayer – "Lord save us from wanting to express an opinion to everyone on every topic that arises." If we don't wish to be shunned it behoves many of us to watch our buttons!

Advertisement.
Dazzlingly beautiful tortie kitten, charming, intelligent, very highly strung, needs wonderful home immediately, to get away from bossy mother and four horrid brothers.

Anonymous.
A grandmother is a woman who has no children of her own so she loves the boys and girls of other people.

Grandmothers have nothing to do, they only have to be there. If they take you for a walk, they go slowly past beautiful things like leaves and caterpillars.

They never say "Come on quickly" or Hurry up for goodness sake". They are usually fat, but not too fat to tie up shoelaces.

They wear spectacles and sometimes take out their teeth. They can answer every question, for instance why dogs hate cats and why God isn't married. When they read to us they don't leave out anything. They do not mind if it's always the same story.

Everyone should have a grandmother, especially those who have no television. Grandmothers are the only grown-ups who always have time.

Mr Harland Maxwell.
Live for today. Your past, like that of most others, is a mixture of good and bad. But it's beyond recall or repair. The future is equally an unknown quantity. So live for today, every day. Enjoy the now. This is life! Fill it, and relish it. Then, when it comes, do the same tomorrow!

Mrs W. B. Harby.
We were all lined up along the edge of the pavement waiting to see the Duke of Edinburgh drive by. The little girl next to me cried: "Lift me up, lift me up!" I told her she would be able to see him all right. "Yes," she answered, 'but he won't be able to see me!"

Miss M. L. Simcox, Wimborne, Dorset.
Here are a few further suggestions on the subject of constipation.

1. Sweeten your afternoon tea with honey. 2. Put a tablespoonful of bran in your breakfast muesli, or cereal. 3. A teaspoonful Black Molasses in hot water, or in your "Elevenses" . Molasses is also pleasant on your bread and butter, or in porridge. 4. Licorice root. Obtain and put a piece in your tea, to be sucked afterwards to your heart's content. 5. Eat a bran biscuit (health food stores, of course) with your tea. 6. Have a good raw salad every day, with dessertspoonful of one of the golden oils – corn, safflower, olive or wheatgerm. 7. Eat plenty of fresh fruit and figs, prunes, etc. 8. Just one thing more – Dandelion coffee. I feel confident you will find relief. Best wishes. Yours sincerely.

Your prayers are requested for:
. . . For all members of Grace Family who may be in hospital or undergoing treatment, that they may soon be restored to normal health again. For all members of the Family wherever they are.

For all those who are afraid and over-anxious, that they may have the belief that there is nothing in this world that we need dread.

For yourself. That, before your eyes close in sleep, you commit yourself to the One who knows all your needs before you make your

requests. To be aware of His faithfulness throughout the night and of His loving-kindness in the morning. Join Robert Louis Stevenson in the following:
"Be with our friends; be with ourselves. Go with each of us to rest. If any stay awake, temper to them the dark hours of watching. When the day returns, return to us, our sun and comforter, and call us up with morning faces and with morning hearts – eager to labour – eager to be happy, if happiness be our portion. And, if the day be marked for sorrow, may we be strong to endure it. We thank and praise Thee; and in the name of Him to whom this day is sacred, commit ourselves to Thee."

Frances Hamilton, Kirkcudbrightshire, Scotland.
I would like to pass on to the readers the recipe for my wholemeal scones which give us so much pleasure.
Ingredients: ¾lb wholemeal flour, 2oz margarine, 1 saltspoon salt, 1 teacup milk and water mixed.
Method: Mix the salt and the flour. Rub in the margarine, add the milk and water to make a stiff dough. Knead for 8 minutes. Roll out, form into scones and bake in hot tins 425°F, Gas 7 for about 20 minutes.

Mr P. Hastings, Havant, Hants.
I have used Hawthorn tablets for some months for palpitation of the heart, which they have regulated.

Mr George Reed.
I feel I must write to express what I think about heart transplants, and wonder how many other members of 'the Family" think the same as I do.
Surely as we were made in the image and likeness of God, our life span should not be tampered with. I do not find it easy to believe that we were meant to be patched up with 'spare parts" from another person's body.

ONE more step along the world I go,
one more step along the world I go,
from the old things to the new
keep me travelling along with you:

And it's from the old I travel to the new;
keep me travelling along with you.

2 Round the corner of the world I turn,
more and more about the world I learn;
all the new things that I see
you'll be looking at along with me:

3 As I travel through the bad and good,
keep me travelling the way I should;
where I see no way to go
you'll be telling me the way, I know:

4 Give me courage when the world is rough,
keep me loving though the world is tough;
leap and sing in all I do,
keep me travelling along with you:

5 You are older than the world can be,
you are younger than the life in me;
ever old and ever new,
keep me travelling along with you:

Sidney Carter (1915-)

Some of my Favourite Remedies

by Thomas Bartram

Fellow, National Institute of Medical Herbalists

Doctors are overworked. Hospital waiting lists can reach astronomical heights. Is there anything we can do to support their treatment . . . to help while waiting for a hospital bed? Today, your health is in your hands.

However elemental the effort, or small the benefits, some amelioration may be brought about by natural pharmacy. Relief is possible. No promise of a cure is made. This selection is a small facet of forty years clinical experience. It is intended for those interested in self-sufficiency.

These pages do not replace professional medical advice. Those with doubts about their health and those who are pregnant are advised to consult their doctor or health professional.

For further information refer to 'Bartram's Encyclopedia of Herbal Medicine'. Check with your doctor or health professional if you are taking anti-clotting or blood-thinning drugs under medical care. The diabetic or pregnant should also check with them.

Abortion (Threatened). *Agnus Castus*
Abscesses, boils. *Echinacea, Slippery Elm powder compress.*
Accidents, bruises, (See also: Wounds) *Echinacea, Comfrey compress.*
Acne. *Blue flag root, Red Clover, Locally: Calendula cream or ointment, Tea tree oil: dab oil on face.*
Adrenal gland stimulants: *Liquorice, Ginseng, Wild Yam, Borage.*
Ageing. *Hawthorn, Red Clover, Ginkgo, Ginseng, Vitamin E, Honey.*
Alcoholism. *Blue Flag root.*
Allergies. *Echinacea, Pulsatilla, Garlic, Honey, Grapeseed, Vitamin B6.*
Alzheimer's disease. *Ginkgo biloba is said to ameloriate symptoms.*
Amenorrhoea. *Motherwort, Agnus Castus.*
Angina pectoris. *Hawthorn, Motherwort, Vitamin E.*
Anorexia nervosa. *Papaya, Wild Yam.*
Antibiotic alternatives. *Echinacea, Wild Thyme, Cloves.*
Antihistamine alternative. *Nettles.*
Antioxidants. *Pumpkin seeds. Selenium. Zinc.*
Anus, itching. *Pilewort, Witch-hazel extract (local).*
Anxiety states. Mild to moderate. *Lemon Balm tea, Ginseng. Oats. Passion flower.*
Apoplexy. *Lavender, Mistletoe, Marjoram.*
Appendicitis. *Wild yam.*
Appetite, loss of. *Papaya, Apples, Wormwood, Sorrel.*
Arterio-sclerosis. *Hawthorn, Motherwort, Vitamin E*
Arthritis. *Garlic, Prickly ash bark. Devil's Claw.*

Aspirin poisoning. *Papaya, Blue flag root.*
Aspirin, alternative. *White Willow bark.*
Asthma. *Iceland moss, Lobelia, Elecampane, Hyssop. Nettles.*
Atherosclerosis. *Garlic.*
Athlete's foot. *Echinacea, Comfrey cream or ointment. Crushed Garlic poultice.*
Autism. *"It's all in the gut!" Gluten-free diet. No milk or dairy products. Supplement: vitamin B12. Oily fish.*
Bacillus coli. *Papaya, Peppermint.*
Back-ache. *St John's Wort, Balm, Rosemary.*
Back-ache. (from urinary disorders) *Buchu.*
Back-ache. muscle pain. *Wild yam, Devil's claw.*
Back-ache. Old spinal injuries. *Prickly ash bark.*
Back-ache. womb disorders. *Wild Yam.*
Back-passage disorders. *Pilewort, Figwort, Wild yam.*
Bad breath. *Papaya, Milk thistle, Diluted Tea tree oil.*
Bed sores. Local *Comfrey cream, ointment or lotion.*
Bed-wetting. *Cranesbill.*
Belchings, sour. *Chamomile, Aniseed, Wormwood.*
Bell's palsy. *Valerian.*
Benzodiazepines. Alternatives — *Valerian.*
Bile: to stimulate secretion of. *Milk thistle, Blue flag root, Wild Yam.*
Biliousness. *Milk thistle, Artichoke, Seaweed & Sarsaparilla.*
Bladder: pain on passing water. *Cranesbill, Shepherd's Purse, Slippery elm powder.*
Bleeding, to stop. *Comfrey, Marigold, Nettles, Tormentil.*

Blood-platelet-clumping-reducer. *Grapeseed, Oily fish.*
Blood, expectoration of. *Cranesbill, Comfrey, Marigold.*
Blood, impure. *Echinacea, Blue flag root.*
Blood pressure, high. *Garlic, Mother wort, Vitamin E, not megadoses, Avoid Ginseng, Oily fish for Omega-3-fatty oils, Potassium-rich foods.*
Blood pressure, low. *Prickly ash bark.*
Body odour. *Wild Yam, Thuja, Sage tea.*
Boils. *Echinacea. Poke root, Marshmallow, cabbage or Slippery elm poultice.*
Bowel inflammation. *Slippery elm, Agrimony.*
Brain booster. *Ginkgo biloba.*
Breasts, painful. *Poke root, Red clover.*
Breasts, sense of fullness. *Poke root.*
Breasts, discomfort. *Evening primrose, Starflower oil.*
Breasts, to reduce. *Poke root.*
Breasts, to stimulate secretion of milk. *Fenugreek seeds.*
Breath, offensive. *See: Halitosis.*
Breathlessness. *Hawthorn, Lily of the valley.*
Broken bones. *Fenugreek seed tea, Comfrey poultice.*
Bronchiectasis. *Iceland Moss, Lobelia.*
Bronchitis. *Lobelia, Iceland Moss.*
Buerger's disease. *Motherwort, Wild yam, Hawthorn, Vitamin E.*
Bunions. *Local Comfrey cream, ointment or lotion.*
Burns *(see your doctor) Local dressings – Honey, Comfrey, Houseleek.*
Bursitis (house-maid's knee, etc) *Local: Comfrey cream, ointment or lotion.*
Caffeine syndrome *Papaya, Valerian.*
Calculus, urinary. *Pellitory-of-the-wall.*
Calmer-downer. *Kava kava, Valerian, Lemon balm, St John's Wort. Passion flower.*
Candida albicans. vaginal infections. *Agnus castus.*
Candidiasis, monilia, infection of the vagina. *Goldenseal.*
Carbuncles. *Echinacea, Blue flag root, Cabbage poultice.*
Cartilage injuries. *Comfrey cream, ointment or lotion.*
Catarrh. *Goldenseal, Hyssop.*
Change of life. *Agnus castus, Helonias.*
Chestiness. *Iceland Moss, Lobelia.*
Chickenpox. *Poke root, Agrimony, Chamomile. Echinacea, Marigold (Calendula) cream locally. External: Dilute Tea Tree oil to take irritation out of spots.*
Chilblains. *Prickly ash bark.*
Cholecystitis (inflammation of the gall bladder) *Milk thistle, Wild yam, Blue flag root.*
Cholesterol, to reduce: *Artichoke, Garlic.*
Chronic Fatigue Syndrome (ME). *Kava Kava Supplement, Magnesium.*
Circulation, poor. *Prickly ash bark, Hawthorn.*
Cirrhosis of the liver. *Wild yam, Milk thistle, Blue flag root.*

Claudication, intermittent. *Hawthorn, Vitamin E.*
Coeliac disease. *Wild yam, Gluten-free diet.*
Cold hands. *Ginger, Cayenne pepper.*
Colds. The common cold. *Echinacea, Eucalyptus inhalent, Liquorice, Tea Tree oil as an inhalant, Chicken broth.*
Colic, intestinal. *Ginger, Chamomile, Wild yam, Peppermint, Fennel.*
Colic, kidney. *Buchu.*
Colic, liver. *Wild yam, Milk thistle, Fennel.*
Colitis, ulcerative. *Echinacea, Wild yam.*
Constipation. *Senna, Ginger.*
Convalescence. Recovery from illness or operation. *Ginseng, Honey.*
Corns. *Local – Comfrey.*
Coronary heart disease. *Garlic, Not with anti-clotting drugs or aspirin.*
Cough, dry. *Iceland moss, Angelica, Elecampane.*
Cough, moist. *Lobelia.*
Cramp. *Cramp bark, Prickly ash bark, Lavender, Ginger, Butcher's Broom.*
Crohn's disease. *Wild yam, Chamomile tea.*
Cuts. *Local treatment – Echinacea, Comfrey, Calendula.*
Cystitis. *Buchu, Uva ursi.*
Diabetes. *Milk thistle. Aloe vera.*
Dandruff. *Rosemary lotion, Cook with olive oil.*
Debility. *Agnus castus, Red clover, Ginseng.*
Dementia. *Ginkgo biloba appears to slow down the stroke-related symptoms in mild and moderate cases.*
Depression. *St John's wort, Valerian, Kava kava, Lemon balm, Ginkgo biloba, Ginseng, (not anxiety disorder, heart palpitations, manic-depressive illness, or asthma). Rosemary inhalent.*
Dermatitis. *Echinacea, Local: Marshmallow & Slippery elm cream.*
De-tox. *Cleansing of the system with Castor Oil packs, colonics & massage. Chlorella.*
Diarrhoea. *Wild yam, Peppermint.*
Digestion. *Chamomile, Artichoke, Ginger, Peppermint.*
Dizziness. *Rutin, Hawthorn.*
Diverticulitis. *Wild yam, Goldenseal, Fresh Ginger Tea. To reduce flatulence: Slippery Elm, Goldenseal.*
Dog bites. *Wipe with Tincture Calendula, Tincture Myrrh, or Tincture St John's Wort, Follow with Slippery Elm poultice.*
Dropsy. *Buchu, Dandelion, Chamomile.*
Duodenal disorders. *Papaya, Goldenseal.*
Dysentery. *Wild yam.*
Dyslexia. *Starflower oil, Evening primrose.*
Dyspepsia. *Papaya, Chamomile.*
Ear noises. *See: Tinnitus.*
Ear-ache. *Echinacea, Valerian.*
Eczema, dry. *Echinacea.*
Eczema, moist. *Red clover.*
Energy booster. *Ginseng.*
Epistaxis, nose-bleed. *Cranesbill. Local: plug with witch-hazel & cotton wool.*
Erysipelas. *Echinacea.*
Eruptions. *Red clover, Echinacea.*

Eyes, inflamed. *Echinacea, Bilberries.*
Eyes. Styes. *Echinacea.*
Eyes, swollen lids. *Buchu.*
Fainting. *Lemon balm.*
Fevers. *Yarrow, Elderflowers.*
Fibrositis. *Black Cohosh. Local: Comfrey.*
Finger nails splitting. *Echinacea.*
Flatulence. *Fennel, Caraway, Papaya, Wild yam, Ginger, Peppermint*
Furuncles. *Echinacea, Blue flag root.*
Gall stone diathesis: tendency to form stone. *Wild yam.*
Gall bladder inflammation. *Wild yam, Milk thistle, Blue flag root. Consult your doctor for gallstones, hepatitis etc.*
Ganglion, cystic tumour on a tendon. *Prickly ash bark.*
Gastric ulcer. *Papaya, Slippery elm powder.*
Gastritis. *Papaya, Chamomile, Mint, Dandelion.*
Gastro-enteritis. *Papaya. Aloe vera.*
Gingivitis, gum disorders. *Slippery elm powder, Poke root.*
"Gone all to pieces" syndrome. *Valerian.*
Gout. *Wild yam, Chamomile, Comfrey tea. Celery seeds.*
Gravel in urine. *Buchu, Apples, Slippery elm (to facilitate passage of gravel), Apricots, Parsley, Nettles.*
Greasy skin. *Milk thistle.*
Haemochromatosis. Bronzed diabetes, *Milk thistle.*
Haemorrhoids (piles) *Pilewort, Figwort. Chickweed, Plantain.*
Halitosis, bad breath. *Wild yam, Gargle: dilute Tea tree oil.*
Hay fever. *Honey in the comb. Nettles.*
Head lice. External: *Tea tree oil.*
Headache. *Betony, Lemon Balm, Valerian, Vervain, Feverfew, Butcher's broom.*
Head-noises. See: *Tinnitus.*
Heartburn. *Cinnamon.*
Heart and circulation. *Garlic, Hawthorn, Artichoke, Honey, Starflower oil. Evening primrose oil, Ginkgo, Ginseng, Soya isoflavones, Oily fish for Omega-3- fatty oils. Grape seed.*
Hepatitis. *See your doctor, Wild yam, Milk thistle.*
Hepatitis C. *Castor oil packs over liver area, 3 days in succession on a weekly basis.*
Hernia, hiatus. *Papaya, Goldenseal.*
Herpes zoster. See under: *Shingles.*
Hiccough. *Papaya, Onion juice, Chamomile.*
Hoarseness of speech. *Echinacea, Poke root, Iceland moss. Horehound, Honey & Lemon.*
Hormones, including pre-menstrual symptoms. *Evening primrose oil, Starflower oil, St John's Wort, Agnus castus, Black cohosh.*
Hormone replacement therapy alternative. *Black cohosh.*
Hormone system: to sustain balance: *Starflower oil (borage).*
Hydrocele. *Pulsatilla, Poke root.*
Hypoglycaemia. *Echinacea.*

Hysteria. *Valerian.*
Immune system, to stimulate. *Echinacea, Garlic, Ginseng (Siberian). Astragalus.*
Impetigo. *Echinacea, Blue flag root, External: Wipe with dilute Tea Tree oil or Calendula lotion.*
Impotence. *Agnus castus.*
Incontinence of urine. *Cranesbill.*
Indigestion. *Papaya, Artichoke, Peppermint.*
Infection. *Echinacea. Aloe vera.*
Infertility. *Agnus castus.*
Inflammatory condition. *Grapeseed. Aloe vera.*
Influenza. *Echinacea, Chicken broth, Tea Tree oil as an inhalant: 2 drops to bowl of hot water.*
Insomnia. *Valerian, Hops, Lettuce. Lemon balm tea.*
Intermittent claudication. *Ginkgo biloba.*
Intestinal colic, abdominal cramp. *Papaya, Wild yam.*
Irritable bowel syndrome. *Peppermint.*
Irritability, nervous. *Valerian, Lemon balm tea.*
Ischaemic Heart Disease. *Hawthorn, Lily of the Valley, Vitamin E.*
Itching of skin. *Echinacea, Wild yam, External: Tea tree oil.*
Jaundice. *Agrimony, Milk thistle.*
Jet lag. *Ginseng, Gotu kola, Capsicum, Garlic, Kola.*
Joints swollen and painful. *Devil's claw.*
Joint mobility. *Devil's claw, Ginger.*
Kidney stone, tendency to form stone. *Buchu.*
Kidney weakness *(see your doctor), Buchu, Parsley, Juniper.*
Labour pains: to assist. *Agnus castus, Helonias.*
Lacerated wounds. See: Wounds.
Lactation, to stimulate. *Fenugreek seed tea.*
Laryngitis. *Poke Root, Lobelia, Echinacea.*
Lassitude. *Hawthorn.*
Legs, aching. *Hawthorn, Motherwort.*
Legs: locking at the knee. *Prickly ash bark.*
Leg ulcer. *Echinacea, Blue flag root, Honeydressing.*
Legs, pins and needles. *Cramp bark, Vitamin E.*
Legs, giving way sensation in ankles. *Cramp bark, Calcium & Magnesium supplement.*
Leucorrhoea, vaginal discharge. *Agnus castus.*
Lichen planus. *Echinacea.*
Lips, sore. *Slippery elm powder, Poke root, Dilute Tea tree oil.*
Liver. disorders. *Wild yam, Milk thistle, Agrimony, Cynara Artichoke.*
Long life. *Ginkgo, Watercress, Broccoli.*
Low mood. *St John's wort.*
Lumbago. *Buchu, Black Cohosh.*
Lymph-adenoid disorders. *Red clover, Poke Root.*
Marasmus, wasting, emaciation. *Echinacea.*
Mastitis. *Red clover, Poke root.*
Masturbation, help break the habit. *Agnus castus.*
Maternity aid. *Agnus castus, Motherwort.*
Measles. *Marigold petals, Saffron, Agrimony.*
Memory and concentration. *Ginkgo biloba.*
Ménière's disease. *Valerian.*
Menopause. *Agnus castus, Black cohosh, St John's wort, Sage.*

Men's disorders. *See: Prostate gland.*
Menstruation, painful. *Agnus castus, Lavender.*
Menstruation, excessive bleeding. *Cranesbill.*
Menstruation, irregular. *Motherwort, Lavender, Feverfew.*
Mental confusion. *Ginkgo biloba.*
Mental performance *Enhanced by Ginkgo biloba, Ginseng.*
Metabolism, to stimulate. *Ginseng, Nettles.*
Migraine, nerve origin. *Valerian.*
Migraine, sick headache. *Feverfew, (not in presence of aspirin or NSAID drugs).*
Migraine, hormone imbalance. *Agnus castus.*
Migraine, kidney malfunction: *Buchu.*
Migraine, congested liver. *Milk thistle, Dandelion, Wild yam.*
Morning sickness of pregnancy. *Ginger.*
Morning stiffness. *Devil's claw.*
Motion sickness. *Ginger, Papaya.*
Mouth ulcers. *Echinacea, Poke root, Goldenseal.*
Mucous colitis. *Wild yam, Peppermint.*
Muscle, aches and pains. *Devil's claw, Prickly ash bark, External: Tea Tree oil.*
Nails. *Paint: Tea tree oil or Tincture Myrrh.*
Nappy rash. External: *dilute Tea Tree oil.*
Nerve tensions. *Valerian.*
Nerve tonic. *St John's Wort.*
Nettle rash, hives. *Red clover.*
Neuralgia. *Chamomile.*
Neurasthenia. *Valerian.*
Neuritis. *Cramp Bark, Chamomile tea.*
Nose-bleed. *Cranesbill, Marigold.*
Numbness. *Lavender, Wormwood. Sage.*
Nymphomania. *Agnus castus.*
Obesity. *Evening Primrose.*
Osteo-arthritis. *Black Cohosh, Devil's Claw, Guaiacum.*
Osteoporosis. *Black Cohosh, Calcium & vitamin D, 1000mg daily.*
Ovaralgia, pain in an ovary. *Agnus castus.*
Pain. *Turmeric. Boswellia.*
Palpitation. *Hawthorn, Balm, Lavender.*
Peptic ulcer. *Papaya, Goldenseal. Aloe vera.*
Personality unstable: *Valerian.*
Phlebitis. *See your doctor. Hawthorn. Echinacea. Butcher's Broom. Vitamin E*
Physical performance decreased. *Ginkgo biloba, Ginseng.*
Piles. *see 'Haemorrhoids'.*
Pleurisy. *See your doctor, Iceland Moss, Angelica, Sage Marshmallow.*
Pregnancy, vomiting. *Agnus castus, Helonias, Raspberry leaf tea.*
Pregnancy, nervous restlessness. *Raspberry leaf tea.*
Pre-menstrual tension *(PMT) Agnus castus, Valerian, Evening primrose oil, Starflower oil, St John's Wort, The liver needs B vitamins and magnesium to metabolise oestrogen properly.*
Prostate gland. Benign prostatic hyperplasia. *(BPH), Saw palmetto, Soya isoflavones. Pumpkin seeds. Tomatoes.*

Pruritis, intense itching. *Echinacea.*
Psoriasis. *Echinacea.*
Pyorrhoea, purulent disease of the gums. *Echinacea.*
Quinsy, acute suppurative tonsillitis *Poke root, Cinquefoil, Cudweed, Wormwood.*
Rashes, dry skin. *Blue Flag Root, Yellow Dock, Seaweed & Sarsaparilla.*
Rashes. moist skin. *Echinacea, Red clover.*
Raynaud's disease. *Ginkgo biloba, Hawthorn. Ginger.*
Relaxation – to promote. *Kava kava.*
Respiratory ailments. *Iceland moss, Garlic.*
Restlessness. *Lemon balm tea.*
Restless legs. *Zinc.*
Rheumatic fever. *Black Cohosh.*
Rheumatism. (acute). *Black Cohosh.*
Rheumatoid arthritis. *Devil's claw, Ginger.*
Rickets. *Dock root, Horsetail, Comfrey tea, Nettle tea, Calcium/Magnesium supplements.*
Sciatica. *Black Cohosh.*
Seasonal Affective Disorder (SAD). *St John's Wort, Valerian, Gotu Kola, Hops, Liquorice, Siberian Ginseng.*
Sexual debility, *Damiana, Ginseng, Ginkgo biloba.*
Shellshock and explosive shocks *(as in air-raids of war-time), Valerian.*
Shingles. *Valerian, Wiping over affected area with pear juice.*
Sickness. *Ginger, particularly during chemotherapy or after anaesthesia.*
Sickness (altitude). *Ginkgo.*
Sinus disorders. *Garlic, Poke Root.*
Skin complaints. *Echinacea, Starflower oil, Evening primrose oil.*
Sleep problems. *Kava kava, Valerian, Milky drink with honey.*
Smell, loss of sense of. *Papaya, Zinc supplement.*
Smelly feet. External: *Tea tree oil.*
Sneezing, uncontrollable. *Chamomile tea.*
Sore throat. *Chamomile, Echinacea, Poke root, Chicken broth.*
Spina bifida, neural-tube birth defects. *For women at risk: Folic Acid supplement.*
Sprains. Local – *Comfrey.*
Sterility. *Agnus castus, Wild yam.*
Stomach, sour: *Chamomile, Balm, Agrimony.*
Stomatitis, inflammation of the mouth. *Echinacea.*
Stress, nervous effects of. *Valerian, Black Cohosh, Ginseng, Lemon balm, Kava kava, St John's Wort, Passion Flower.*
Stroke, to reduce incidence. *Garlic, Honey.*
Stye. *Echinacea*
Sunburn. *Cold tea wipes.*
"Superbug" *(methicillin-resistant staphylococcus aureus), Tea Tree oil.*
Swollen ankles. *Buchu (due to kidneys), Hawthorn (due to heart).*
Synovitis. *Devil's Claw.*
Tachycardia, rapid heart beat. *Hawthorn.*
Thrombosis. *Hawthorn, Motherwort, Vitamin E.*

Thrush, vaginal. *Goldenseal, Pulsatilla,* External: *Dilute Tea Tree oil, Yoghurt inhibits infection.*
Thyroid gland, over-active. *Passion flower.*
Thyroid gland, under-active. *Kelp. Soya. Blue Flag Root.*
Tinnitus, ringing in the ears. *Parsley tea, Plantain, Ginkgo biloba.*
"Tired-all-the-time" syndrome. *St John's Wort, Ginseng.*
Tonic, general. *Echinacea, Ginseng.*
Tonsillitis. *Echinacea, Poke root.*
Toothache. *Suck a clove.*
Travel Sickness. See: *Motion sickness.*
Trench mouth, bacterial infection of the gums: *Echinacea.*
Trichomonas, vaginal infection. *Agnus castus.*
Tuberculosis. *Iceland Moss, Elecampane, Liquorice.*
Tuberculosis, ill-effects of BCG vaccine. *Echinacea.*
Ulcers of the mouth. *Echinacea.*
Ulcers of the legs: see, *Leg Ulcers.*
Ulcerative colitis. *Slippery elm powder, Wild yam.*
Under-weight. *Agnus castus.*
Uric acid diathesis. *Black Cohosh. Celery seeds.*
Urinary infections. General. *Buchu, Uva ursi, Cranberry, Echinacea.*
Urinary disorders, pain on passing urine. *Buchu, Goldenseal. Uva ursi.*
Urinary disorders, incontinence. *Cranesbill,*
Urinary disorders. Always passing urine. *Pulsatilla.*
Urinary disorders, retention of urine. *See your doctor, Magnesium, 360mg daily for 2 months, Uva ursi.*
Urticaria. *Blue Flag Root.*
Uterine cramp. *Agnus Castus, Cramp bark.*

Uterine haemorrhage *Shepherd's Purse, Cranesbill.*
Vaccination, ill-effect of. *Wild yam, Thuja.*
Vaginosis. External: *Dilute Tea Tree oil.*
Varicose ulcer. See *Leg ulcer.*
Varicose veins. *Hawthorn, Motherwort, Horse-chestnut, Vitamin E, Butcher's Broom.*
Vegetarian Health Hazards. *Vitamin B12, Calcium, Zinc.*
Venous disorders. *Hawthorn, Horse-chestnut.*
Vertigo, giddiness. *Ginkgo.*
Vincent's disease. *Echinacea, Tincture Myrrh, Tincture Goldenseal.*
Vision weak. *Bilberries.*
Vitality. *Ginseng.*
Vitamin deficiency. *Multivitamin supplement.*
Vitiligo. External: *Black Pepper extract.*
Vomiting. *Papaya, Onions, Fennel.*
Vulva, inflammation of. *Agnus castus.*
Warts. *Dandelion or Celandine – juice of fresh plant – local.*
Whooping cough. *Red clover, Lobelia, Iceland moss.*
Wind, to expel. *Ginger.*
Womb, catarrh of. See: *Leucorrhoea.*
Womb, pain in. *Agnus castus, Black Cohosh.*
Womb, change of life. *Agnus castus.*
Worms. *Garlic.*
Wounds, bruises. *Where skin is broken – Marigold (Calendula). Where skin is unbroken (Arnica) Comfrey compress.*
Wounds, suppurating. *Echinacea. Comfrey or Slippery elm powder poultice.*
Wounds, broken bones. *Echinacea & Goldenseal to avoid infection, Comfrey poultice.*
Yeast infections. *Garlic.*

Note:

If you are already taking prescribed medication, consult your doctor before taking herbal supplements.

Kava Kava. Should not be taken by those with Parkinson's disease, or who have been prescribed benzodiazepines.

Ginger. Should not be taken together with aspirin or anti-clotting or blood thinning drugs.

Devil's Claw. Not used in pregnancy, breast-feeding, gallstones, or gastric ulcer.

Echinacea. Not used in pregnancy, asthma, diabetes or leukaemia.

Garlic. Not used with aspirin, anti-clotting and blood-thinner drugs.

Ginkgo biloba. Not used with anti-clotting and blood-thinner drugs. Increases blood flow in the brain and extremities.

Valerian. Should not be taken with other sedatives.

St John's Wort. The most popular anti-depressant in Germany. It is an antidote to some prescription medicines, (Department of Health).

Ginseng. Not used: High Blood Pressure or diabetes.

Saw Palmetto. See your doctor to make sure your symptoms are not due to some more serious underlying condition.

Goldenseal. Avoid during pregnancy & breast-feeding.

With many of the above remedies you may have to take them for two months before seeing results. No supplement is a miracle cure. You will still need regular exercise, no smoking, low alcohol and a healthy diet.

©*Thomas Bartram, Bournemouth, England.*

Acknowledgements

A. A Cup that cheers; A male OAP; Mr. R. B. A.; D. S. Abbott; Mrs. D. Adams; Mrs. Nora Adamson; Robert Addison (14); Mrs. G. Alexander; Mrs. Allaway; Mr. W. Allen; Mr. H. C. Allsopp; Alpenlandische Beinenzeitung; An American magazine; An Indian; Mr. John Anderson; Mrs. F. G. Annert; Miss G. E. Arthurs; G. E. Ashby; Miss H.Ashington; Mrs. Enid Ashley; Mr. Aspinall. **B.** Mr. L. P. B.; Mrs. J. B.; A. R. B.; Mrs. E. B.; Mr. J. B., Coventry; Mr. M. B., Kidderminster; Mrs. R. B., Leeds; Mrs. H. N. B., North Walsham; S. B., Swansea; Mrs. L. Bacon; Mr. B. J. Bailey; Mr. L. Bailey; Anthony Baird; Mrs. H. Baker; Mr. R. Baldwin; Lady Eve Balfour; Mr. John Balfour; Mrs. H. Ball; Beatrice Ball; The Balti Garden; Mr. J. D. Banham; Mr. L. P. Bannerman; Mr. Percy Barker; Mr. J. Barlow; F. Barnes; Harry G. Barnes; Ray Barnes; Mrs. Bridie Barrett; Mrs. M. Basson; Mrs. D. Bateman; Miss M. I. Bateman; Mrs. D. H. Baxter; Mr. J. P. Beach; Beaconsfield reader; Sharon Bebbing; Bedtime Story; Mrs. M. Bedwell; James Beech; Miss Lois Beechey; Mrs. H. Beecroft; Miss F. E. Bellingham; Mr. And Mrs. E. Benjamin; R. S. Bennett; Mrs. D. E. Bennett; Miss Ann Bentley; Mrs. E. A. Bickers; Mr. H. Bignold; Mr. J. Blake; Margaret Blakesby; Mrs. Katherine Blanchard; Mr. S. Blyth; Madame Helene Bonner; Mrs. Mary Booker; Mrs. Amy Bostock; Mrs. E. Boult; Miss Gladys Bowden; Mrs. G. Bradley; Miss A. Bradley; Eva Breakstone; Roy Briggs; J. T. Brining; Mr. E. Britton; T. Brookes; Mrs. Gladys Brown; Josephine Brown; Miss Audrey Browning; Stella Bryant; Mrs. Gladys Bunker; Miss Thelma Burnett; Mr. C. Burrell; Agnes M. Burt; Mrs. D. Burton; Mrs. S. Busby; Miss L. Butcher; Mrs. N. Butler; Mr. W. G. Butler; Samuel Butler; Howard Bygrave. **C.** John C.; A. H. C., Brighton; Mr. A. H. C., Canada; Mr. A. H. C., Derby; S. H. C., Devon; Mrs. F. H. C., Dublin; L. S. C., Glasgow; Miss C. C., Gloucester; Mrs. V. C., Manchester; Mrs. L. C. C., Oswaldtwistle; Charles Cameron; Miss O. Campbell; Miss L. N. Candlin; Mr. C. W. Carmichael; Barbara Cartland; Mr. V. Cartwright; Mrs. Oria Cartwright; Mrs. G. L. Cave; Mrs. I. M. Cawker; Mr. Chalk; Harold Chambers; Mrs. L. Chambers; Miss B. Chantrey; Mr. C. Chapman; Mrs. M. Chapman; Vera Chapman; Barbara Charles; Mr. T. Charlesworth; Mrs. F. H. Chubb; Cigarettes Anonymous; Mr. I. W. Clark; John G. Clark; Fred Clarke; Mrs. J. V. Clarke; Cleveland Plain Dealer; Mrs. L. Clegg; Mrs. E. L. Coggan; Mrs. Coles; Mrs. W. Collett; H. C. Collins; Mrs. H. Collins; Mrs. P. Collins; Mr. R. W. Collins; The Communicator; George Coo; Archibald Cook; Mrs. L. Cooke; Mrs. Cooper; Joan E. Coudret; Miss A. Crossley; Ronald Crossley; Mr. E. Crowe; Mrs. Anne Cumming; Mrs. M. Cumming; Mr. B. Cunningham; Mr. J. D. Curtis. **D.** L. D.; Mr. G. D., Swansea; Mrs. D. Dailey; Miss Grace Dainton; Mrs. Marjorie Dale; Mrs. C. W. Daniels; Miss E. Darlington; Lydia Darnton; R. R. Davey; Mr. Edwin Davies; Mrs. Stefni Dawn; Mrs. Day; Joan S. de Boisy; Dr. T. de la Torre; Simon and Helen de Yong; Mrs. Frank Deacon; Deborah; Philadelphia; C. Keith Denny; Mrs. L. A. Derry; Mrs. S. A. Dicker; Mrs. L. Digby; H. Jay Dinshah; Mr. S. Dobson; Mrs. Ken Dobson; Nell Dollimore; Miss A. Donald; Miss Margaret Dunlop; Mrs. J. B. Dyer. **E.** Mrs. Blanche, E.; Miss I. M. E.; Mrs. G. E.; Mr. J. E., Chatham; Mr. A. S. Earp; Mrs. Eaton; Miss I. Edgington; J. Edmunds; Anne Edwards; Barbara Edwards; Mr. Arnold Edwards; Mrs. Helen Edwards; Miss Celia Effer; Miss Barbara Elliott; Mrs. E. M. Ellis; Mrs. M. Ellis; Mrs. Shirley Ellis; Mrs. S. Elmington; Caroline Espey; aged 9; Mrs. L. Evans; Mr. J. Evans; Mrs. I. G. Evans; Miss Irene Everton; Mrs. J. Ewart; Exerpted; Mrs. Ivy M. Eyre. **F** Mrs. D. F., Bournemouth; Mrs. E. Fairman; John Fawcett; Mrs. Lena Feick; Mrs. Feick; Mrs. Earl Feick; Miss M. Felgate; Feminine writer; Fenland Citizen; Gracie Fields Film struck; Financial Times; Mrs. W. Fisher; Mrs. D. M. Fisher; Gwen Fletcher; F. Foley; Mrs. Nora Ford; Mrs. W. A. Forster; Mrs. A. Foster; Mrs. K. Fox; Mrs. A. J. Fox; Mr. M. J. Fox; Mrs .Foxton; Miss M. Freeman; Mr. Harry Freeman; Marjorie Friend; Fruiterer's Shop; John Fuller; William Furlong. **G.** T. A. G., Mrs. M. W. G., N. Yorks; Mr. Jim Galbraith; R. M. Gale; Mrs. Lisa Gantenbein; Ken Gaskell; Miss Nora Gayton; Dr George Gemmill; Ryan Gibbs; age 9; Mr. Giles; C. Giles; Mr. J. L. B. Gill; Mrs. F. Glenna-Hills; Phyllis Goodship; Graeme Gorden; Jimmy Gordon; Mrs. L. Gordon; Grace Post; Mrs. D. M. Grace; Monica Grant; Moira Grassby; Grateful Reader; Mr. B. M. Gray; Mrs. Marjorie Gray; Mr. F. Green; Jack Green; Miss M. Green; Mrs. Barbara Groves; Mrs. Helen Guest. **H.** M. E. H.; Mrs. A. H.; Mrs. C. H., Liverpool; Mrs. Norman V. Habberfield; Mrs. Haddon; Wilfred Hadley; Miss Evelyn Haig; Mrs. Sally Haines; Mrs. E. Hall; Mrs. M. Hall; Lady Halsey; Frances Hamilton; Mrs. J. K. Hammond; Mrs. L. Hammond; Mrs. Margaret Hanson; Mrs. W. B. Harby; Mrs. Hardiman; Mrs. Winifred Hare; Harfield Parish Magazine; Jeanette Harper; Mrs. M. J. Harries; Miss H. Harris; Miss K. Harris; Mrs. Olive Harris; Mr. T. H. Harris; Mrs. Edith Harvey; Mr. P. Hastings; Mildred Hatch; Mrs. W. E. Hay; Helen Hayes; Mrs. I. Hayhurst; Mrs. J. I. Hazelton; Health Conference; Mrs. Jessie Heaps; C. Henderson; Miss Herapath; Mrs. A.Hewlett; Stanley Hickman; Jessie Hicks; Mrs. S. Higginson; Elizabeth Hildreth; Mrs. E. M. Hill; Miss Joan Hill; Dulcie Hills; L. G. Hird; Mrs. H. Hitchings; Mrs. M. M. Hoare; Miss E. A., Hobden; Mrs. O. Holman; Horticulture Week; Mrs. D. Hoult; D. E. Howard; Mrs. May Howard; Mr. W. Hubbard; Mrs. M. Hughes; Ruby Hughes; Muriel Humphrey; Miss D. Hutchings; Barbara Huttmann. **I.** Mrs. Alex Ingrey; The Irish Digest; Mrs. C. M. Irvine; Mr. E. Irving; Mr. H. J. Irwin; Mrs. D. B. Isaac. **J.** Mrs. H. J.; Yvonne J., (10); Mrs. H. J., Essex; Mrs. B. H. J., London; Miss A. M. Jackson; Mr. L. Jackson; Mrs. Nellie Jackson; Mrs. I. Jacobs; E. James; Mr. L. James; Mrs. E. Jamieson; Mr. S. L. Jamison; Mrs. E. Jarvis; Mollie Jarvis; Mrs. Norah Jeffery; Mrs. M. Jenkinson; Miss M. Jenkinson; Joan Jensin; The Jewish Vegetarian; John; Miss C. L. Johnson; Mr. J. E. Johnson; Mrs. J. Johnson; Mrs. H. Johnson; Mrs. M. Johnson; Mary Johnson; G. Bryan Jones; G. J. Jones; Sir Henry Jones; Mrs. J. Jones; Mrs. M. E. Jones; S. R. Jones; Ian

B. Jordan; Ruth F. Julian. **K.** Mrs. B. K., Birmingham; Mrs. K., Norway; Eileen Kelly; Mary Kendle-Jackson; Bill Kennedy; Mrs. R. Kennedy; Mr. Jerry Kerr; Mrs. N. W. Kerr; Rebecca Killworth; Madeline King; Miss H. W. Kingsnorth; Mrs. I. Kinscott; Mr. L. I. Kirk; Dorothy Knopp; Lelord Kordel; A. B. Kretschmar; Lis Kurtz. **L.** Mrs. F. L.; Mrs. B. L., Inverness; J. V. L., London; Roy Albert Lain; F. E. Lambert; Mabel Lambros; Fraulein Erika Lang; Mr. J. C. Langley; Mrs. M. Latchett; Daphne Lawes; Mr. J. Leach; Mrs. E. D. Leatherbarrow; Mrs. Lucy Leathley; Miss H. M. Legg; Mr. T. Lemon; Mrs. E. Lewis; Ralph Lewis; Daphne A. J. Lincoln; Dr E. Linnell; Barbara Lister; Miss Little; Eileen Littlewood; Liverpool Store Magazine; Lone Pine; James Long; Mrs. Lucy Long; Mrs. P. Long; Mrs. L. Louis; Miss Gertrude Loveless; Mr. V. Lucas; Mrs. Ida Lunt; Miss R. Lupton; Mrs. Joy Luton.

M. E. M.; J. V. M.; Mrs. D. M. M.; Mr. H. L. M., Brighton; H. C. M., Limerick; Miss M. M., Pulborough; Mr. M. Mace; Mrs. Margaret Mackenzie; Mollie MacKillop; Miss M. Mair; Miss E. Mallinson; Miss E. Barbara Manning; Mrs. D. Mansfield; Mrs. Florence K. Mansfield; Miss M. Mansley; Miss M. Marchant; Miss C. Marjorum; Mrs. Eileen Marsh; Mr. H. Marshall; A. Marshall-Taylor; Mrs. J. Martin; Mr. Alfred Martinet; C. Martinet; Mrs. Elizabeth Martyn; E. W. Marwick; Josephine Mason; Mr. K. L. Mason; Mrs. M. Mathieson; H. Maxwell; Mr. Harland Maxwell; Mrs. R. F. May; The Countess of Mayo; Mr. J. L. McD.; Mrs. C. McDonald; Mrs. Angus McIndoe; Mrs. W. G. McNeel; Mrs. E. McPherson; Mrs. L. R. Meeker; Member of Parliament; Miss J. Mercer; Mrs. B. Mildenhall; Mrs. Amy Miles; Miss E. L. Millar; Mr. H, C Miller; Miss Hilda Mills; Mr. L. Mitchell; Mrs. Mitchell; Mrs. Moeder; Betty Morales; Veronica Moretti (age 11); Doris Morgan; Mrs. M. J. Morgan; Mrs. G. Morrell; Miss Mabel Morton. **N.** Mrs. J. N., Cambridgeshire; Mrs. C. Nelson; C. H. Nelson; Miss E. Nesbit; Mrs. J. Newbold; Mr. F. T.Newman; Mrs. Shirley Newman; Mrs. Margaret Nisbet; Mrs. Freda Norman; Gerald North; Mrs. Emma Northe; Mr. Arne Notland. **O.** Mrs. A. Oates; Oggi Illustrator; Mrs. Oliver; Dr. Noel Olsen; Gwen Oxberry. **P.** C. H. P.; Mrs. I. E. P.; Mrs. N. P.; Mrs. P. P., York; Leslie Parker; Miss C. Parnell; Mrs. L.A. Parnell; Jack Parr; D. Parsons; Joyce Parsons; Mr. H. Patterson; Mrs. Payne; Mrs. Jeannie Peck; Mrs. Pennyfeather; Mrs. Penson; A. H. Penylan; Mr. L.Percy; Mrs. Perry; Mrs. Perry; Laurence Peter; Nicola Peterson; Miss C. Pettit; Winifred Pettitt; Mrs. C. Philip; Mr. Guy Ragland Phillips; Mr. L. V. Phillips; Mrs. L. J. Picton; Mr. C. W. Piggott; Elsa Pike; Mr. John Piner; Marian Pitt; Leo T. Pivirotto; Mrs. L. Plowright; Ellen Poole; Mrs. I. E. Pope; Mr. A. Poulter; T. Powell; Mr. John Preston; Mrs. Helen Price; Mrs. Prosser; Mrs. Beryl Prutty. **R.** Mrs. K. R.; Mrs. P. A. R.; Miss C. R., Kent; Mrs. C. N. R., N. Ireland; Phyllis Rabbitts; Irene Railton; Mrs. M. M. Rainey; Mr. E. Raynor; Mr. George Reed; Mrs. E. Reeves; Miss J. E. Reid; Paul Rendall; Miss B. Rew; Mr. G. Richards; Mr. D. F. Richardson; John Richardson; Mr. R. J. Richardson; Alice Richmond; Dr R. A. Rigg; Ian Roberts; Miss Joan Roberts; V. Roberts; Mrs. A. B. Robertson; Mrs. Clare Robertson; Jimmy Robinson; Miss Jessie Robinson; Mrs. Mary Robinson; Mrs. S. Robinson; Miss O. Robotham; Mr. R. G. Rollinson; Mrs. S. J. Rondesbosch; Miss D. A. Roth; Gennen Roth; Ezra Rubinstein; Dr John Rudkin; Kennedy Runion; Dr. Benjamin Rush; Arthur Russell; Leslie Russell. **S.** Miss A. S., Ohio; A. T. S.; Miss A. L. S.; Mrs. A. C. S.; Mrs. E. M. S.; Mrs. H. S., Glasgow; Mr. Ted S., Guildford; Mrs. E. D. Saberton; Stephen Sagamang, age 4; Ruth Salmon; Max Samuels; Mr. J. Saunders; Cyril Scott; Eva I. Scott; Mrs. Hilda Scott; Mrs. M. Scott; Dolly Sewell; Miss Enid Shaw; Mrs. Sheldon-Flynn; Shepherd of the hills; Mrs. H. Short; Joyce Sibbick; Signs of the Times; Miss M. L. Simcox; Mrs. E. Simpson; Mr. T. Simpson; Mrs. L. E. Sinclair; Mr. L. J. Slaugenwhite; Jerome Frank Slezak; Mr. Smart; Mrs. H. A. Smart; J. Smith; Miss Smith; Mr. A. W. Smith; Mrs. Ada C. Smith; Mrs. J. Smith; Mrs. L. Smith; Mrs. L. M. Smith; Mr. M. Smith; Mrs. P. Smith; Mr. Jack Smithson; Mr. P. Smithson; Mrs. Sheila Smithson; Yvonne Smithson; Mrs. L. B. Snook; Sister L. B. Snook; A. Southwood; Miss Elizabeth Sparrow; Dr. H. E. Spencer; Mr. Arthur Spencer; Winifred Spray; Mr. C. W. Staddon; Stephen; aged 14; Miss P. Stephens; Sallie Stephens; Mr. L. R. Stewart; Mrs. M. Stievenard; Irene Stockley; A. S. Stokes; Miss N. Stott; F. A. Stoughton; Sturdy Octogenarian; Mrs. H. A. Sturt; Sunday Post; Sunny Sunset; Sunshine Magazine; Florence Swann; Mr. E. Symons. **T.** C. T.; Miss B. T.; Mrs. T.; Mrs. L. T.; Lipika Tandon (14); George Taylor; Miss E. Taylor; Mr. A. L. Taylor; Mrs. Taylor; Mrs. B. M. Taylor; Mrs. Pearl Taylor; Mrs. Jeanette Tempest; The Kent Messenger; Mr. J.Thomas; Mrs. L. Thomas; Mrs. Yvonne Thomas; L. Thompson; Mr. C. H. Thompson; Mrs. B. S. Thompson; Mrs. Emily Thompson; Mrs. F. Thompson; Mrs. R. Thompson; Mr. T. Thompson; Miss Emilie Thomson; Mr. H. Thorne; Mrs. O. E. Thurlow; John Tobe; Mr. William Tompkins; G. M. Trevelyan; Mrs. Try; Mr. Francis Tucker; Mrs Tucker; Cyril Turner; Mrs. Turton; Mrs. Jenny Turton; L. M. Twichell. **U.** Uncle Willie; Mrs. N. Upchurch. **V.** Miss R. V.; Mrs. A. V., Norfolk; Louise Vacher; Mr. P. Vance; Mrs. Oliver Veltom; Mary Vincent. **W.** J. W.; Mrs. A. C. W., Norwich; A. Waerland; Mr. George Walker; Teresa Waller; Nancy Walmsley; Ruth Walsh; Mr. J. Walters; Mr. F. J. Warnes; Elsie Watkins; Mr. J. M. Watkins; Mrs. Myra Watkins; Mrs. Joan C. D. Watson; Mrs. J. Watts; Mrs. I. Weaire; Weekly News, Somerset; Miss Weeks; Mrs. E. C. Weightman; Mrs. E. L. Weightman; L. Weismann; Neville and June Wellington; Mrs. L. Wells; Mr. Kenneth Weston; June White; Margareta White; Mrs. L. Whitton; Mrs. Dora Whyte; C. H. Wickett; Mrs. R. Wiebelitz; Mary Wilcox; Mr. E. Wilkinson; Albert George Williams; Elizabeth E. Williams; Fred Willings; Mr. A. Williams; Mr. L. Williams; Mrs. M. W. Williams; Mrs. O. Williams; Mrs. V. Williams; Harry Willis; K. H. Wilson; Mr. K. Wilson; Reverend Arthur J. Winter; Edward Winckly; Mrs. G. Winnett; Mrs. Wendy Wisdom; Miss Hilda Wood; Mrs. Woodford; Alan Woodhouse; Miss G. Wright; Miss L. Wright; Miss L. A. Wright; Mrs. Audrey Wright; Mrs. E. Wright; Mrs. R. J. Wright; Mrs. T. M.Wright; P. W. Wright; G. Wyatt.

Index